A GEOGRAPHY OF SUBSAHARAN AFRICA

A GEOGRAPHY OF SUBSAHARAN AFRICA

Harm J. de Blij

Michigan State University

RAND M^cNALLY & COMPANY · *Chicago*

Rand McNally Geography Series
Edward B. Espenshade, Jr., *advisory editor*

Alexander, *World Political Patterns,* 2nd Edition
De Blij, *A Geography of Subsaharan Africa*
Espenshade, ed., *Goode's World Atlas,* 12th Edition
Espenshade, ed., *Rand McNally Regional Atlas,* 2nd Edition
Highsmith, Jensen, Rudd, *Conservation in the United States*
Murphey, *An Introduction to Geography*

AAG Monograph Series
1. Hartshorne, *Perspective on the Nature of Geography*
2. Meinig, *On the Margins of the Good Earth*
3. Alexander, *Offshore Geography of Northwestern Europe*

PREFACE

The regional text is an established part of the geographic literature. Each continent has been treated by scholars in this field, sometimes several, and with a varying degree of success. This volume, though a regional text on Africa, differs in many ways from almost all its predecessors. In the first place, it does not cover all of Africa simply because Africa is a physical whole; Africa is a whole in practically no other sense. No one would deny the influence of the Arab world, the world of Islam, the Middle East on Subsaharan Africa. But the contrasts between black and Mediterranean Africa are vast. To venture beyond the "real" African cultural realm into the heart of another world is to cover every square mile of a land mass bounded by sea water, but that does not seem adequate justification for the practice. To use the "impact" argument in the present-day world implies that more than just North Africa would have to be included. Indeed, other than perhaps Latin America and Australia, what could justifiably be left out on that basis?

In the second place, this book, unlike many regional texts, does not attempt to be factually complete. So many texts have, for every country or region, maps and descriptions of geology, soils, climate, vegetation, resources, population, cities, physiographic provinces, lakes, rivers, and so on and on. This one does not. Not every irrigation scheme and hydroelectric plant appears in the index, perhaps not every large city is mentioned. What has been tried—doubtlessly not everywhere with success—is a thematic approach, using the political boundaries as dividing lines and focusing upon a specific aspect of the country in question rather than all its general geographic qualities.

The writer of a regional text cannot, of course, be qualified in every systematic field of geography, and almost inevitably he will know certain parts of a continental area better than others. My own interests have been in physical and political geography, and I have done some historical and urban work; much of what I have written will be biased in one or more of those directions. But mostly I have tried to keep a certain focus when writing about each entity: in Kenya, it is land; in Uganda, S. B. Jones's field theory model is applied; in Nigeria, the political geography of federation; and so on. This is not to deny that I have added some sections in the interests of completeness; the first three chapters, making use of some terms that most students hear in their introductory courses, are examples. But except in some few cases where it seemed unavoidable, I have tried to escape gazetteer writing.

No one who has the temerity to write a regional text of this scope should expect to produce something without shortcomings. Even where the thematic approach has been successfully applied, a chapter will penetrate certain problems and aspects of a country, but, as a result, will be shallow in others. I feel it is worth the price. If he uses a text that is all-embracing, what is the lecturer going to do? Summarize the text? That is not the purpose of the classroom, although sometimes it is the use to which the classroom is put.

I want to emphasize, however, that this book is intended as an introductory text to some of the aspects of geography in Subsaharan Africa, and nothing more. I hope that readers in my own field as well as those in the other social sciences will not assume it to represent anything else.

I owe much to many people as this book is completed, but to none more than Professor Peter Gould of the Pennsylvania State University and Mr. Donald Capone of Michigan State University. Professor Gould's extensive criticism of every chapter is gratefully acknowledged; he did this work while in Africa and when other things were pressing, and his suggestions and encouragement have been invaluable. Mr. Capone, one of my graduate students in the Department of Geography at Michigan State University, gave up all the joys of a Michigan summer to produce, from my scant sketches and instructions, maps that speak for themselves. His involvement and interest in the entire work, his questions and suggestions leading to useful discussions were a source of constant stimulation.

Various people lent a hand when needed: Mr. Voris King did the calculations for the population map of South Africa and took over my duties at registration to save me three precious days. Mrs. Norma Wolff searched library shelves for needed materials. Mr. Robert Hansen worked on climatological data. Mr. Adhemar Byl read and commented usefully upon a large part of the book, Mr. Alan Best provided certain base maps. Professor James King of the University of Utah supplied several photographs from the collection gathered during his field work in East Africa, and Mr. Martin Billings permitted me to use his photographs of Angola. Several agencies were helpful in providing illustrations: the United Nations, the South African Tourist Corporation, the South African Information Service, the Belgo-American Development Corporation, the French Embassy in New York, the East African Railways and Harbours, and others assisted me in this way. Mr. Dennis Enberg provided some cartographic assistance.

This book could not have been written without the provision of time and a conducive environment, such as I found at Michigan State University, enabling me to return to Africa at short notice in the middle of the year and yet to retain a light teaching load. Thanks are due to Dr. Charles C. Hughes, Director of the African Studies Center at this university, and Dr. Lawrence M. Sommers, Chairman of the Department of Geography.

The reading and retyping of the manuscript, which benefited immeasurably from the expert editorial work of Miss Lucia Boyden, was speeded by the help of Miss Beverly Hamilton and Mrs. Nancy Weiss. My secretary, Miss Nancy Gray, performed a variety of functions in this and other connections. To all go my heartfelt thanks.

H. J. de B.

East Lansing, Michigan
October 28, 1963

Table of Contents

MAPS

by Donald L. Capone

Part 1

INTRODUCTION

1

SIGNIFICANT FEATURES OF THE PHYSIOGRAPHY
OF SUBSAHARAN AFRICA

HAVING LONG BEEN referred to as the "dark" continent, Africa is now frequently described as "unique." Yet Africa is neither the largest nor the most densely populated continent, its range of climates is not extreme, and its historical development not without parallels. Africa's forests are no denser than those of the tropical Americas, its mountains no higher than those of Asia, and its white population no greater than that of Australia. In view of its area, the resources of the continent are by no means spectacular.

What, then, merits the application of the term "unique" in any geographical consideration of the African land mass? One justification emerges from a study of the physical geography of the continent. Africa's physiographic features, in combination, are not repeated in similar form anywhere else on the land surface of the earth. The present landscape of Africa, and indeed of any continent, is the result of geologic processes which have continued over many millions of years. The interaction between the forces of uplift and those of weathering and erosion have resulted in a physiography which is complex, but a valuable key to the past. There is reason to believe that the peculiarities of Africa's landscape can be explained in terms of the unique role played by the land mass in the evolution of the morphology of the earth.

One of the striking features of the African continent is its size. Its area of well over 11.5 million square miles makes up about one-fifth of all the land of the earth and is exceeded in this respect only by Asia. Dakar, Senegal, and Cape Gardafui, Somalia, are separated by some 5,000 miles, and the distance between Tunis, Tunisia, and Cape Town, South Africa, is similar. In spite of its size, however, Africa is remarkably compact. There are no lengthy island arcs off its shores, and there are no really large bays and estuaries to indent its coasts. What appears on maps as a very straight coast line is indeed so in reality, with very few exceptions. Unlike Europe and North America, Africa is not flanked by extensive continental shelves, and in general the adjacent ocean floor drops sharply to great depths.

Not only does the ocean floor descend rapidly, the land rises almost equally abruptly, very near the coast in many areas. Thus, Africa lacks really extensive coastal plains. There are exceptions, such as the delta of the Niger River, the coastal plain of Moçambique, and the plain of Somalia, but more commonly Africa, and especially Subsaharan Africa, is surrounded by what has become known as the Great Escarpment, an often spectacular mountain wall leading from the narrow coastal belt to the interior plateau. Thus, Africa, whether below sea level or above, is ringed by a severe declivity or wall with a vertical extent of thousands of feet. In Natal, South Africa, for instance, the decline from Drakensberg Plateau to the bottom of the continental slope involves more than 20,000 feet.

The Plateau and the Basins

Africa is indeed almost entirely an extensive plateau, high in the east and lower toward the west. In the east, it includes the Drakensberg Plateau in South Africa, the Ethiopian Massif in the north, and intervening regions such as the East African Plateau and the Highveld of the Transvaal and Southern Rhodesia. It culminates in the great mountains of East Africa, where Mount Kilimanjaro reaches over 19,340 feet, the highest point of the continent. Although the Drakensberg Plateau reaches 11,000 feet, and elevations over 14,000 feet occur in Ethiopia, the average height of this eastern backbone of the African Plateau is perhaps between 5,000 and 6,000 feet. The relative lack of interruption of the eastern section of the plateau is remarkable: from Natal to the northeastern Sudan, the Great Escarpment is almost everywhere prominent in its development.

Westward, the general level of the plateau drops, and several great depressions interrupt it. These basins have been filled with many feet of sedimentary deposits, beneath which the crystalline rocks of the plateau are buried. In the south, the Kalahari Basin is an extensive sand desert. Vast quantities of loose material, supplied by the surrounding plateau, have been deposited in this tectonic depression. In Central Africa, the Congo Basin forms a sharp contrast to the high East African Plateau. It is separated from the Kalahari Basin by the Bihé Plateau, which is essentially a westward continuation of the eastern highlands and has escaped the forces which

The Great Escarpment on the Natal–Basutoland Border, Southern Africa. Here, the escarpment is more prominent than anywhere else in Subsaharan Africa, and the edge of the highlands illustrated lies at over 10,000 feet above sea level. The scarp, which in this area is carved in basalt, is retreating under erosion. (South African Railways)

The Descent from the Plateau to the Coastal Belt. In many areas such as the Drakensberg of South Africa, the Great Escarpment is actually a series of steps, leading from the plateau to the coast. Each step represents an erosional phase.

4

MAJOR PHYSIOGRAPHIC FEATURES

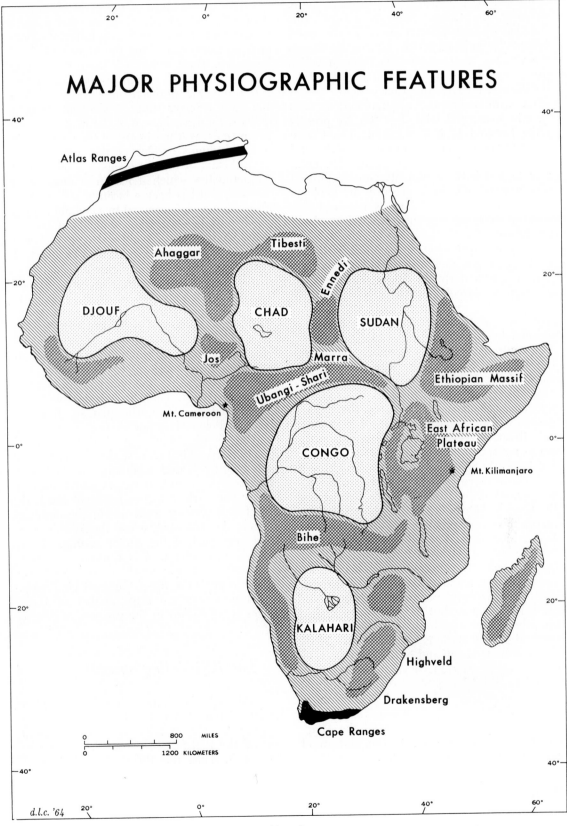

Atlas Ranges

Ahaggar

Tibesti

Ennedi

DJOUF

CHAD

SUDAN

Jos

Marra

Ethiopian Massif

Ubangi - Shari

Mt. Cameroon

East African
Plateau

CONGO

Mt. Kilimanjaro

Bihe

KALAHARI

Highveld

Drakensberg

Cape Ranges

0   800   MILES

0   1200 KILOMETERS

d.l.c. '64

Map 1

depressed the regions to the north and south. Actually, the Congo Basin is entirely surrounded by such plateau areas. To the north is the Ubangi-Shari divide, and to the west is the Crystal Mountain Range, through which the Congo River cuts a narrow gorge. Like the Kalahari Basin, the Congo depression is filled with sediments, accumulated in this case in an ancient lake of which the present Lake Leopold II is a remnant. The Congo Basin is often compared to a soup plate, and the comparison is very appropriate. The great lake in which the sediments were deposited was drained relatively recently in geologic time, and the exposed floor is low and flat, some areas lying less than 1,500 feet above sea level.

To the north of the Ubangi-Shari divide lie three major interior basins. Each is well defined, particularly the Sudan Basin, which corresponds largely to the political entity known by the same name. This, the easternmost of the three northern depressions, is drained by the White and Blue Nile rivers. The contrasts between the Sudan Basin and the adjacent Ethiopian Plateau need not be emphasized. Much of the basin lies below 1,000 feet in elevation, and in the south is the famed Sudd region, possibly the world's most extensive marshland. Here the great Nile River barely succeeds in penetrating the dense masses of floating vegetation, its total fall in nearly 800 miles being under 140 feet.

The western boundary of the Sudan Basin is marked by the Plateau of Darfur and the Ennedi Plateau, and there the crystallines reappear in such prominent landmarks as the Marra Mountains. Beyond lies the Chad Basin, the core of which is Lake Chad and the Bodele Depression. Formerly much more extensive than it is today, Lake Chad has dwindled to a swampy area which is inundated after heavy rains but is being encroached upon by Sahara sands from the north. In the north, the Chad Basin is bounded very clearly by the Tibesti Massif and in the northwest, by the Ahaggar Plateau. From the southern boundary, the Ubangi-Shari divide, the Shari River drains into Lake Chad. The western margin of the Chad Basin is less well defined, although a southward extension of the Ahaggar Plateau reaches close to the plateau of northern Nigeria, the Jos Plateau.

The westernmost of the great basins, the depression of Djouf, occupies the western Sahara Desert and reaches its fullest development in the region along the Mauritania-Mali boundary. It is separated from the coastal belt by high ranges such as the Futa Jallon and forms the drainage area for the upper and middle Niger River. The Djouf Basin is perhaps the least known of the major African depressions, as it lies in one of the most empty and forbidding regions of the great desert. Nevertheless, it clearly displays a number of characteristics which it has in common with the others: it has been a basin of sedimentary accumulation, it is rimmed by crystalline areas which pass beneath the sediments of the interior, and it lies largely between 500 and 1,500 feet above sea level, only the heart of the basin lying as low as 500 feet.

The African Plateau, therefore, extends from the Futa Jallon in the west to Ethiopia in the east, and from the Tibesti and Ahaggar in the north to the Drakensberg in the south. Though interrupted in places by tectonic depressions, causing the crystallines to be covered by more recent sediments, the plateau is by far the dominant physiographic feature in Africa. There is considerable landform variation within the plateau, but the structure below does not change. Europe has its Alps, South America its Andes, and Asia its Himalayas, but Africa does not possess such lengthy folded mountains. In fact, the only sizeable mountain ranges which have a history and surface expression involving folding of sedimentary rocks are in the extreme north of the continent, where the Atlas Mountains form part of the Alpine chain and are as such an outlier of this Eurasian orogeny, and in the extreme south, where the Cape Ranges occupy the tip of the great land mass. In terms of surface area, neither of these ranges is significant in the vastness of Africa.

The Rift Valley System

Although the plateau is not interrupted by folded mountains, it is broken by a series of great troughs or rifts which extend from beyond the Red Sea in the north to Natal in the south. This, the Rift Valley System of

The Cape Ranges Along the Southern Margin of Africa. With the Atlas Ranges of North Africa, the Cape Ranges represent the only major folded mountains in Africa. The Hex River valley is one of the series of valleys separating the parallel folded ridges. In the western Cape, the east-west orientation of the folds is disturbed, and the Cape Ranges there trend in several directions. (Satour)

The Cape Coast Near the Cape Peninsula. The rugged cape coast line provides a strong contrast to the smooth coasts of South West Africa and Natal. Promontories such as this jut out everywhere along the Cape coast, and beneath the water are dangerous reefs and banks.

East Africa and its bifurcations, is one of those features which have contributed to Africa's reputation of physiographic uniqueness: although there are rifts elsewhere in the world, nowhere are they known to be so extensive, prominent in development, and problematic in terms of genesis. Few problems have aroused as much controversy as the question of their origin. It was J. W. Gregory who, in 1896, recognized the nature of the parallel-sided depressions which he encountered in his travels through East Africa and proposed the name Rift Valleys for them.[1] Ever since, hypotheses have been advanced to account for their extent, location, geologic and geomorphic significance, age, and history.

Since Precambrian times, the vast continental shield of Africa and Arabia has been stable except for those epeirogenic movements which created, among other features, the great depressions of the west. Uplift and denudation have cleared the eastern backbone of the shield of sedimentary cover, and it is there that the Rift Valley System reaches its culmination. Great fractures have caused lengthy strips of the plateau surface to subside between parallel walls. The major trend

---

[1] J. W. Gregory, *The Great Rift Valley* (London: John Murray, 1896).

7

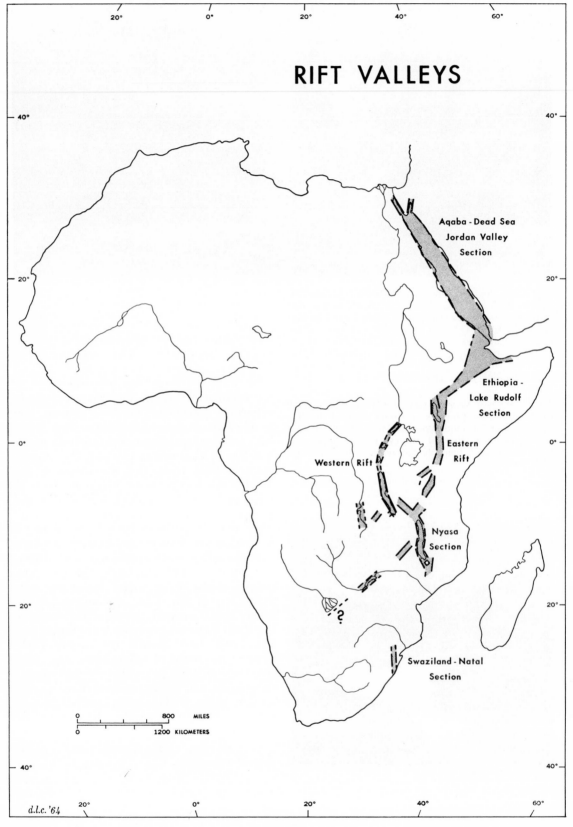

RIFT VALLEYS

Aqaba - Dead Sea
Jordan Valley
Section

Ethiopia -
Lake Rudolf
Section

Eastern
Rift

Western Rift

Nyasa
Section

Swaziland - Natal
Section

0   800   MILES
0   1200   KILOMETERS

d.l.c. '64

Map 2

Within the East African Rift Valleys. A number of lakes remain in the trough created by the rifts, including the great Lakes Tanganyika and Nyasa. Many smaller lakes, some slowly drying up, also still occupy parts of the rift floors. A number of these are very salty. Illustrated here is Lake Naivasha, just to the north of Mount Longonot in the Eastern Rift. The rift wall can be seen in the background, and the mounds across the lake are clearly lava extrusions.

of these *graben* is north-south, with subsidiary faults running north-northwest and north-northeast. In East Africa, the meridional trend predominates. The entire system may conveniently be divided into six individual sections:

    a. Aqaba–Dead Sea–Jordan Valley Section Red Sea
    b. Ethiopian Section and Lake Rudolf
    c. Eastern Rift of East Africa
    d. Western Rift of East Africa
    e. Nyasa Section and Bifurcations
    f. Swaziland–Natal and Kalahari Floor Section

The Red Sea, which lies between the Aqaba and Ethiopian sections, is itself a great rift valley, but its characteristics are somewhat different from those of the other parts of the system. The East African rifts have been studied most intensively and are perhaps best known. The Eastern and Western rifts of East Africa display virtually all the characteristics of the rifts anywhere. There, great lakes have filled the troughs formed by the faulting, volcanoes have erupted within and beyond the rims of the rifts, the entire plateau has undergone tilting, affecting the drainage patterns associated with the developing *graben*, and

great variations exist in the degree of prominence displayed by the valleys.

In spite of their length, which must be measured in thousands of miles, the rift valleys over great distances are remarkably uniform in their width. The lakes of the Nyasa Section and the Western Rift of East Africa show variations in breadth of tens of miles, but the narrowest is over twenty miles, and the widest under sixty. Although there are some places where these limits may be exceeded, they generally hold true, so that the rift, wherever it may be observed, whether in Swaziland, Kenya, or Ethiopia, is unmistakable in its appearance. From the plateau rim, the land falls steeply to a flat lowland which often possesses climatic and vegetational characteristics utterly different from those above the fault scarp. Beyond, the wall marking the opposite fault can be seen to carry the surface back to plateau elevations.

There is no such uniformity as far as the floor of the rifts is concerned. The narrow strip of land which has dropped between the parallel faults lies far below sea level in some places and thousands of feet above in others. The degree of variation may be observed especially well in the Western Rift of East Africa, where the floor of Lake Tanganyika

The Rift Valley in Swaziland. The 2,000-foot-high wall of the Swaziland Rift Valley rises above the "Lowveld" floor, the sunken block. Headward erosion is driving the wall back from its original topographic position, but its vertical prominence is little changed. Turning around, the photographer would see a similar scene.

is as much as 2,140 feet below sea level. Some miles to the north, however, but still to the south of Lake Kivu, the elevation of the floor of the rift is over 5,000 feet *above* sea level. Nevertheless, the adjacent plateau towers above the floor and is separated by a prominent escarpment almost everywhere, so that the depth of the rift valley must be measured from the upper to the lower surface and not simply by the level to which the fault block has foundered.

East Africa is a land of great volcanoes, and the volcanism is directly associated with the rifting. The exact relationship between the great volcanic mountains and the faults creating the rifts is, however, not known. Some of the volcanoes lie within the region separating the Eastern and Western rifts of East Africa. Of these, Mount Elgon is a prominent example. Certain volcanic cones lie within the very rift, such as Mount Longonot, which has undergone very recent growth, evidencing continued rift movements. Other volcanic peaks lie outside the area enclosed by the East African Rifts; the greatest of all, Mount Kilimanjaro, belongs to this group. Thus, there is no simple areal correlation between rifting and volcanism. The matter can, of course, be approached from the standpoint of degree of intensity of faulting; thus, the faults with the greatest throws must be

associated with the largest amount of volcanic activity. This theory is not tenable either, since some of the most tremendous faults occur in the Tanganyika area of the Western Rift, where volcanism is, for all intents and purposes, nonexistent.

The earth movements which shaped the Rift Valley System have not yet ceased. Earthquakes are common in the Rift Valley north of Lake Albert,[2] and lavas have recently blocked the valley north of Lake Kivu and altered its outflow.[3] An increasing body of evidence is accumulating in support of the theory that the rifts are still developing. In geologically recent times, lakes of much greater extent than those of today occupied the rifts, leaving sedimentary deposits as proof of their existence. In addition, they possessed a fish fauna that left fossil evidence for its distribution. The reconstruction of the history of the great lakes and the interruption of the drainage lines connecting them has been greatly facilitated by this peculiar fauna. Today, the rifts contain a number of basins

[2] E. Krenkel, "Die Erdbeden Ostafrikas," *Centralblatt für Mineralogie*, XXII (1921), 705–13, 743–51.
[3] N. Boutakoff, "Ecoulement Primitif du Lac vers le Nord," *Bulletin de la Société de Géologie Belgique*, XLIII (1933), 50–56.

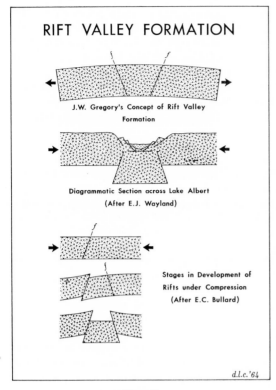

Map 3

When rift valleys form, they may be caused by either tensional or compressional forces. J. W. Gregory first recognized the Rift Valley System as a tectonic feature due to faulting. Observing the angle of declination of the walls bounding the floor, he stated: "The Rift Valley is bounded by faults which have been proved to occur in so many parts of its course that they probably bound the whole length. These faults are normal (tensional) except for a reverse fault . . ."[4] Thus, Gregory visualized long, narrow strips of crustal material sinking between blocks of a plateau which retained its original elevation. This concept appears to contain a mechanical impossibility which has frequently been emphasized. A block between normal, tensional faults will not sink unless this tension pulls the supporting flanks away. Clearly, should this process take place, the sinking crust will displace vast amounts of molten material, much of which will be extruded along the faults. Significantly, however, the volcanism that accompanied rifting was localized, even if extensive. In several areas, volcanism accompanied initial rifting, then ceased as rift movements continued. The uplift of Ruwenzori could also be viewed as inconsistent with the tension hypothesis: in a sinking floor affected by tension, it is not likely that a mountain mass would be pushed to great height at the same time.

All these apparent contradictions in the physiography of East Africa caused Wayland and Willis to propose an alternative hypothesis involving not tension, but compression. Boundary faults, it was suggested, are steep upthrusts, and the rift blocks are wedges which widen in depth and are held down by pressure from the overriding plateau edges.[5] As the plateau edge rides up a high-angle thrust plane, its forward section is left unsupported and slumps down in strips. The

of internal drainage. Some of these basins are connected, others are not. Lake Magadi and Lake Natron, in the Eastern Rift, lie at approximately the same elevation, but they are separated by a rise in floor level within the rift. And even within the rifts themselves, nonvolcanic mountain masses may occur. Within the structural confines of the Western Rift, between Lakes Albert and Edward, lies the towering horst of Ruwenzori, which at 16,794 feet rivals the greatest volcanoes of the east. Rising from a floor which is itself thousands of feet below the adjacent plateau, Ruwenzori reaches elevations of 10,000 feet above the plateau surface. It would seem unlikely that it is merely a remnant of the plateau, unaffected by the downward movements of rifting, for there is little to suggest that the plateau itself stood at 17,000 feet. Ruwenzori, a mass of gneisses and schists showing evidence of recent uplift in the south, seems to have been pushed upward while the surrounding floor was depressed.

---

[4] J. W. Gregory, *The Rift Valleys and Geology of East Africa* (London: Seeley, Service and Co., 1921), p. 358, point (7). Note also point (9): "With the exception of one reverse fault, there is no evidence along the Rift Valley of the reverse faulting and intense folding which accompany mountain building under lateral pressure."

[5] E. J. Wayland, "The African Bulge," *Geographical Journal*, LXXV (April, 1930), 381–83.

visible walls thus resemble those produced by normal faults, often arranged in successive steps.

Until twenty-five years ago, this suggestion was based on field evidence as scanty as that of Gregory. In 1936, however, it was reinforced by the results of a gravity survey carried out by E. C. Bullard.[6] Bullard found the plateaus to be very nearly in isostatic equilibrium, while over the rifts of Lakes Albert and Tanganyika, among other sites, the observed values of gravity were abnormally low. The deduction was, then, that an excess of sial underlies the fault blocks. This would mean that if the blocks were free to move, they would rise in order to restore isostatic equilibrium. Consequently, it was believed that they were being held down by the overthrusting plateau edges.

Under these conditions, the rising of Ruwenzori is explicable, but neither hypothesis provides a totally adequate explanation for all the phenomena observed. It has been indicated that the question of volcanism is no more solved by compression than it is by tension, since the process of thrusting would appear to involve preventing the outflow of any lava. The interpretation of Bullard's gravity data is not agreed upon, and though most geologists are willing to admit that compression has played a role in certain parts of the rift valleys, few would accept without reservation the Wayland-Willis idea.

Lake Victoria

An important aspect of the central section of the East African plateau, perhaps containing the answer to the rift problem, is the gigantic, but shallow, Lake Victoria. Reaching its greatest depth (270 feet) toward the east, this basin appears to have formed as a result of relative or actual subsidence. Both along its periphery and on its floor are numerous drowned valleys to support this assertion, and Wayland suggested that the lake actually occupied the area of a former divide, which drained to the Congo in the west and the Indian Ocean in the east. After rifting interrupted this pattern, subsidence created the present basin. On the eastern side, where the lake is deepest and depression strongest, lava extrusion has also been heaviest.

The existence of Lake Victoria appears as incompatible with a hypothesis of rift valley formation based solely on compression as the distribution of lava extrusion is to the tension idea. Pointing to the absence of positive anomalies in the gravity survey, Alex L. du Toit wrote: "On the contrary, we see Lake Victoria almost surrounded by rift valleys and we cannot but conclude that, deprived of much of its lateral support, that block dimpled at its center and so enabled the lake—with its typical drowned topography—to come into being . . . Gregory's interpretation is accordingly and wholeheartedly upheld."[7]

Recent research on the Pleistocene history of the East African plateau has brought to light a number of additional factors which affect the interpretation of the sequence of events involving the rifts and Lake Victoria. During the Pleistocene, a succession of pluvials (wet phases) and interpluvials occurred there. Sediments were deposited which are today seen in the form of terraces, and these have been affected by rift movements. Such terraces, representing the various pluvials, are found in river valleys as well as lake basins. In the vicinity of Lake Naivasha in the Eastern Rift, they betray the existence of a very large lake, comparable to those of the Western Rift of today, during Pleistocene times and into the period when early man was present there. Indeed, terraces containing artifacts have not only been disturbed by fault movements, but covered by volcanic outpourings.[8]

In the Lake Naivasha area of the Eastern Rift, the Kamasian beds are early evidence of a former lake within the rift valley. In the

[6] E. C. Bullard, "Gravity Measurements in East Africa," *Transactions of the Royal Society of London* (A), CCXXXV (1936), 445–531.

[7] A. L. du Toit, *Our Wandering Continents* (London: Oliver & Boyd, 1937), p. 255.

[8] F. R. C. Reed, *The Geology of the British Empire* (London: Edward Arnold and Co., 1949), p. 57.

Western Rift, however, there are deep sediments of a large lake existing in pre-Kamasian times. These Kageran beds, first recognized by Wayland in Uganda, suggest that rifting on a major scale in the Western Rift preceded that in the Eastern Rift.[9] This information permits a tentative theory of the sequence of events in the plateau region. First, in pre-Pleistocene times, the Victoria block subsided, causing extensive river reversal, particularly in the west, and drowning of river valleys, especially in the east. This was followed closely by extensive rifting in the Western Rift, and finally, probably in mid-Pleistocene times, rifting reached its culmination in the Eastern Rift, accompanied by volcanism. The problem of the mechanism is not solved, and many lines of evidence are in apparent conflict. What is clear is that no single force must be invoked as an all-embracing answer; there is indisputable proof for tension as well as compression, volcanism and quiescence, seismic activity and apparent stability. Seen alone and without reference to the other physiographic peculiarities of Africa, the rifts are indeed a vexing problem. Considered together with such features as the great basins, the Great Escarpment, the nonfolded shield, and African drainage lines, however, they appear a natural consequence of the process of evolution of the continent.

African Drainage Lines

Several of the great basins which depress the African Plateau are drained by large rivers. The Sudan Basin contains the White Nile and also part of the Blue Nile, the Congo Basin holds the great Congo River, and the Djouf Basin is the catchment for the upper and middle Niger River. A glance at the map of the major drainage lines of the continent indicates that several of these rivers have certain characteristics in common, some of which are easily explained by the plateau nature of the continental land mass, while others seem contrary to what would be ex-

pected. The course of the Niger River is a good case in point. In a continent that has been tilted strongly to the west, it is indeed surprising to find a river rising some dozens of miles from the West African coast, then heading straight into the central regions of the Sahara Desert, only to make a 90-degree turn there and proceed southeastward to its delta. In the process, it passes through extensive braided sections and plunges over some great falls. In the southern part of the continent, the Zambezi River likewise starts its course in the western part of the land mass, proceeds in a southeasterly direction as if to enter the Kalahari Basin, then abruptly turns northeast, plunges over the Victoria Falls, and passes through a number of gorges and across rapids before forming a small delta on the Moçambique Coastal Plain. Not far to the south, on the other hand, the Orange River rises in the Basutoland Highlands within sight of the Indian Ocean and flows across the entire southern width of the land mass, through the southern extremity of the Kalahari Basin, over the Aughrabies Falls, and into the Atlantic Ocean.

The Congo River, commencing its course (as the Lualaba) on the northern flank of the South Equatorial Divide, flows northward, not west, for many miles, and changes course abruptly to cross through the Crystal Mountains before entering the sea. Throughout its course, the Congo is interrupted by rapids and falls. The White Nile River, after rising on the East African Plateau (the rivers draining into Lake Victoria may be considered the headwaters of the White Nile), makes a spectacular turn in the northern Sudan, as if to enter the Sahara interior, then continues northward on its way to the great delta.

Neither are these characteristics of course direction confined to the large and well-known rivers. In Angola, the Cunene River flows south as if to enter a basin of internal drainage, Etosha Pan in northwestern South West Africa, but although there is a fossil drainage channel linking the Cunene with the pan, the present river elbows toward the sea, plunging over the Ruacana Falls. In the Rhodesias, the Kafue River, a major tributary of the Zambezi, flows southwest, apparently with the same goal (the Kalahari Ba-

[9] S. Cole, *The Prehistory of East Africa* (London: William Clowes and Sons, 1954), p. 44.

sin) as the upper Zambezi River, but then angles sharply to flow due east before entering the Zambezi.

The impression conveyed by the river pattern is that the upper parts of the major courses drain into the interior basins of the continent, and that the rivers were subsequently reoriented to the coasts. Thus, the upper Niger, upper Zambezi, and others are probably direct descendants of rivers of great age, while the lower courses of these rivers are younger, having been the means by which the interior lakes were drained. This is possibly why the lower and upper courses of the same river seem so unrelated in several cases, particularly in terms of direction.

The question now remains how the great basins of internal drainage came to be drained toward the oceans, and how some of these basins, such as Chad, retain their original condition even today. What prevented headward erosion from capturing the interior lakes for so long? The African shield being so ancient, why have some of the most significant changes taken place so very recently?

The Aughrabies Falls on the Orange River, South Africa. The total height of the falls exceeds 600 feet, and the gorge, part of which is illustrated here, is some 11 miles in length. (Satour)

Madagascar

Some of the answers to these questions may be forthcoming through an analysis of the relationships between Madagascar and Southern Africa. It is opposite the west coast of this great island that the Zambezi River today reaches the sea, and it is along the coast of Moçambique that Africa possesses

The Victoria Falls on the Zambezi River, Rhodesia. Here the Zambezi River leaves its upper course, adjusted to the plateau surface, and plunges over a 350-foot-high wall into its middle (gorge) tract. The falls are sustained by basalt which was extruded at about the same time as that underlying the Drakensberg. Here, however, the rock is cut by two planes of weakness: a series of parallel faults and a joint system, and these two planes intersect at a very low angle. The falls have been carved out of these lines of weakness in the rock, so that a series of elbow canyons marks previous positions of the drop. About eight such locations have been recognized. Today, the Victoria Falls are about a mile in width, and the illustration shows the Zambezi River at low volume.

one of its few really large coastal plains. The possibility has been put forward that Madagascar was once connected to the African continent. J. H. Wellington, in an effort to explain the peculiarities of the Zambezi drainage system, suggested a reassembly which places Madagascar in the area presently occupied by the coastal plain.[10] Others, such as A. L. du Toit, have considered, largely on petrologic grounds, that any such connection should be to East Africa, not to Southern Africa.

Madagascar, like much of Africa, is formed of ancient crystalline rocks which rise to form a plateau which, in the east, reaches heights of over 10,000 feet above sea level. The eastern margin of the island, along the remarkably straight coast line, is marked by a great escarpment which rivals in degree of development anything Africa's mainland has to offer. Westward, the crystallines pass beneath a sedimentary cover ranging in age from the late Paleozoic in the east to the Quaternary in the west; the sediments dip westward and create a cuestaform topography. The sequence of sedimentation throughout the Mesozoic is very similar to that of Southern Africa; when the subcontinent was being covered by the great Karroo succession of glacial, lacustrine, continental, and other deposits, Madagascar underwent corresponding periods of deposition. Although Madagascar's fauna today shows marked differences from that of Africa (there are no carnivores, no poisonous snakes, and there are marsupials), until the Cretaceous, the fossil sequence is very similar to that of adjacent Africa.

If post-Cretaceous sediments are removed from the Moçambique Coastal Plain (which thereby disappears) and from the western regions of Madagascar, the two opposing coasts show outlines which are far more in agreement than those of today. Objections to the reassembly based on present-day coasts are not valid, since coasts of accumulation would be expected to show considerable change over a period of some 80 million years. Wellington, rather than focusing

his attention upon the actual region of reassembly, considered the effect such reassembly would have had upon the interior, and particularly upon the Zambezi River system.

The northern Kalahari Basin, the early recipient of the upper Zambezi River, possesses a great interior delta, the Makarikari Depression, Okovango Swamps, and Lake Ngami. Lake Ngami is the remnant of a lake which was once much more extensive, and occasional periods of heavy rain indicate what much of this region may have looked like before water began to flow to the coast. Indeed, the drainage lines of the South Equatorial Divide to the north often show, as does the Kafue River, upper parts of their courses directed toward the delta. Today, with only the Linyanti and Okovango rivers flowing into the depression (and the Linyanti is in the process of being captured by the Zambezi system), sands are encroaching upon this region, which was once one of permanent inundation.

In a continent tilted toward the west, with the eastern plateau separating the interior basin from the sea, it might be considered likely that headward erosion would eventually cause drainage toward the Atlantic Ocean. Nevertheless, the Okovango has not been reversed, the Cunene has not captured the basin, and the major drainage today is to the east. Plunging, in the process, over the 360-foot wall of the Victoria Falls, the Zambezi has rapidly cut its way down into hard granites below the falls, eventually meandering across the flat Moçambique Coastal Plain. What afforded the river the opportunity to penetrate a plateau which had for millions of years held the Kalahari Basin contained as an interior basin of accumulation?

One possibility is the fragmentation of that plateau and the removal of much of the barrier. On its way to the ocean, the Zambezi River receives the waters of the Shire River, which drains Lake Nyasa. Lake Nyasa is itself in a rift valley, and its floor lies over 1,000 feet below sea level. The rift faults can be traced southward until they disappear beneath the sediments of the coastal plain. No known rift faults then occur until in the latitude of Swaziland. The suggestion is that the faults did indeed exist, and that they were

[10] J. H. Wellington, *Southern Africa* (Cambridge: Cambridge University Press, 1955), I, 460–73.

instrumental in the fragmentation of this part of Africa by permitting the breaking away of Madagascar. In the reassembly, the spur of Cape St. André would lie immediately south of Lake Nyasa. Thus, the high shield of the island filled what is today a gap in the African plateau, bringing to this region elevations similar to the Drakensberg to the south and the East African Plateau and Ethiopian Massif to the north. Preventing eastward drainage until the breakaway occurred, it has permitted the escape of the Zambezi River, the only major stream to penetrate the plateau backbone of east Africa from Basutoland to Eritrea (the Limpopo, also allowed to flow east by the breakaway, is a minor stream compared to the Zambezi).

It is now possible to suggest a relationship between the Great Escarpment, the enormous depressions of the plateau, the rift valleys, and the drainage pattern of Africa, which together form the four most important physical features of the continent. The very extensive plateau must have been affected by moist as well as dry climates, accumulation as well as denudation, tilting and depression as well as faulting. Hence, as the interior basins subsided due to initial tectonic forces, they became receptacles for tremendous sedimentary accumulations which, by their sheer weight, depressed the basins even further. Rivers emptied into these interior basins, which began to form lakes. Then, something occurred which caused the shield to fragment, creating great troughs where the forces of fragmentation were severe. These, the rift valleys, heralded a new episode in the history of the land mass. Probably even before those of today came into existence (although they may have had forerunners), Madagascar was separated from the continental block. As this occurred, rivers found their way out of the basins of interior drainage, which were emptied, leaving only the mass of sediments to attest to the nature of the conditions of accumulation. This process was long in completion and is not yet finished. Some rivers have cut deep valleys on their way to the sea, but they fail to drain parts of the basins and capture must still take place: Lake Chad and the Okovango Delta are examples of this. Meanwhile, an escarpment was formed around the coast and began to retreat under the attack of subaerial erosion. Where Madagascar broke away, such an escarpment has formed and lies along the eastern border of what is today Southern Rhodesia. It is not as prominent as that of the Drakensberg, but, for reasons which will be indicated later, it is probably younger. The rifts continued to develop and forecast the further fragmentation of the great shield.

The point may now be raised that, while Madagascar provides the answer to some of the physiographic problems of Southern Africa, there remains the question of why the Niger, Congo, Orange, and other rivers drain into the Atlantic Ocean. In addition, the absence of large fold mountains has not been accounted for, nor is it clear why Africa should display these characteristics, and not Asia, Europe, or North America.

The answer appears to be that there is a great deal of similarity between what happened along the Moçambique Coastal Plain and what occurred elsewhere along the coasts of Africa, especially Subsaharan Africa. In order to account for all the factors that make Africa physiographically unique, it seems absolutely necessary to invoke the hypothesis of Continental Drift. For these purposes, this involves an African shield surrounded by the other continental masses of the Southern Hemisphere and India, the whole forming one great supercontinent which is known in the literature as Gondwana (sometimes also as Gondwanaland). It is of this Gondwana that Africa was the core, and so, uniquely, it possessed no coasts until the supercontinent fragmented. This fracturing provided Africa with the beginnings of its Great Escarpment, permitted its rivers to flow to sea level, and is now affecting the interior of the African land mass itself.

"Africa Forms the Key"[11]

The astounding similarities between the opposing shores of the South Atlantic Ocean have been a subject for discussion since long

---

[11] Du Toit, *op. cit.*, p. iii.

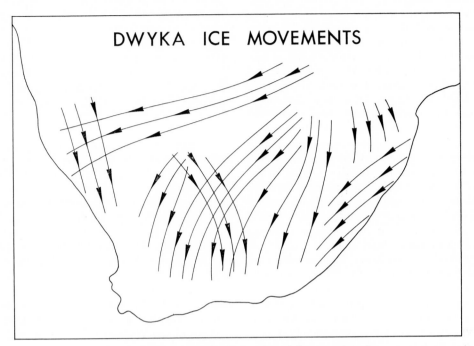

DWYKA ICE MOVEMENTS

Main Movements of the Dwyka Ice Sheets (After A.L. du Toit)

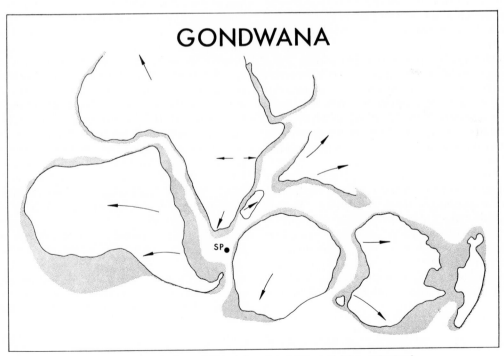

GONDWANA

SP●

A Reconstruction of Gondwana (After A.L. du Toit, L.C. King, and others).
For these purposes, the outlines of the Continental Shelves are used.

d.l.c. '64

Map 4

before the hypothesis of Continental Drift was established. Indeed, if the continental outlines are cut from a globe or map and fitted together, it will be seen that virtually every bulge on one land mass fits into an indentation in the other. The Niger Delta, which would seem to invalidate this statement, is a recent product of deposition and not involved in the hardrock jigsaw. Of course, the simple fact that the west coast of Africa and the east coast of South America fit together is not proof of their former unity. Coastal outlines change as geologic time progresses, and perhaps the fit was not nearly as good in the past as it is today. The fact remains that the present-day correspondence is one of a series of lines of evidence pointing, many would say indisputably, to a former close connection between these land masses.

Although A. Wegener is generally considered the father of the hypothesis of Continental Drift,[12] his presentation of the idea was based on so much unreliable evidence that it fell into disrepute because it was so vulnerable. The hypothesis has never completely recovered from its stormy birth, although Du Toit's 1937 treatise did much to answer the major criticisms. Du Toit, a South African geologist, established a set of criteria on the basis of which Continental Drift should be studied, and he himself collected an imposing amount of evidence to place the hypothesis on a strong foundation. Most of his work was done in Africa and South America, in an effort to prove their former union. During the course of his researches, he unearthed a vast quantity of detail which proved to be of far greater importance than its function in substantiating the union.

Africa, although presently astride the equator and famed for its hot climates, has not always experienced these conditions. Toward the end of the Paleozoic, the southern part of the continent underwent extensive glaciation, and the tills which were left by the great ice sheets have since compacted into tillites. These tillites, along with the striated and polished floors, erratics, and other glacial fea-

---

[12] A. Wegener, *Die Entstehung der Kontinente und Ozeane* (English translation: *The Origin of Continents and Oceans* [London: Methuen and Co., 1924]).

tures, give evidence of greatly reduced temperatures in areas which today are under the tropical sun. The discovery of the tillite (which, along with intercalations, reaches 2,000 feet at several Cape localities) in South Africa has been followed by similar finds to the north, as far as the Congo. Striations in the rock floors underlying the glacial debris indicate that the dominant direction of ice movement was not, as might be expected, from south to north, but the reverse, with a northeast-southwest direction being particularly frequent. The deposition of the Dwyka Tillite was followed by a lengthy sequence of sedimentation, including almost every conceivable variety of rock, until the crust, tiring under the weight of the layers, yielded and, in the late Jurassic, permitted the extrusion of thousands of feet of basaltic lava. The entire succession, known as the Karroo System, measures at maximum theoretical development some 40,000 feet. Today, the great lava plateau with which the sequence culminated is being broken up by erosion, but parts of it survive in the Drakensberg, at Victoria Falls, and elsewhere.

The Karroo succession, although best developed in Southern Africa, is by no means unique to the subcontinent. The discovery of glacial deposits in South America, India, Madagascar, and Australia, and sequences of deposition resembling the Karroo succession in all but the last of these areas, became a cornerstone for the hypothesis of drift. Not only were there found to be striking similarities between the actual rock types, with a final outpouring of basalt in South America, Africa, India (where the Deccan Plateau is a remnant), and Antarctica, but the fossil content of the various types, faunal as well as floral, showed marked similarities. Soon, biologists came to be among the strongest supporters of the idea.

With the continents in their present position, the near-contemporaneous glaciation of areas as far apart as India and South America must be ruled out unless the entire globe experienced such glaciation. Of all the continental blocks of the Southern Hemisphere, Africa was glaciated most strongly. Contemporaneous beds in the Northern Hemisphere show no evidence of widespread glaciation.

Hence, there are two possibilities. One is that the high latitudes, during the Paleozoic, were the regions where glaciation was prevalent, and that polar wandering took place at such a pace as to affect all the widely dispersed areas that were glaciated. The objection is that the North Pole would have had to wander sympathetically and would have caused similar extensive glacial conditions; there is no evidence for this. The other possibility is that the continents themselves were grouped in a different manner. It is thought that the South Pole may have been some hundreds of miles southeast of the present site of Durban, South Africa, and that Antarctica, Southern Africa, Madagascar, southern India, and South America were all so grouped as to be covered by an ice sheet. Indeed, when the widely separated areas of glaciation are thus reassembled, the area actually covered by the late Paleozoic glaciers is not very different in size or shape from the area affected by the latest Pleistocene glaciation in the Northern Hemisphere, an area which is well known. The reassembly—Gondwana—shows how areas in equatorial Africa might have been affected by peripheral glaciation, and it also explains why there should be similarities in the sedimentary sequence which followed the ice age.

In the proposed arrangement, Africa thus formed the heart of Gondwana. It alone possessed no coasts, for it was bounded everywhere by land. Not surprisingly, it developed basins of internal drainage, although it is possible that some rivers flowed from Africa onto the adjacent land. The discovery, in South America, of a lenticular bed of sand and gravel containing diamonds which were thought to have formed in Africa caused speculations that a river transported them there, and several suggestions have been made that some of the erratics found in the glacial beds of South America are recognizable as bedrock in Africa, whence they appear to have come.

Significantly, Southern Africa possesses one of the two folded mountain belts of the entire African continent and the only one in Subsaharan Africa. The Cape Ranges were formed well before the Karroo deposition began, and thus before the late Paleozoic ice age. If Africa was at this time adjacent to South America, it would seem that an equivalent of the Cape Ranges should occur on the opposite side of the Atlantic and indeed, there is such an equivalent. The Sierras of Buenos Aires show structural, lithologic, and even topographic similarities, as described by, among others, Keidel.[13] The Falkland Islands are likewise related to this structure, as might be expected from their location.

This is not the place for a defense of the hypothesis of Continental Drift, which finds its strongest support in those areas where its manifestations are commonplace. The facts remain that without it, the essential unity of African physiography is lost, and that there is a real need for it, not only from the point of view of the geologist, but also from that of the geomorphologist and physiographer. Africa does not have its Andes, Alps, or Himalayas because it remained when the blocks which once enclosed it began to drift away, leaving it a high, rigid, crystalline shield. Having possessed no coast line for millions of years, it did not experience coastal accumulations and did not crumple on its margins. But, though rigid, it could not escape the effects of the forces which came to fracture Gondwana, of which it was the core. Surrounded by great escarpments where the break had taken place, experiencing monoclinal subsidence where the supporting neighbor had gone (as in Natal), the interior of the shield itself began to fail. As the rivers found their way to the coasts, great faults ran through the backbone of the plateau, and the Rift Valley System came into prominence. The Madagascar separation, permitting the Zambezi to reach the sea, was preceded by similar events involving the Niger, Congo, and Orange rivers.

Although there is not yet a satisfactory answer to questions concerning the mechanism of Continental Drift, it is clear that the actual process of separation is of an oscillatory nature, involving, in any given area, tensional as well as compressional forces. It is, thus, not surprising that the rifts show the

---

[13] J. Keidel, "La Geologia de las Sierras de la Provincia de Buenos Aires y sus relaciones con las montanas de Sud Africa y los Andes," *Anales de la Ministerio de Agricultura de Argentina,* XI, No. 3 (1931).

19

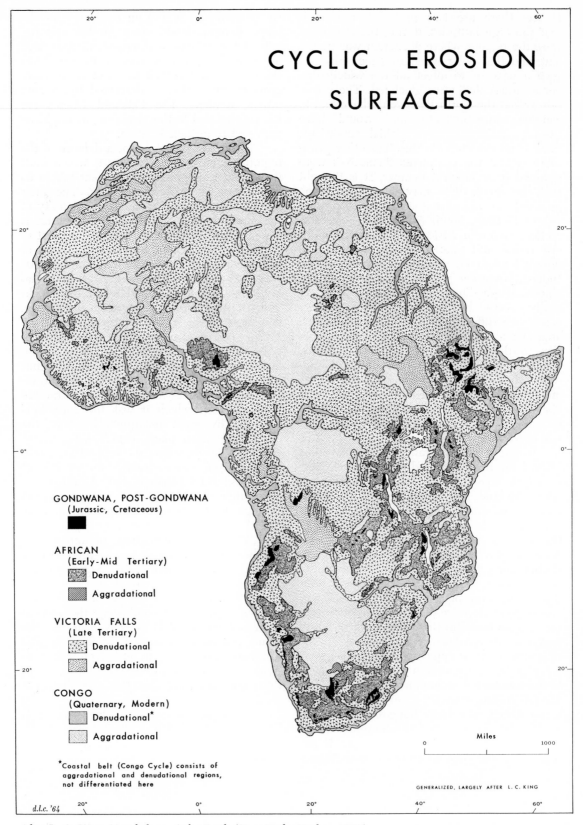

CYCLIC EROSION SURFACES

GONDWANA, POST-GONDWANA
(Jurassic, Cretaceous)

AFRICAN
(Early-Mid Tertiary)
Denudational
Aggradational

VICTORIA FALLS
(Late Tertiary)
Denudational
Aggradational

CONGO
(Quaternary, Modern)
Denudational*
Aggradational

*Coastal belt (Congo Cycle) consists of
aggradational and denudational regions,
not differentiated here

Miles
0   1000

GENERALIZED, LARGELY AFTER L. C. KING

d.l.c. '64

After L. C. King, *Morphology of the Earth* (New York: Dutlon, 1963).

Map 5

The Gondwana Erosion Surface in the Basutoland Highlands, Drakensberg, Southern Africa. and which has been elevated to about 10,000 feet in this area. The retreating escarpment is This is a remnant of the erosion surface that once extended across the Gondwana land mass, reducing the areal extent of the Gondwana surface still remaining. (Satour)

effects of both, causing some confusion about the dominant force present. There are many other unsolved problems in connection with the actual process. Why Gondwana—and its Northern Hemisphere counterpart, Laurasia —remained unbroken until the late Mesozoic is not certain. Many paleontological details remain to be uncovered. The absence of final proof does not, however, impair the value of the hypothesis for which Africa forms the foundation and which is indispensable for an understanding of Africa's physiography.

Cyclic Erosion Surfaces

While the African continent was for so long a period a part of the Gondwana supercontinent, it partook of the beveling the entire land mass experienced. Thus, after the extrusion of the Drakensberg basalts, which spread across much of South America, India, and Antarctica, Gondwana was planed prior to the final fragmentation which was to carry the separate remnants to their present locations. The surface which extended across the supercontinent is referred to as the Gondwana cyclic erosion surface, and its equivalents have been recognized in Africa as well as other continental areas, cutting across the basalts, crystallines of the ancient shield, and other rock formations. This Gondwana surface is one of a series of cyclic erosion surfaces which have been identified and mapped, in places as far apart as Brazil, Africa, and Australia, by Lester C. King.

King has placed the entire field of geomorphology on a new footing, using Africa and the other fragments of Gondwana as his laboratory.[14] He has suggested that, if such plantation as described above is a reality, the remnants of the cyclic erosion surfaces on the various segments of Gondwana should still be recognizable, just as other correlations can be made in stratigraphy and paleontology. Surfaces which developed in Gondwana before fracturing are the Pre-Karroo surface (which Wellington had recognized as the Pre-Karroo Peneplain before King came to realize its greater significance[15]) and an Intra-Karroo surface. The Pre-Karroo surface was created across much of Gondwana before the great sequence of the Karroo was deposited. It is now being exposed where the overlying Karroo beds are eroding away. The Gondwana surface, on the other hand, having developed just prior to fragmentation and across the beds which represented the culmination of Karroo accumulation, has not been buried and has been under constant attack by subaerial erosion since the Cretaceous. Hence, it survives only on elevated plateau regions, and the prime example is the upper surface of the Basutoland Plateau.

In order for surfaces as old as the Gondwana to survive even in small part, it is clearly necessary to postulate the retreat of slopes as the dominant mode of erosion. Indeed, the acceptance of the concept of peneplantation would automatically invalidate the bulk of King's work, and hence he has developed the ideas of Walter Penck and has much refined them.[16] The surfaces of Gondwana, and indeed erosion surfaces everywhere, are thought to be pediplanes, formed by the backward erosion of scarps according to certain rigid physical laws.[17] Thus, when Gondwana splintered, one of the immediate results was the

initiation of retreat of the slope of the embryo Great Escarpment, and a Post-Gondwana surface began to develop. Since much depends upon the elevation of the area undergoing planation above sea level, however, and considerable uplift occurred soon after the initiation of the Post-Gondwana cycle, its areal extent is limited. Hence, in the Early Tertiary, a surface formed in Africa which covers most of the plateau today; this is the African surface. The African surface has its equivalent in South America, where it is known as the Sul-Americana surface, the most widespread of Brazil's erosion surfaces. "Study and mapping of this surface in Brazil have left an indelible impression . . . of its identity with the African cyclic landscape, as judged from its visible features."[18]

Two additional major cycles of erosion have affected the African plateau since the African cyclic erosion surface formed. The first of these developed in the Late Tertiary, and the latest is a Quarternary surface. Only along the major rivers and in marginal regions are they extensive in their areal development. The Late Tertiary surface (called the Victoria Falls Cycle by King) is particularly well developed in the Limpopo, Zambezi, and Congo regions, where it forms the rise from the Quaternary in the valleys to the African surface of the Plateau.[19] The Quaternary surface appears confined to the very marginal areas, but is very extensive also in the Congo Basin. Hence, it has been called the Congo surface, and it is this surface which extends over much of the Moçambique Coastal Plain, up the Zambezi River as far as the Kariba Gorge, and along the entire coast of Southern Africa. Because of its youthfulness, the Quaternary surface has not had sufficient time to develop extensive planed regions across hard bedrock.

From this summary of the recognized ero-

---

[14] L. C. King, "The World's Plainlands: A New Approach in Geomorphology," *Geological Society of London Quarterly Journal*, CVI (1950), 101–31.

[15] J. H. Wellington, "The Pre-Karroo Peneplain in the South-Central Transvaal," *South African Journal of Science*, XXXIII (1937), 281–95.

[16] L. C. King, "Canons of Landscape Evolution," *Bulletin of the Geological Society of America*, LXIV, No. 7 (1953), 721–53.

[17] L. C. King, "The Uniformitarian Nature of Hillslopes," *Transactions of the Edinburgh Geological Society*, XVII, Part 1 (1953), 81–102.

[18] L. C. King, "A Geomorphological Comparison between Eastern Brazil and Africa," *Geological Society of London. Quarterly Journal*, CXII (1957), 445–74.

[19] L. C. King, *South African Scenery* (Edinburgh: Oliver & Boyd, 1951). See map in rear. It has, since completion, been revised to some extent, additional Late Tertiary topography having been recognized in the southeast, particularly Swaziland and Natal.

sion surfaces in Subsaharan Africa, especially Southern Africa, it might be deduced that everywhere in Africa and the former components of Gondwana there should be a steplike ascent from the Quaternary on the coast, via the Late Tertiary and the African surfaces, to the remnants of the Gondwana surface. Although this steplike appearance is not everywhere immediately evident, there are places where it is dramatically displayed. The ascent from the coastal regions of Natal to the top of the Drakensberg is one. There, it is possible to stand in such a position as to observe the Gondwana atop the Drakensberg, the African surface to the northwest, the Late Tertiary underfoot, and the Quaternary in the valleys of the eastward-flowing rivers. This situation prevails across rocks which dip in several directions, which have been faulted extensively, and which have been affected by monoclinal folding; the landscape retains evidence of the reality of geomorphic evolution.

A vast quantity of research remains to be done on the physiography and geomorphology of Africa. Mapping of erosion surfaces, analysis of the rifts, and hydrographic study of many river basins are just a few of the many topics yet inadequately considered. As more becomes known, it is clear that the individual features of Africa's physiography may have a common history. The escarpment of the Futa Jallon and that of the Drakensberg bear considerable resemblance to each other. The Zambezi River and the Niger appear to have undergone similar stages in their erosional history. The rifts of Nyasaland are structurally and topographically comparable to those of East Africa and beyond. The possibility of their interrelationship appears strong, and Continental Drift and the concept of former unity of Gondwana provide the link.

2

CLIMATOLOGICAL ASPECTS OF SUBSAHARAN AFRICA,
WITH REFERENCE TO ASSOCIATED FEATURES

THE GREAT BULK of Subsaharan Africa lies between the tropics. Only the southern part of the continent, including most of the Republic of South Africa, is not part of tropical Africa south of the Sahara. Consequently, the image most often associated with Africa is one of heat and humidity, and over a large part of the region this impression is verified by the facts. The equator more or less bisects the area here under consideration, and, as a result, much of it is under rainforest and savanna conditions.

Africa's climates, however, do not lack diversity. Because of the elevation and extent of the African Plateau, the escarpment which forms its rim, the narrow coastal belt, and the ocean currents along the shores, there is considerable variation, although perhaps not as much in temperature as in precipitation. While there are places along the slopes of Mount Cameroun which receive as much as 400 inches of rainfall annually, areas in the same general latitude in northern Kenya are semiarid. Large portions of the Congo Basin experience over 75 inches of rainfall each year. Freetown, Sierra Leone, on the west coast, has an average annual precipitation well in excess of 170 inches. In contrast, Port Nolloth, on the Cape coast just south of the mouth of the Orange River, has just over 2 inches, and Khartum, in the Sudan, less than 6. Although there are extremes of this kind on every continent, the areas affected are so large in Africa that they take on great significance there. The Sahara Desert is the largest area in the world

which can be climatically so defined, and the Kalahari Desert of Southern Africa, with the coastal Namib Desert, occupies about half of the combined areas of South Africa, South West Africa, and the High Commission Territories (Basutoland, Bechuanaland, and Swaziland). The vastness of the tropical basin of the Congo requires no elaboration, and the heat and humidity of West Africa, from the Niger Delta to Cape Verde, are legendary.

The Tropical Climates

Climatologists have devised systems of regional classification of climates, providing at the same time a basis for the cartographic representation of the situation and a framework for description.[1] The Köppen system (see Map 6) produces a rather symmetrical pattern for Subsaharan Africa.

RAINFOREST

A large part of equatorial Africa is under tropical rainforest conditions, best exemplified by the region near the confluence of the Congo and Ubangi rivers. There, the enervat-

---

[1] For some examples, see D. B. Carter, *Climates of Africa and India According to Thornthwaite's 1948 Classification,* The Johns Hopkins University Laboratory of Climatology, *Publications in Climatology,* Vol. VII, No. 4 (1954).

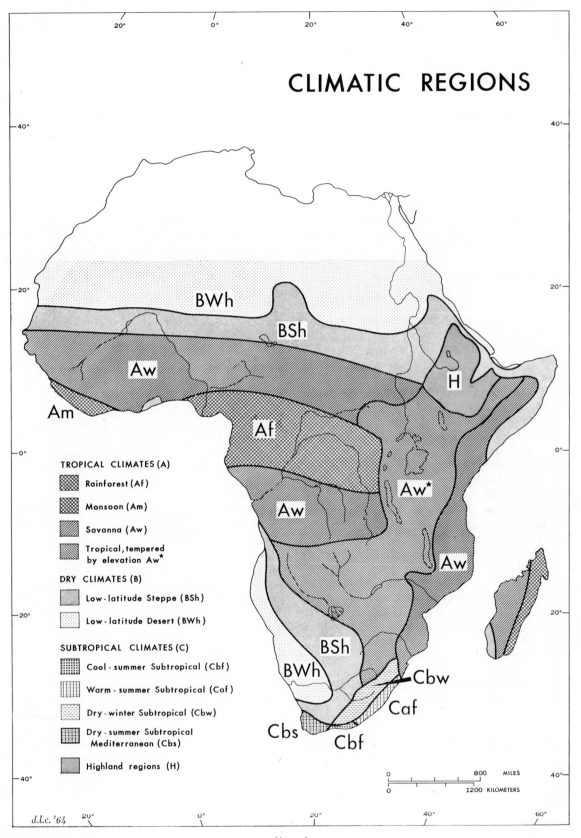

CLIMATIC REGIONS

BWh

BSh

Aw

Am

Af

Aw*

Aw

Aw

H

TROPICAL CLIMATES (A)

Rainforest (Af)

Monsoon (Am)

Savanna (Aw)

Tropical, tempered
by elevation Aw*

DRY CLIMATES (B)

Low-latitude Steppe (BSh)

Low-latitude Desert (BWh)

SUBTROPICAL CLIMATES (C)

Cool-summer Subtropical (Cbf)

Warm-summer Subtropical (Caf)

Dry-winter Subtropical (Cbw)

Dry-summer Subtropical
Mediterranean (Cbs)

Highland regions (H)

BSh

BWh

Cbw

Caf

Cbs

Cbf

800 MILES

1200 KILOMETERS

d.l.c. '64

Map 6

FIGURE 1
TEMPERATURE AND PRECIPITATION AT NOUVELLE ANVERS, CONGO

	J	F	M	A	M	J	J	A	S	O	N	D	
Temp.	79.2	80.1	79.2	78.1	79.2	78.4	76.5	76.3	77.0	77.4	77.9	78.1	Year Range 3.8
Prec.	4.1	3.5	4.1	5.6	6.2	6.1	6.3	6.3	6.3	6.6	2.6	9.3	Year Total 66.9

ing conditions of high temperature and humidity prevail which seem to dominate almost every aspect of life in the tropics. The seasons pass virtually unnoticed, as the unbroken monotony of hot, rainy days is only slightly ameliorated by the nightly drop in temperature of about 15 degrees Fahrenheit. Even so, "night is the winter of the tropics," for the annual temperature range (the difference between the means for the warmest and coolest months) is less than the daily range, as illustrated by conditions at Nouvelle Anvers, Congo (see Figure 1).

It is a common misconception that the hottest temperatures recorded are those of the tropics. In fact, daytime temperatures there rarely rise above 100 degrees Fahrenheit and are usually in the high eighties. More important is the high precipitation and its even distribution through the year; the tropical rainforest does not have a real dry season, although there is usually a distinct period of maximum precipitation. In places, due to the migration of the heat equator and associated factors, there is a double maximum of rainfall.

As a result of the warmth and moistness of the tropics, the growing season is uninterrupted, and luxuriant vegetation exists. The excessive amount of rain causes heavy latozation of the soils, which in consequence are rich in residual iron and aluminum, but poor in many essential plant nutrients. As will be seen subsequently, the actual area covered by the vegetation climax known as the rainforest is only a portion of the region which is under the climatic type of the same name. The great problem of the rainforest areas does not lie in the clearing of dense vegeta-

tion. It involves, rather, the soil quality, the high incidence of diseases stimulated by the heat and humidity, and the absence of the dry period required for the harvesting of grain crops. Malaria, yellow fever, sleeping sickness, and a host of other plagues afflict all of the tropical regions and much of the remainder of Subsaharan Africa, but it is in the tropics that their severity is greatest and the battle against them still in the beginning stages. For all practical purposes, pastoralism is impossible, and agriculture has developed in a shifting form which is an adaptation to the limitations of the region.

As a result, Africa's tropical areas have suffered from lack of advancement. Communications, health conditions, education, and other forms of organization have lagged there, compared to Africa's more favored parts. Apart from some rubber, the tropical lowlands of Africa have not produced significant resources, and in the absence of the impetus provided by resource exploitation, most of the work of improving conditions there remains to be done.

In the region of the Congo Basin, two major air circulations have been recognized as important in creating the conditions described above. There is a constant inflow of moderately moist air from the southwest. These air masses originate over the relatively cool waters of the South Atlantic Ocean, and there are no great mountain barriers to hamper their eastward progress, often to the very eastern edge of the basin of the Congo River. From the northeast come the trade winds, which travel in exactly the opposite direction. Thus, a zone of convergence is created, which is thought by some climatologists to be a major contributor to the processes of precipitation affecting the region.

This, however, is only one possibility. For many years, it was held that South Africa's interior rainfall originated in the southeast trades, until studies of the upper air circulation completely revised the matter. Similarly, some climatologists hold that the bulk of the Congo Basin's moisture comes from the east, rather than the west, and they assert that the upper air circulation may provide an answer similar to that found in the case of the South African Plateau. Those who feel that the southwesterly influx is the major source of Congo rainfall support their hypothesis by pointing to the effect that the high plateaus and mountains of East Africa would have upon moisture-laden air from the Indian Ocean traveling westward. By the time such air would reach the eastern Congo, they reason, much of that moisture would have been removed by orographic processes.

The assertion that air masses of differing character, converging in a zone across the Congo Basin, cause precipitation there leads to a re-examination of popularly held ideas concerning the nature of precipitation in tropical areas. There is increasing evidence that such rainfall does not simply derive from heat-of-day thermal convection areas located at random across the vast region. Although convection clearly plays a part, and the monotony of late-afternoon showers, so frequently described by observers, no doubt is a reality, there are also periods of rain which fail to conform to this pattern. Apparently, major disturbances attended by severe thunderstorms and heavy precipitation can be recognized, and these seem to originate from the meeting of contrasting air masses and to have linear characteristics. They appear to move across the country in the manner of the familiar frontal systems of the middle latitudes,

but there is doubt regarding their direction and velocity. So uncertain are climatologists about this problem that some suggest that these zones move eastward, carried by the southwesterlies, while others believe that they move in an opposite direction and are pushed by the prevailing easterlies.

Along the coastal belt of West Africa, rainforest and tropical monsoon conditions also prevail, but in this case they give way rapidly to drier conditions in the interior. The obvious cause of the heavy coastal precipitation (except for a small area along the Ghana-Togo coast, to be discussed later) would appear to be orographic, with moist air flowing toward the plateau edge of the continent. Conditions in West Africa are exceedingly complex, however, and much remains to be learned concerning them. In addition to the orographic type of precipitation, especially evident in the high Cameroun interior behind Douala, convectional rainfall also probably occurs. Furthermore, the vertical zone of contact between the interior and maritime air masses produces rain, although there is no agreement concerning the mechanism involved. Finally, disturbances of other kinds have been recognized, one of which is in the category referred to as the easterly wave. This results from horizontal contact between the surface, moist air of the southwesterlies and the upper layer of the easterlies. The turbulence resulting in rainfall is created within the lower air mass, but the whole system is carried westward by the easterlies.

The double rainfall maximum (monsoon) recorded over a section of the West African coast has also proved problematic. One maximum (in June at Axim, Ghana, and in August in Freetown, Sierra Leone) occurs "normally," as pressure systems move northward during the Northern Hemisphere summer. Then, when the zone of convergence between the

FIGURE 2
PRECIPITATION AT AXIM, GHANA, AND FREETOWN, SIERRA LEONE

	J	F	M	A	M	J	J	A	S	O	N	D	Total
Axim	2.0	2.4	5.0	5.6	16.5	21.0	6.1	2.1	3.3	8.0	7.5	3.5	83.0
Freetown	0.6	0.5	1.1	5.4	14.8	21.3	36.8	39.6	32.5	15.2	5.3	1.3	174.4

FIGURE 3
TEMPERATURE AND PRECIPITATION AT BATHURST, GAMBIA

	J	F	M	A	M	J	J	A	S	O	N	D	Year Range
Temp.	74	75	76	76	77	80	80	79	80	81	79	75	7
Prec.	0	0	0	0	0.2	2.9	10.9	19.6	10.0	3.7	0.2	0.1	Year Total 47.6

FIGURE 4
TEMPERATURE AND PRECIPITATION AT SALISBURY, SOUTHERN RHODESIA

	J	F	M	A	M	J	J	A	S	O	N	D	Year Range
Temp.	69.7	68.8	68.2	65.7	60.6	56.9	56.1	60.2	66.4	70.7	70.7	69.6	14.6
Prec.	7.5	7.4	4.5	1.0	0.5	0.1	0.0	0.1	0.3	1.1	3.7	5.8	Year Total 32.0

southwesterlies and the easterlies is still far to the north, and the inflow of moist air is apparently uninhibited, a rapid decline in precipitation occurs—more rapidly in the region of Axim than in Freetown. It has been suggested that the cause might well be sought in the South Atlantic Ocean, which is, at that time, under an anticyclone which may extend somewhat north of the equator and may just be able to influence the southern parts of the littoral. This may be one explanation for the differences between Axim and Freetown, whose rainfall patterns are shown in Figure 2.

The mechanism behind the low-sun (winter) maximum is also still a subject for debate. It is possible that the zone of convergence between the southwesterlies and the easterlies remains sufficiently close to the coast, during the winter season, to permit an occasional incursion of moist, maritime air. Some have attributed the southerly winds of winter to the normal land and sea breezes resulting from the differential heating of land and sea, and the influx of moist air by means of this system.

It will have been noted that frequent reference has been made to the zones of convergence between air masses possessing different characteristics. Climatologists are only now beginning to understand the characteristics of this zone, or series of zones. A more complete discussion of this feature is postponed until later.

SAVANNA

Literally surrounding the "core" of tropical rainforest conditions in Subsaharan Africa is the tropical *savanna*, which extends over most of the land mass. The major difference between rainforest and savanna conditions lies not so much in temperature as in amount and distribution of precipitation. Temperature conditions show a slightly greater annual range which, however, usually is less than 15 degrees Fahrenheit. Total annual precipitation, on the other hand, is significantly less toward the outer margins of the region, and there is a distinct dry season. It should be emphasized that there is no sharp break between the rainforest and savanna, so that the inner margins of the latter resemble the rainforest. The heart of the savanna, nonetheless,

Savanna Vegetation and Fauna, Rhodesia. Each dry period, the drinking places reduce in number and shrink in size, and animals congregate in huge concentrations around those that still provide some water. These giraffe are representative of a species occurring throughout the savanna lands of Southern and Eastern Africa. Note the bushy growth in the background and the large tree nearby. The annual rainfall in this area is about 30 inches.

displays conditions which cannot be confused with the wet rainforest, as exemplified by Bathurst, Gambia (see Figure 3).

A large portion of Subsaharan Africa lies at considerable elevations, which have a moderating effect on the heat of the tropics. Thus, the rainforest region does not extend across all of equatorial Africa, being interrupted by the East African Plateau. The location of these plateau regions and their height affect both temperature and rainfall conditions. Douala, Cameroun, less than 5 degrees north of the equator and on the west coast, has an average annual rainfall of over 400 inches,

while Nairobi, Kenya, which lies just south of the equator but on the plateau and in the east, has only about 34 inches of rain annually. Although the plateau is largely mapped as savanna, many individual stations, for instance, Salisbury, Southern Rhodesia, have climatic data to show that they should be classified as temperate climates (see Figure 4). The moderating influences of the elevated plateau have been of profound importance to the course of settlement, particularly white settlement, in Subsaharan Africa. Kenya's White Highlands, the Katanga-Copperbelt region, the Southern Rhodesian Plateau, the Bihé Plateau of Angola, and the South African Highveld would, without their elevation, be continuations of the normal African savanna, with all its liabilities. Instead, these areas possess climates which rank among the most acceptable, to whites, in the world.

The savanna vegetative association is unmistakable. Tall grasses and scattered, flat-topped trees give much of Africa's savanna lands an appearance which has appropriately been termed "parkland." Although hard and not particularly nutritious, the grasses sustain the bulk of Africa's cattle population. This, also, is the land of the great herds of antelope. There, in regions as yet remote from the advancement of civilization, elephants, buffalo, eland, giraffe, wildebeest, and countless other species roam by the thousands. Aware of the dangers facing this unparalleled heritage, man has established a number of game reserves in which Africa's fauna find refuge.

Three general areas of savanna may be recognized in Subsaharan Africa. The first lies to the north of the rainforest zone in West Africa, where the increasing dryness renders the belt rather narrow. Its boundaries there are indistinct. A second area lies to the south of the Congo Basin, covering much of the South Equatorial Divide. The third and largest zone occupies the great highlands of the

east, and, surprisingly, it extends all the way to the coast of Equatorial Africa. From what is known of the general atmospheric circulation, it might be presumed that the windward coasts of East Africa would be moister than they are. On the other hand, the coastal savanna of East Africa yields rapidly to the desert of Somalia northward, and to the rather dry coastal plain of Moçambique southward.

The air masses which appear to affect this eastern part of Africa originate in three separate areas. In the heart of savanna East Africa, the annual migration of the wind and pressure belts is reflected by the alternation of northerly winds (during the period from October to March, the Southern Hemisphere summer) and southeasterlies (during the Northern Hemisphere summer). In addition, there is an occasional westerly component, carrying air from the South Atlantic Ocean across the Congo Basin and into the eastern highlands.

Thus, the air reaching the eastern part

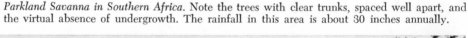

Parkland Savanna in Southern Africa. Note the trees with clear trunks, spaced well apart, and the virtual absence of undergrowth. The rainfall in this area is about 30 inches annually.

The Margin of the Desert, Griqualand West, South Africa. This area lies in the northern Cape Province, and the stony ground and little tufts of vegetation would seem to render any form of agriculture or pastoralism impossible. Yet in territory like this, goats and sheep manage to survive, often destroying what vegetation is left and promoting desert encroachment. (South African Information Service)

of Africa from South Africa to southern Ethiopia would appear to possess all the characteristics favorable to precipitation, and yet relatively little rainfall is recorded. Several factors might explain this apparently anomalous situation. As is indicated below, there are reasons to believe that the inflow of air from the northeast as well as the southeast takes place in a rather thin layer, above which there is air which is much drier. In the case of South Africa, the trades which hit the Great Escarpment may have a vertical extent of less than 10,000 feet, and thus fail to cover the interior highlands. In East Africa, also, the air mass would have to be of great depth in order to carry much moisture onto the plateau. Of course, if there is indeed a drier layer of air overlying the trade-wind layer, the vertical development of clouds and, consequently, the rainfall would be inhibited.

In addition, attention has focused upon the actual path of these "monsoon" winds from the east. Actually, the northeast trades have traveled great distances across land rather than water; some of the air flowing in from the north has moved around the western side of the Ethiopian Plateau. Those winds coming from the northeast travel parallel rather than into the land, and this has the effect of reducing the precipitation. The moister air flowing in from the south has moved long distances across warm water, but, as it approaches the coast, its trajectory, too, becomes more meridional. If these air masses struck the coast at right angles, considerable precipitation would result. Their paths, however, appear to be among the causes underlying East Africa's rainfall deficiency.

Surface divergence and subsidence of air also create dry conditions. This situation appears to prevail over much of the eastern savanna land of Africa, and it is a contributing factor in the picture of dryness. Possibly the island of Madagascar affects the mainland. It is high, with a steep eastern slope directly in the path of the southeast trades. Indeed, Madagascar's eastern escarpment shows the sort of precipitation to be expected

31

in windward equatorial regions (around 100 inches annually). But western Madagascar receives less than 30 inches over extensive areas, and a large part of the African continent lies in the lee of the great island mass. There, the winds become more meridional, the air subsiding and divergent, and again the situation is one of rainfall deficiency.

Exactly what does produce the rainfall on the savanna lands of eastern Africa is still uncertain. Nairobi (34 inches) and Dar es Salaam (45 inches) are near the lower limit of savanna moisture conditions, and yet one city lies in what would appear to be an orographically favorable position, and the other is on the coast. It is much less easy in these areas to trace the effect of zones of convergence than it is in West Africa. Lines of disturbance have been noted forming in the air mass when it is still over the ocean, and these then move toward the coast in a west-northwesterly direction. Since a situation seems to prevail which is not entirely dissimilar to that recorded in West Africa (a moist lower layer overlain by a drier air mass), the disturbance may likewise be of the character of an easterly wave. It is also possible that surges of air from the south, invading the southeasterlies, produce the disturbance recorded. In the interior, the western part of East Africa's plateau may be affected by invasions of air from the Congo Basin and, ultimately, the South Atlantic Ocean. Finally, the great South African anticyclone, to be discussed later, may influence the weather of the savanna lands of East Africa.[2]

Steppe and Desert

Along the northern and southern margins of the savanna lie Africa's extensive steppe lands. In the north, the steppe forms the belt of transition between savanna and Sahara, and in the south it is the heart of the Kalahari. The steppe is marked by sparse grasses

which, however, support cattle in many areas. Pastoralism in these regions with unreliable precipitation and dry winters is a precarious enterprise, severe cattle losses being a frequent occurrence. Notwithstanding this, the practice continues, with the result that overgrazing creates dustbowl conditions and erosion, permitting desert encroachment. In parts of northern and southern Subsaharan Africa, desert advancement is a real threat.

The variable steppe precipitation does not usually exceed 20 inches annually. In Africa's low-latitude steppes, where evaporation ratios are high, the effectiveness of even this moderate amount is greatly reduced. Almost always, the rain which falls is concentrated during the high-sun season, with the winter period being extremely dry, as exemplified by Mogadishu, Somalia (see Figure 5). The African steppe is not devoid of tree growth, and, particularly in the Kalahari Basin, a thorny acacia manages to survive on the generally poor and shallow soils. Its existence is of great importance to the cattleman, for without the shade trees of the steppe the cattle would not survive.

In the desert, Africa's climates reach many of their extremes. Although outside the scope of this book, the Sahara is of significance in this respect, for its influences are felt far beyond its technical limits. In the dry Sahara originates the harmattan, a wind which sweeps south toward the Gulf of Guinea. There, also, daytime temperatures have been known to exceed 130 degrees Fahrenheit in the shade. Deserts are regions of extremes, and hot days may be followed by cold nights, as the cloudless sky permits the loss of great amounts of long-wave radiation in short periods of time. As a result, the environment is hostile and inhospitable. Mechanical erosion is dominant; soil-forming processes are slow and ineffective; vegetation is sparse or nonexistent; and only the hardiest of animals survive.

Some of Subsaharan Africa's desert areas are almost completely dry. In the southwest is the Namib Desert, which lies adjacent to the Kalahari. A combination of factors produces dryness there. The Namib lies in the northwestern and southwestern (dry) quadrants of the Kalahari Anticyclone, so that

---

[2] For a summary of various views regarding this problem, see G. T. Trewartha, *The Earth's Problem Climates* (Madison: University of Wisconsin Press, 1961), pp. 121–37.

FIGURE 5
TEMPERATURE AND PRECIPITATION AT MOGADISHU, SOMALIA

	J	F	M	A	M	J	J	A	S	O	N	D	
													Year Average
Temp.	77	79	81	82	80	77	75	76	76	77	76	77	78
													Year Total
Prec.	0	0	0	7.0	2.2	3.5	2.0	0.6	0.5	0.7	0.4	0	16.9

FIGURE 6
TEMPERATURE AND PRECIPITATION AT SWAKOPMUND, SOUTH WEST AFRICA

	J	F	M	A	M	J	J	A	S	O	N	D	
													Year Range
Temp.	62.6	63.1	63.3	59.9	60.6	58.5	56.5	54.9	56.1	58.1	58.6	61.5	8.4
													Year Total
Prec.	0	0.1	0.2	0	0	0	0	0	0	0.1	0	0	0.6

the pressure situation prevents precipitation. In addition, the coastal margin (to a width of only a few miles, however) is influenced by the Benguela Current, which produces relatively cool temperatures, and, not infrequently, a fog which forms over the water and drifts slowly inland. Namib conditions are typified by Swakopmund, South West Africa (see Figure 6). This station indicates the cooling effect of the Benguela Current, lying as it does within the tropics.

The interior of the Namib Desert, merging into the western Kalahari, is somewhat less dry. Five inches of rain are recorded about 70 miles inland from Swakopmund, and the region around the capital of South West Africa, Windhoek, actually gets about 15 inches. The coastal regions of the southwest are the driest, but, with the ascent of the plateau, the precipitation totals rise, to drop again toward the heart of the Kalahari.

Mediterranean Climate

The southern tip of the African continent just penetrates those latitudes which partake of the cyclonic storms and westerly winds reminiscent of the regime of the Mediterranean region proper. In this area, rainfall comes in moderate amounts and is concentrated during the winter period. Vegetation is xerophytic and similar to the chaparral, maquis, and other types of Mediterranean vegetative associations found throughout the world. Where the rainfall is between 20 and 30 inches annually, sclerophyllous bush thrives. Soils are generally poor, but the region is one of ridges and valleys, and some of the valleys contain soils of good quality. Slope incidence is high, and rock outcrops

FIGURE 7
Temperature and Precipitation at Cape Town, South Africa

	J	F	M	A	M	J	J	A	S	O	N	D	
Temp.	69.9	70.3	68.1	63.2	58.9	55.7	54.7	55.6	57.9	61.2	64.4	67.9	Year Range 15.6
Prec.	0.7	0.6	0.9	1.9	3.8	4.5	3.7	3.4	2.3	1.6	1.1	0.8	Year Total 25.3

give parts of the zone an impression of barrenness.

In the small Mediterranean region of Southern Africa, the months of January and February, being almost constantly cloudless, are the warmest. The annual range of temperature is of the order of 15 degrees Fahrenheit, the normal warmest and coldest months averaging approximately 70 and 55 degrees, respectively. During the clear summer months, the area is thought to be under the influence of stable air associated with the subtropical high-pressure belt; in winter, the westerly wind belt migrates northward and brings with it the cyclonic storms producing rain and many gray, overcast days. Although only a small part of the subcontinent is affected, the region of Mediterranean climate is flanked by a belt of steppe having low-sun precipitation maxima. The classic example of the type is Cape Town (see Figure 7).

Humid Subtropical Climate

Along the southeast coast of Southern Africa lies a narrow region of true humid, mesothermal climate, characterized by summer maxima in precipitation. Somewhat cooler than the tropical savanna to the north, summers in this area are nevertheless hot, with lower temperature conditions mainly in the winter period. The region is limited by the rapid rise of the plateau slopes toward the interior. Except for some frost due to katabatic flow (air drainage), which is confined to val-

ley lowlands, subfreezing temperatures do not occur.

In terms of precipitation, the contrast between summer and winter is not as great as in the interior. Although most rain comes during the summer, there is no month with less than one inch of rain. Rainfall is orographic, as might be expected from the topography of the area and the prevailing winds, but, of course, convectional storms occur in the summer. The coasts are influenced by the warm Moçambique Current, and the southeast trades arrive laden with moisture from these waters. In winter, when the entire system moves to the north, it is the coasts of Moçambique and Madagascar which continue to benefit from the moisture (particularly exposed Madagascar), and the drier period sets in further south. The situation is illustrated by the climatological data of Durban (see Figure 8).

There is a transition zone between the humid subtropical region and the Mediterranean area. Lying just to the west of Port Elizabeth, this area receives the precipitation from the cyclonic storms in the westerly wind belt during its winter, and in summer it is exposed to the onshore winds, as is Durban. There, precipitation may exceed 50 inches annually.

The South African Plateau Climate

The plateau of South Africa is known as the *Highveld,* suggesting its elevated nature

FIGURE 8

TEMPERATURE AND PRECIPITATION AT DURBAN, SOUTH AFRICA

	J	F	M	A	M	J	J	A	S	O	N	D	
Temp.	76.3	76.8	74.9	71.8	67.8	64.8	64.3	65.8	67.6	69.5	72.0	74.6	Year Range 12.5
Prec.	4.6	4.9	5.4	3.4	1.9	1.2	1.2	1.7	3.2	5.1	5.0	5.1	Year Total 42.7

FIGURE 9

TEMPERATURE AND PRECIPITATION AT JOHANNESBURG, SOUTH AFRICA

	J	F	M	A	M	J	J	A	S	O	N	D	
Temp.	65	64	62	59	55	50	50	55	59	61	63	65	Year Range 15
Prec.	5.6	5.0	3.8	1.3	0.7	0.1	0.3	0.6	0.9	2.7	5.1	4.8	Year Total 30.9

and grassland vegetation. There is justification for singling out this region climatically, as its latitudinal location (well outside the tropics) and altitude combine in creating a comparatively cool clime.

Extremes are considerable on the plateau. Summer days can be oppressively hot, while frosts occur in winter. In high regions such as the Drakensberg, snowfalls are not infrequent. Winters are dry, and, after sunny days, rapid radiation losses cause inversions of temperature. Jackson has disproved the long-accepted assertion that Southern Africa is under the influence of cyclonic conditions during the summer and anticyclonic conditions during the winter.[3] It has become clear that the circulation over the plateau is essentially the same throughout the year, namely, a rather weak anticyclone centered over the eastern margin of the subcontinent. In winter,

this cell is somewhat stronger than in summer, when it is forced to move southward. During the dry winter season, the result is a high frequency of westerly and northwesterly winds.

Another common misconception eliminated by Jackson's research involves the source of precipitation for the plateau. It was long assumed that the trades penetrated the entire southern part of the continent, bringing rain not only to Natal, but to plateau areas as well.[4] This would involve the occurrence of easterly winds on the plateau, but observations show that there is no great difference between the summer and winter circulation, that is, northwesterly and northerly winds continue to predominate even during the summer. There is an occasional easterly component, but it is by no means sufficiently strong to account for the entire precipitation regime; it is explained by the southward

[3] S. P. Jackson, "Atmospheric Circulation over South Africa," *The South African Geographical Journal*, XXXIV (December, 1952), 1.

[4] W. G. Kendrew, *The Climates of the Continents* (Oxford: Clarendon Press, 1941), p. 123.

FIGURE 10

TEMPERATURE AND PRECIPITATION AT BLOEMFONTEIN, SOUTH AFRICA

	J	F	M	A	M	J	J	A	S	O	N	D	
													Year Range
Temp.	73	71	67	60	53	47	48	52	59	63	68	72	26
													Year Total
Prec.	3.8	3.3	3.6	1.8	1.1	0.4	0.4	0.5	0.9	1.7	2.1	2.3	21.9

migration of the anticyclone, part of the northern sector of this system.

In summer, the anticyclonic circulation transfers maritime, potentially unstable air from the region of the Limpopo mouth and further north onto the plateau. The actual mechanism producing the rainfall, which is particularly heavy in the east, probably lies in the convergence between the plateau anticyclone and adjacent oceanic anticyclones. In the interior, convectional storms are common, with the formation of cumulo-nimbus clouds, severe thunderstorms, and rapid clearing. Summer days on the plateau are hot, but they are tempered by the elevation. Conditions at Johannesburg, South Africa, illustrate the situation (see Figure 9). The effects of elevation and latitudinal location are indicated by a comparison between the statistics of Johannesburg (6,000 feet) and Bloemfontein (4,500 feet). Lying lower and further south, Bloemfontein's summer temperatures are higher, and winters are much colder, with frosts occurring on one of every four July nights, and severe frosts being experienced each year (see Figure 10).

Because of the decline from the plateau Highveld to the coastal regions, a number of transitional belts are recognized along the escarpment which on a continental scale do not warrant examination. Frequent summer mists occur along these plateau slopes. On the plateau itself, the highest rainfall totals are recorded immediately above the eastern scarp: Havelock in Swaziland receives 74 inches annually. As the figures for the cities given above indicate, the totals decrease rapidly westward and southwestward.

Special Features

A number of aspects of the climates of Africa have been under the scrutiny of meteorologists and climatologists. Many others are still not well understood, owing to the relatively small number of recording stations and consequent scarceness of data. The situation is improving, however, and the mechanisms behind several of Africa's climatic peculiarities have been identified.

INTERTROPICAL FRONT

Because of the vastness, relative emptiness, and isolation of many tropical regions, the processes responsible for equatorial climatic conditions have long been a matter for speculation. In regions where strongly contrasting air masses come into frontal contact with one another, producing situations which are well understood, weather predictions have long been based upon the air mass concept. Barometric changes, wind shifts, temperature variations, and cloud conditions all betray the existence of a contact zone between air masses which differ in terms of stability, humidity, and a number of other features. In the tropics, however, there is indeed converging air, but the precipitation is usually seen as resulting from convection, owing to the great accumulation of surface heat produced by intense radiation. Efforts have been made to apply the frontal concept to equatorial regions as well as middle latitudes. The term

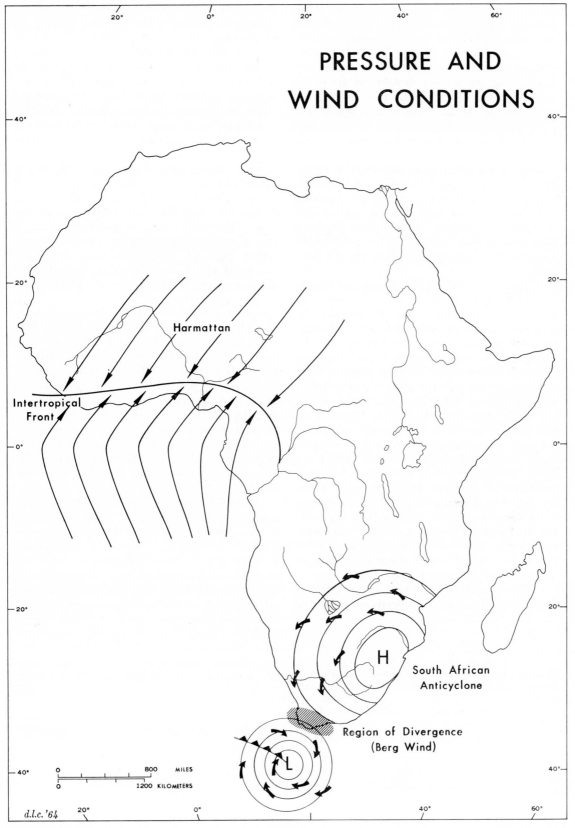

PRESSURE AND
WIND CONDITIONS

Harmattan

Intertropical
Front

H

South African
Anticyclone

Region of Divergence
(Berg Wind)

L

MILES
800

0
1200 KILOMETERS

d.l.c. '64

Map 7

Intertropical Front came to replace Intertropical Convergence, some meteorologists believing that the air masses flowing into the equatorial pressure trough from the north possess qualities which differ sufficiently from those air masses flowing in from the south that the contact plane may be referred to as frontal.[5] Riehl, however, has stated that "the trough is placed so that northern and southern trades reach it after complete equalization of their thermodynamic properties."[6] Stamp, on the other hand, continues to recognize the Intertropical Front as of "supreme importance" in African climatology, pointing out that it is not well defined, particularly in terms of position, presumably implying that comparisons to cyclonic frontal disturbances in the westerly wind belt are not relevant.[7]

There are, undeniably, strong and significant differences between the air originating over the Sahara source area (By virtue of its location and direct association with subtropical high-pressure areas, the Sahara may be considered a source region.) and that air which flows onto the African plateau from oceanic regions. Saharan air is warm and dry; it is also more stable than the moist, warm air originating over the water. Whether or not these differences are strong enough to produce a semblance of frontal conditions upon contact depends to some extent, as Riehl has pointed out, upon the observer's definition of the term *front*. Actually, there are few topographical barriers to the movement of air across the African land mass. As the heat equator migrates, so does the front, resulting in its temporary disappearance from the West African scene when dry Saharan air flows out into the Guinea Gulf.

The frontal concept of tropical African climatology has recently been strongly endorsed by Alissow.[8] It is pointed out that the differences between the two dominant types of air over the central plateau are not confined to humidity conditions; the maritime air is not only moister, it is also cooler than the Saharan air. Using West Africa as the example, the Intertropical Front thus has the effect of limiting the precipitation (whether orographic or of other origin) to its southern side. If the air flowing in from the Guinea Gulf is weak, and that originating in the Sahara is strong, rainfall will occur in only a small section of the coastal strip of West Africa, and all that lies north will continue to be dry until the front retreats from the coast. The front, thus, is not marked by a line of rain-producing cumulo-nimbus clouds; rather, the contact between moist air on the one hand and warm, dry air on the other results in mixing, along the contact plane, higher moisture-holding capacities, lower relative humidity conditions, and an abrupt termination of precipitation. As such, the front does not resemble mid-latitudinal warm or cold fronts, each associated with rainfall. Its behavior is less predictable than the cyclonic fronts of the westerlies. Its migration is the result of contrasts in strength between humid and dry air masses, and in West Africa, its frequent failure to move northward, preventing the penetration of moist air inland, is a prime cause of the unreliability of precipitation only relatively short distances from the coasts.

The Intertropical Front (or ITC, as it is referred to frequently) has been recognized in places other than West Africa. It exists in East Africa, forming the zone of convergence between the air masses flowing in from the northeast and southeast. But in East Africa it has proved a far less useful tool for the interpretation of weather phenomena and the making of predictions than in West Africa. With the recognition of front-like conditions in tropical areas, however, the idea of random thermal convection as the dominant mode of precipitation there has been discredited. Further work will no doubt increase the

[5] C. E. P. Brooks and S. T. A. Mirrlees, "A Study of the Atmospheric Circulation over Tropical Africa," *Geophysical Memoirs*, Vol. VI, No. 55, (1932).

[6] H. Riehl, *Tropical Meteorology* (New York: McGraw-Hill, 1954), p. 238.

[7] L. D. Stamp, *Africa* (New York: John Wiley & Sons, 1953), p. 71.

[8] B. P. Alissow, *Die Klimate der Erde* (Berlin: Deutscher Verlag des Wissenschaften, 1954), pp. 88 ff.

understanding of the nature and effects of the Intertropical Front in Africa.

HARMATTAN

During the winter months, the coastal regions of West Africa are influenced by northeasterly winds emanating from the subtropical high-pressure region over the Sahara Desert. The excessively moist conditions of the coasts are driven away, to be replaced by the dry, often cool air from the interior. Relative humidity percentages may drop to between 10 and 20, skies clear, and the general effect is one of relief for the inhabitants. Known as the *Harmattan,* this outflow of air may be strong and very persistent, affecting not only the coastal regions but continuing far out into the Gulf of Guinea.

While bringing relief to the coasts, the Harmattan is often hot, dust-laden, and stifling in the steppe interior. Its effect on man, animals, and vegetation can be disastrous when its reign is unbroken for long spells. Swirling dust storms and severe droughts occur, and the failure of vegetation and consequent overgrazing result in destruction of the vulnerable grass cover and much-feared desert encroachment.

ANOMALY ON THE WEST AFRICAN COAST

Although most of the coast of West Africa is under tropical rainforest conditions, a small area in the Ghana-Togo-Dahomey littoral is semiarid. Its dryness is reflected in the vegetation, which elsewhere is forest, but there becomes a dry savanna. Rainfall in this area is well below 30 inches, when elsewhere along the coast it is three times as much. Not only do stations in this zone record a low annual precipitation total, they also show dryness during the month of August, when the sun is high and all would seem to point to a maximum of rainfall. In addition, August, although dry and sunny, also has the lowest temperature average for the year.

Several conditions probably combine to produce this aspect.[9] The region in question lies just east of Cape Three Points, where the

coast line bends northeastward. Axim, west of the Cape, records over 80 inches of rain annually, while Accra, just to the east, receives 29. Stations along the dry coast record winds with a westerly component throughout the year. This means that such winds are more nearly at right angles to the coast line west of the Cape, but almost parallel east of it. Such parallel flow could produce divergence and local subsidence, and rainfall would be reduced.

The dryness of the month of August in this region is duplicated in a less spectacular manner elsewhere along the coast of West Africa, and reference has been made previously to the possibility that the strong anticyclone over the South Atlantic Ocean may influence the region. In the BSh area (see Map 6), however, the drought is so much deeper than it is elsewhere along the coast that further explanations are demanded. One such explanation may lie in the appearance, along this part of the coast, of cold water. This may be an extension of the cold Benguela Current, attendant upon the northerly movement of the South Atlantic anticyclone. The water appears to be in this area only from July until September, and may contribute to the August drought in Accra. The entire anomaly has been attributed to this cold water, but it is likely that its influence is confined to the period immediately after the May-June rainfall maximum. The remarkable coolness of the coast during August also may be due to the appearance of this water at that particular time.

BERG WIND

Along the coastal regions of South and Southeast Africa, from Cape Town to Natal, air movement associated with heating takes place from the plateau to the lowlands. Known as *Berg Winds,* the heating has often been considered due to subsidence and compression, but Jackson has shown that this apparently simple explanation does not suffice.[10]

---

[9] Trewartha, *op. cit.,* p. 108.

[10] S. P. Jackson, "Air Masses and the Circulation over the Plateau and Coasts of South Africa," *South African Geographical Journal,* XXIX (April, 1947), 13.

In Cape Town, a warm, clear, winter day marked by the heating of the Berg Wind is commonly followed by cloudiness, fog, and rain. In Cape Town, Port Elizabeth, and other coastal cities of South Africa, the Berg Wind's warming effect is often spectacular.

Jackson, pointing out that subsidence and dry adiabatic heating would appear an obvious explanation for the Berg Wind, proved that the real mechanism has long been misunderstood. In fact, the understanding of the Berg Wind was the direct result of his new interpretation of the circulation on the plateau itself. Katabatically initiated downward flow of plateau air would soon cause temperatures higher than the stable air at subplateau levels, and the air drainage would come to a halt long before the lowlands of the coast could be affected. Hence, it was argued, there must be a pressure situation causing air to be drawn from the plateau. Surface and near-surface divergence is representative of such conditions.

During the southern winter, the Cape is affected by cyclonic storms. On the plateau, the anticyclone is strong. When an anticyclone and cyclone lie in close proximity, divergence occurs, particularly in the region of their closest approach. This takes place when the northeast sector of a storm-producing cyclone and the plateau anticyclone come into contact: air is drawn from higher levels, not only from the plateau (where heating is also recorded), and surface temperatures rise rapidly. As the cyclone progresses on its path toward the east, it brings the frontal storms for which the Cape in winter is noted, rapidly destroying the clear, warm day caused by the initial subsidence. The Berg Wind, first recorded in Cape Town, may later be felt in Port Elizabeth.

The mechanism of divergence explains several of the peculiarities of the Cape and Natal coast lands' winter. In this manner, the limited nature of the areas affected is explained; it had long been a question why the Berg Wind should be concentrated in one region, rather than affecting the entire coastal lowland at the same time. It is now possible to suggest a relationship between the observed winds and the pressure systems that exist, and it has been noted that in terms of speed and direction such a relationship is

real. In addition, the cloudy, rainy weather immediately following the Berg Wind is understandable when it is seen that both are the result of the same depression. Finally, the complete disruption of the normal land- and sea-breeze circulation, which is strong and persistent along the coasts, is explained by the imposition of a powerful pressure pattern. Simple subsidence would be unlikely to disrupt this system so completely.

COLD WAVES ON THE PLATEAU

It has been stated previously that the subtropical anticyclone is the dominant controlling agent in the climate of Southern Africa. It moves north and south with the local winter and summer, the former being cool and dry, the latter, moderate to warm and moist. Throughout the year, however, and especially during the winter months, the plateau experiences repeated invasions of very cold air, which may bring 10 or more degrees of freezing even to the Transvaal, during the months of May to August. These cold spells, or "cold snaps," as they are locally called, are associated with rapidly dropping barometric pressure and southerly winds.

Apparently, the cold waves are associated with the low-pressure cells which, particularly during the winter, affect the Southern Cape. At times, such a depression is very strong and spreads over much of the southern part of the continent, temporarily displacing the usual anticyclone. Then, the cyclone is succeeded by a very strongly developed high-pressure cell, which covers all of the south from the Cape to perhaps as far as the Zambezi. At this time, strong winds blow from the south across the entire plateau, often bringing severe drops in temperature and much discomfort.

Cold waves are especially intense during the late fall and early spring, which, in view of the transitional nature of the anticyclone at that time, is explicable.[11] In winter, although the anticyclone is strong, the cyclones which are associated with the development of the conditions necessary for the cold snap

[11] S. P. Jackson, "Notes on the Occurrence of 'Cold Snaps' at Johannesburg," *South African Geographical Journal*, XIV (December, 1933), 34.

are likewise most fully developed and located farthest to the north, and the result is an increase in the frequency of cold wave occurrences. However, sudden cold snaps may occur even in midsummer. B. S. Young has described the weather of Natal between January 1 and 9, 1960, in these terms, speculating that the marked drop in temperature was the result of conditions similar to those described above.[12] A large low-pressure area was located to the south of the land mass, but it moved unseasonably toward the northeast, trailing a cold front across the country. As a result, temperatures behind the front dropped sharply, but in 48 hours the anticyclone which is normally present over the region was restored. The difference between the summer and winter cold spell appears to lie in the role played by the anticyclone, which in winter sweeps cold air into the interior, after having replaced the invading cyclone. In summer, however, it is the cyclone itself which brings in the cold air; with redevelopment of the high-pressure cell, the invasion is terminated. Young maintains that it is indeed an outbreak of polar air which produces the cold snap, but the actual origin of the low-temperature air masses has not yet been finally determined.

Those mechanisms of African climate which are now becoming understood are clearer only because long-term data are accumulating, and the facilities for meteorologists are expanding, if slowly. Only with upper-air data has it been possible to interpret the observed wind velocities and directions of the plateau, and only through the study of inversions associated with Berg Winds and cold waves have these features become better understood. Although gaps remain, the climatology of Subsaharan Africa is slowly being pieced together.

Climate and Man

Various attempts have been made by climatologists to classify the climates of the world in terms of their suitability for human settlement, efforts which were especially popular during the period when environmental determinism was intensively studied. For Africa, such work was carried out by Brunt and Jackson, who used hourly values of dry- and wet-bulb temperatures for selected stations.[13] Their major interest was to locate those areas in Africa which appeared to be suitable for European settlement for certain periods of the year, as opposed to those which seemed unsuitable all year long.

Of course, there are serious dangers inherent in work of this kind. Philips has pointed out that the influence of wind was discounted in these studies, and many other factors were not taken into consideration. Obviously, a map based mainly upon temperature and humidity shows "suitable" areas in the highlands and along the southwestern desert coast, and it so happens that many of the white settlement concentrations do lie in the higher areas. But have these Europeans come to those suitable areas because the climate there is attractive, or because there is economic opportunity? Would Johannesburg not have attracted a great influx of whites whether its climate was dry-winter subtropical or rain-forest, as long as it proved to lie on the world's greatest gold field? Kenya's Highlands are pleasantly cool on the very equator, but the combination of physical factors has produced excellent soils yielding profits for farmers. Would the Europeans not have come if those same profits could have been made, but in climatically less "comfortable" regions?

Obviously, Africa's environment differs from place to place, and in some places it is easier for individuals, whatever their race, to do certain things than in others. The all-pervading problem in tropical Africa is that of water supply; it affects all those who live on the land, and, not infrequently, also those who live in the cities. Compared to other tropical areas, the percentage of land in Africa that receives a high annual precipitation is relatively small, and a large part of the region that does receive much rain is rather sparsely populated. Most Africans live in the climatic zone defined as savanna, and as has

[12] B. S. Young, "A Summer Cold Spell," *Nucleon*, II (July, 1960), 48.

[13] J. Philips, *Agriculture and Ecology in Africa* (London: Faber and Faber, 1959), p. 52, gives a summary of these efforts.

been indicated, the savanna is subhumid over vast areas. A marked dry season brings serious problems for the pastoralist, and somewhere in Africa thousands of livestock die every year as wells and streams run dry and fodder becomes unavailable. For the agriculturalist, much depends upon the amount of moisture the preceding wet season has brought: adequate rainfall and good crops render survival easier during the lean dry season. But over much of Africa, rainfall variability is high, and a failure of the rains during the wet season brings hunger during the ensuing dry season. The bulk of East Africa's savanna lands, for instance, receive their expected quota of rain during only one wet season out of every three.

Even when the rains do come, their effectiveness is vastly reduced. Often, the rains arrive in severe storms after the sun has parched the countryside for months and has baked the soil's upper layer into a hard, dry crust which defies all farm implements. The result is that much of the rainfall, rather than seeping down into the soils's lower layers, becomes useless runoff—worse than useless, for it contributes to erosion, breaks through the crust to create gullies, and carries great quantities of valuable soil off to the ocean.

When, after the initial onslaught, the soil has been softened and the water begins to seep down, its effectiveness in stimulating plant growth continues to be reduced because, most of the time, there simply is not enough water available. Africa, by virtue of its latitudinal location, receives a great amount of radiation, and the high temperatures cause the evaporation of much of the badly needed water brought by the rains. D. B. Carter's analyses have shown that, except for the rainforest, the vegetation cover requires more than the entire annual precipitation *before* runoff and evaporation. In the global heat balance, low-latitude areas experience the greatest amount of excess insolation (over outgoing radiation). Thus, a rainfall figure of 40 inches, considerable in marine west coast latitudes, may be only one-third as effective in equatorial regions.

These conditions are, of course, reflected by the soils of Subsaharan Africa. It is unfor-

tunately true that few areas possess good soils, and that most of the continent has decidedly poor ones. The high temperatures, the torrential nature of the rainfall, and the parent materials have combined to produce a pedology which is marked by poverty in lime, potash, magnesia, and phosphorus. The lack of organic material (humus) and the tendency to form "hardpan" layers also contribute to render many African soils low in fertility and extremely difficult to work.

Most of these problems stem from the climatic environment under which the soils have evolved. The high temperatures accelerate bacterial activity to the point where much of the product (nitrates of various kinds) is lost before it can be used up by the living vegetation. The nature of the precipitation and the high temperature of the rain water contribute to produce deep soils, leached in their upper horizons of the materials so badly needed there. What remains after the wet season is the evaporated content of the rapidly percolating waters: compounds rich in aluminum and iron. These are the materials that help constitute the "hardpan," through which roots penetrate with difficulty and which facilitates the runoff through which so much rain water is lost. These iron and aluminum compounds color the soils, called *latosols* by pedologists, the familiar reddish-yellow of the tropics.

Practically every aspect of these latosols is disadvantageous to agriculture. As deep weathering takes place, the waters carry the valuable nutrients to horizons farther and farther from the root level of the plants above. With time, the processes affecting the soil make it worse, not better, for more and more of the essentials are carried downward and, eventually, what is left depends upon the composition of the parent material. If it was rich in quartz, a sandy soil remains; if there was much feldspar, a clayey latosol. Both react badly to attempts to use machines in farming. In the case of the sandy soil, compaction is often the result, while the clay variety is extremely difficult to work because of its hardness after exposure and its stickiness when moist.

To be sure, there are some areas where

better soils have evolved, and where soils have been found capable of artificial improvement. As is true elsewhere in the world, alluvial soils are among the best in Africa, and in some areas extensive deposits have been laid down by the great rivers. The Niger becomes braided between Bamako and Timbuktu, and there the alluvial soils form the basis of an extensive irrigation scheme. Similarly, alluvial soils lie between the White Nile and its tributary, the Blue Nile, and another such scheme has been developed there. Projects on a larger or smaller scale can be found along almost every sizeable river in Subsaharan Africa, the Juba in Somalia, the Zambezi in Rhodesia and Moçambique, the Orange, Vaal, and Pongola in South Africa, and so forth.

Certain nonalluvial soils also have been found to be of good quality, such as those on the South African Highveld, the Southern Rhodesian Plateau, and the Highlands of Kenya, as well as on the slopes of the Cameroun Highlands. These soils have resulted from particular parent materials and unusual climatic conditions, and they support the few really important cash-cropping regions of the continent. But there is nothing in Africa to compare with the agricultural cores of Europe and Anglo-America in terms of size and yields per acre, and in a continent where the vast majority of the people still make their living off the land, this is a somber reality.

The traditional method by which the African living on the poorer soils has countered the problem has been that of shifting cultivation. With increasing population growth and pressure and the expansion of cash cropping, this process has become more and more difficult, and the introduction of change in an organized fashion, however problematic, has become imperative. Although shifting cultivation ought not to be dismissed as wasteful and ignorant, as Europeans unaware of its background have done, its effects are undesirable. It is destructive and promotes soil erosion, often ruining areas beyond repair and initiating gullying that cannot be halted.

The introduction of changes, however, is a difficult process. Changes must come in land-tenure systems, techniques of cultivation must be improved, and the regular use of fertilizers, in areas where these are applicable, must be encouraged. But changing peoples' association with their lands is difficult, foreign agricultural techniques may be completely unsuccessful in Africa, and the presence, over extensive areas, of the tsetse fly precludes the raising of cattle and, therefore, the local production of fertilizer. Means to store and conserve water must be established under local responsibility, a practice remarkably absent in Subsaharan Africa in spite of its difficult environment.

Among the most spectacular changes introduced have been those involving irrigation schemes, whether the barrages were built specifically for the purpose of irrigation (as at Gezira on the Nile) or initially for the production of electric power (as on the Volta River in Ghana). Africa is especially well endowed with hydroelectric potential, totalling perhaps 40 per cent of that of the world, and many hydroelectric projects have associated benefits in that they facilitate the irrigation of adjacent lands. On these irrigated lands are examples of individual land tenure, cash cropping, mechanization, cooperative ventures, and other aspects of progress that must come to agriculture in Africa. In the case of the Sansanding scheme on the Niger and the Gezira scheme on the Nile, these projects have come to form the economic core areas of Mali and Sudan, respectively. But even the smallest dam built of mud and branches is of significance, for every drop of Africa's water must be put to use.

Irrigation projects do not escape the environmental obstacles Africa puts in the way of progress in agriculture. The number of acres that can be irrigated depends upon the number of square miles of catchment area, the amount of rainfall received there and its reliability, and the climatic conditions at the irrigated area, among other factors. Much depends also upon the physical characteristics of the storage reservoir, the loss of water by evaporation from it, and the efficiency with which the irrigation water can be distributed to the cropped areas. This, of course, is true of any irrigated area, but the particular vagaries of the African climate emerge again as major problems. A very small rainfall during

Soil Erosion in the Eastern Region of Nigeria, West Africa. Deep soils, a moist climate, and tropical vegetation which is easily disturbed and destroyed combine to produce tremendous scars in the landscape. The scale of this particular area of erosion can be realized from the height of the tall trees at the forest edge about to be attacked. Once such erosion has been initiated, it is very costly and difficult to stop, and in this particular instance, it is going on unchecked, forcing people to leave the areas about to be affected.

Alluvial Soils and Irrigation Along the Orange River, South Africa. Amid the dry steppe lands around Upington, the waters of the Orange and the soils of its valley permit intensive cultivation up to a few hundred yards from the water's edge. The scene is reminiscent of many along the Nile River, and the contrast between the dry, barren landscape and the cultivated belt of green is as great as it is in the Sudan and Egypt. The Orange River is to be the object of a major irrigation and flood-control project exceeding the TVA in size. (South African Information Service)

a wet season in the catchment area, and consequent inadequate replenishment of the water in the storage reservoir, can mean disaster in the intensively cultivated lands, and the low reliability of rainfall has already been emphasized. Just as it is possible to estimate the amount of moisture required by the vegetation cover on the savanna, so the number of acre-feet required by a planted crop can be calculated. The acreage that can be irrigated is related to the amount of water provided by the catchment area; if it fails to produce that water, and the storage reservoir empties, crop failures result. Thus, what may happen on the smallest scale to an individual's grazing land somewhere on the plateau can be paralleled by major problems in large irrigation projects. The dams are built to regulate the water supply and raise the water level for purposes of distribution, but in the end that supply is still dependent upon the annual precipitation and its variability.

Every country in Subsaharan Africa shares in some measure in the severe problems presented by the climatic environment. Although it is indeed possible, on a continental scale, to marshal a number of exceptions which would seem to give cause for optimism, these are islands in a sea of difficulties. Only one country, South Africa, shows a really significant degree of climatic and pedologic diversification, but it lies almost entirely outside of tropical Africa. More money has been spent on the improvement of agriculture in South Africa than in any other African country, yet even there droughts, soil erosion, vegetation depletion, low yields on farmland, and desert encroachment rank among the major concerns.[14] Improving the use made of the limited opportunities for agriculture provided by the climatic environment over much of Africa is a slow and difficult process. It involves far more than the study of meteorology and pedology and the understanding of the mechanisms behind the processes observed. It involves more even than the introduction of fertilizers and improved farming methods. Many aspects of the African peoples' ways of life are responses to the rigors of the environment. To counter the consequences of that environment is but one step. It must be accompanied by changes in those ways, and that is quite another.

---

[14] South Africa is presently engaged in the development of the Orange River Project, which will outrank the TVA in size when completed in the 1970's. See A. S. Reyner, "Water Conservation Projects in the Republic of South Africa," *Journal of Geography*, LXII, No. 5 (May, 1963), 197.

3

AN OUTLINE OF THE HISTORICAL GEOGRAPHY
OF SUBSAHARAN AFRICA: PEOPLES AND REGIONS

SUBSAHARAN AFRICA's early history is known only in fragments, due to the paucity of documentation. During the last few years, however, a concentrated effort has been made to reconstruct the African past. This is partly because of the unprecedented involvement of academicians in the African field, and it is also a consequence of independence for Africa's political entities. Africans themselves desire to re-establish their links with a history full of achievements which was interrupted by the colonial episode. Still held by some observers of the African scene, however, is the opinion that Africa at the time of colonization was a continent of tribal savages completely devoid of political sophistication, economic organization, and artistic achievement. This false image is now being destroyed.

Indeed, the very lateness of the European invasion of Africa is evidence for the degree to which Africans were organized. While sometimes at enmity with one another and even willing to cooperate with European and Arab in the evil of slavery, they protected their inland trade routes effectively. For example, in the hinterlands of the Gold Coast trading stations and in the gold-producing areas of Southern Rhodesia, the African middlemen successfully repelled for centuries European efforts to encroach.

If it cannot be claimed that Africa during the past several hundred years was in the center of the world stage, it must be emphasized that during hundreds of thousands of years previously, Africa was indeed the heart of the inhabited world. There, the evolution of Homo sapiens has been traced from very early beginnings, when the making of tools commenced. Africa's Pleistocene stratigraphy has yielded an orderly sequence of objects made by man's ancestors, ranking from the earliest stone pebble tools to hand axes. At Olduvai, in Tanganyika, a sequence covering about two and a half million years has been found. Perhaps during the later phases of the Pleistocene glaciation, which was felt in East Africa as a series of wet and dry periods and was reflected by variations in the Rift Valley lake levels, the use of fire was discovered. That may have been 50,000 years ago, during a dry period which probably coincided with a glacial advance and possibly brought colder weather to equatorial regions. Man sought shelter in caves, began to make new and different tools, including many with wooden handles, and started to use bone and wear skins. Finally, Homo sapiens appeared on the scene—in Africa probably an early ancestor of the present-day Bushman. The entire sequence is recorded in Africa more perfectly than anywhere else, and "there is little doubt that throughout all but the last small fraction of [the] long development of the human form, Africa remained at the center of the inhabited world."[1]

The Bushman in all probability was not

---

[1] R. Oliver and J. D. Fage, *A Short History of Africa* (Harmondsworth: Penguin Books, 1962), p. 15.

Bushman Paintings, South Africa. Much has been learned about the former distribution of the Bushmen, the animals they hunted, and their modes of hunting and dress from paintings such as these found in caves and on protected rock ledges throughout Southern Africa. The large antelope above seems to be an eland, the others possibly springbuck.

Bushwomen and Children, South West Africa. The number of Bushmen is dwindling. Some still live virtually without shelter, with merely a windbreak for sleeping. Many wear less clothing than those in this illustration. The men of the family shown here are probably off hunting, while the women and children await news of a kill. If the animal killed is large, all may move to the place where it dropped and remain until the meat has been eaten. Note the sandy soil underfoot and the vegetation in the background, which suggest that this is by no means the driest part of the Bushman's environment (South African Information Service)

A Bushman in the Kalahari Desert. This young man is demonstrating one of several means by which the Bushmen hunt. In addition to the bow and (often poisoned) arrow, the Bushmen use the spear to hunt such animals as ostriches, buck, and even giraffe. They set traps and snares and also may poison water at a drinking hole not used by themselves. In addition, they are known to use the method of disguise very effectively and display an almost unbelievable knowledge of the habits of their prey. Unfailing trackers, Bushman hunters read the veld like a book and are able to locate animals by the most minute bits of evidence. (South African Information Service)

the only occupant of the African stage at this early time. It is thought that a distinct Negroid type appeared in the forests of the west (whereas the Bushman occupied the eastern highlands), and in northeastern Africa a later arrival was a Caucasoid, proto-Hamitic type. This last representative migrated into northern and eastern Africa, along the Mediterranean coast and the East African lakes, and

made major contributions to the cultural development of the continent by introducing the idea of barbs for spears and arrows, special chiseling tools for wood and bone, and pottery.

Archaeologists, anthropologists, linguists, and historians have attempted to reconstruct the events that followed the arrival of man on the African scene. Using linguistic phenomena in present-day Africa as their guide, researchers suggest that, in addition to the languages of the Hamitic people of the northeast and the Khoisan language of the southern Bushmen, two major ancient language groups existed in the Africa of about 5,000 years ago. Perhaps the region of Lake Chad formed a dividing belt between them; in any event, there seems to have been a Western Sudanic and an Eastern Sudanic group. The former existed in the forests and savanna lands of West Africa, and the latter extended from Lake Chad to the Nile River. When one studies the individual languages within each group, it quickly becomes clear that they have been developing in separate ways for many centuries, because they differ greatly from each other. When this situation is compared to that prevalent among the Bantu group of languages predominant in Africa south of the equator, it is noted that these Bantu languages are much more closely related to each other, so that they may be considered to be much younger. From this and other data, it is deduced that the peopling of Africa to the north of the equator, east and west of Lake Chad, took place long before that of southern Africa. That is, the arrival of the modern inhabitants of southern Africa and the displacement of the Bushmen and Pygmies by Bantu peoples occurred possibly after A.D. 1, while agriculture and its consequent expansion of population had been felt for more than 3,000 years previous in Sudanic Africa.

The agricultural revolution experienced by Subsaharan Africa came in several distinct phases. In the savanna lands, the growing of cereals probably was first learned in the east and then spread to the west. But many of the crops found in other parts of Africa were introduced from other continents and probably did not arrive until after the beginning of the Christian era. Bananas and yams, for instance, came from Asia, possibly during the first centuries A.D., and the present-day staples of corn and cassava came from the Americas as late as the sixteenth century. Thus, the southern part of Subsaharan Africa apparently lagged some 3,000 years behind the Sudanic regions in this field, perhaps the major reason why the dispersion of the Bantu-speaking peoples came so late.

Contact with Asia brought more than food crops to Subsaharan Africa. Immigrants arrived from Southeast Asia, including Indonesia, and they settled along the East African shores, later to migrate to Madagascar, where they became the ancestors of the present-day Malagasy people.[2]

One of the remaining questions connected with the peopling of Subsaharan Africa involves the location of the core region from which the Bantu spread. Some researchers favor the theory that this dispersal took place from the southern margins of the equatorial forests, while others suggest that the Cameroun Mountains and the surrounding forests formed the Bantu heartland. Whatever the answer may be, the use of iron was probably discovered in Africa while this migration was in progress, and the hunting, fishing, and gathering early Bantu were superseded by the expanding agricultural and pastoral later Bantu. These later representatives conquered and absorbed Bushmen and Pygmies, but their competition with the more stubborn Hamites of the east was lengthy and less successful. There, too, much intermixture took place, and eventually the Hamitic people were displaced or absorbed also, leaving linguistic and somatic evidence of their former hegemony.[3]

While all these changes were in progress in Subsaharan Africa, and the coming of cultivation and iron implements was producing major population growth and migrations, the focus of an even more important transformation lay in the northeast of the continent, whence the concept of organized agriculture

had spread. For there in Egypt, urban centers began to develop, great strides were made very rapidly in political and religious thinking, great artistic achievements occurred, and economic activity was carried farther than ever before. In an amazingly brief period, political unity was achieved in the most highly complex, most densely populated state of its time. For several thousand years, Dynastic Egypt was the heart of power and the source of ideas for Africa and the world. The empire expanded southward and subjugated Africans; slaves were brought to the cities; trade connections extended well into the Subsaharan part of the continent.

By the last millennium B.C., Egypt had begun to lose power, and it eventually was overrun by Assyrians, Persians, Greeks, and Romans. But beyond Nubia, Cush survived as a remnant of the civilization for another ten centuries, now in closer proximity to black Africa and counting many black African subjects, although led by Caucasians. Its decline came soon after the beginning of the Christian era and was due in large part to a shift in economic power to the rival trading state centered on Axum in the northern Ethiopian highlands. When the final collapse of Cush occurred, many of its leaders may have fled westward, taking with them their ideas and knowledge about various aspects of state organization. In any event, in order to follow the evolution of politico-territorial organization in Africa south of the Sahara, it is necessary to survey the political situation in widely separated parts of the continent, and especially in West Africa.

Early African States

Progress was being made in Subsaharan Africa in the sphere of socio-political organization, not on a scale comparable to that of Egypt, but the advances were by no means insignificant. Indeed, to some extent they were influenced by Egyptian thinking, and one of the striking characteristics of widely separated African states is that some of the prevalent practices are so alike that they must have had a common origin. Egypt no doubt gave to

---

[2] *Ibid.*, p. 32.

[3] The Hamitic peoples extended far into Southern Africa, and some believe that the Hottentot people, related to the Bushmen, originated in the mixture of Bushman and Hamitic strains.

SOME PRE-EUROPEAN STATES

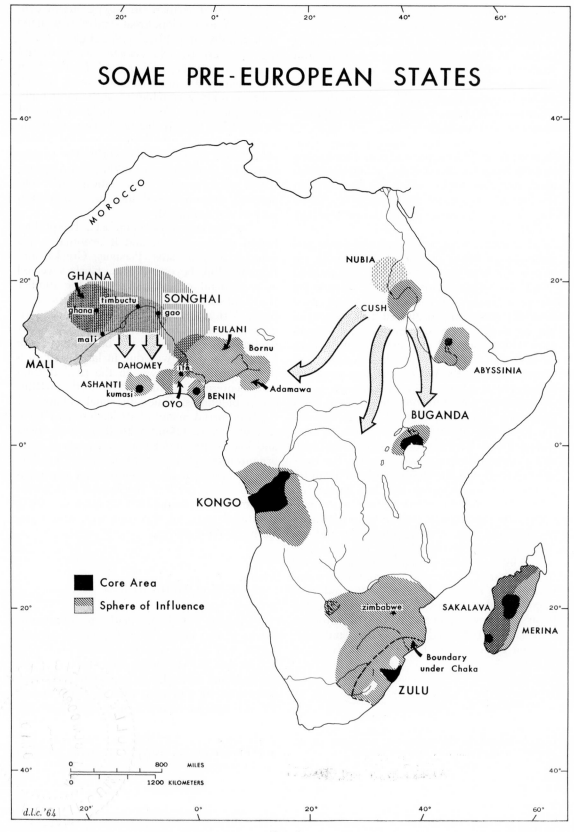

MOROCCO

GHANA

ghana

timbuctu

SONGHAI

gao

mali

FULANI

Bornu

MALI

DAHOMEY

ifè

Adamawa

ASHANTI

kumasi

OYO

BENIN

NUBIA

CUSH

ABYSSINIA

BUGANDA

KONGO

zimbabwe

SAKALAVA

MERINA

Boundary
under Chaka

ZULU

Core Area

Sphere of Influence

0   800   MILES

0   1200 KILOMETERS

d.l.c.'64

Map 8

Subsaharan Africa the idea of the divine powers of kings. African states, during the first ten centuries of the Christian era, existed in areas as far removed as present-day Mali and Southern Rhodesia, Katanga and Chad. They mined the gold of West Africa and Southern Rhodesia and the copper of Katanga, and they probably built great structures such as Zimbabwe. They were not simply enlarged tribes: their administrative structure was often complex, their populations in several cases must have exceeded a million, and they engaged in trade and commerce.

Most commonly, the early states in Subsaharan Africa were imposed by military conquest, sometimes by invaders from the north and northwest, and at other times by black people who were skillful enough at making and using arms to permit them to subjugate diverse peoples. Such states as were created, therefore, were nearly always imposed upon the agriculturalists of the savanna lands and the forests. They included groups of people with very different customs and languages, and they survived only as long as the conquering minority could manage to extract tribute from the subverted population. Sometimes there was little cohesion in the state, the only real binding agent being the periodic collection of tribute by the ruler and his agents. Often the state would take the form of a cluster, with a strong central kingdom and less effectively controlled provinces around the margin. But internally, these states were not ruled in a hereditary fashion by a succession of descendants of a privileged family. They were not normally feudal in character—although Africa has seen feudalism, for instance in Ethiopia—and the great administrative force serving the divine king was a sometimes endless array of viceroys, officials, chiefs, and other agents.

Having been imposed by conquest upon diverse peoples, these states collapsed when the strength of the controlling minority failed. Often, subverted chiefs were willing to cooperate with new invaders seeking to overthrow the local authority, or would rebel on their own accord if they saw the opportunity to regain their independence. Corruption was rife, especially if the same force ruled for a long period.

What the rulers gained, in addition to the comforts of living off the local agricultural people, was control over trade routes passing through the territory under their sway and a virtual monopoly over their state's own external trade. Most probably, the first of these loose states were created in those regions where the trade routes passed, yet not very far (on a continental scale) from the regions where so much political progress had been made. This means that several of them are likely to have been located in the Sudanic belt east of Lake Chad, and that, from this general vicinity, these political experiments took place further and further west and south. Hence the apparent similarities in the customs of those states about which something is known.

The earliest of the West African states about which much information has been gathered is *Ghana*. It was located in the western part of present-day Mali, to the north of the major headwaters of the Senegal and Niger rivers. It has not been possible to date the origins of the Ghana state with exactness, but it probably was in existence about the fourth century A.D. Its economic foundations, however, are quite well understood. The river valleys to the south contained alluvial gold, much of which was mined and exported northward. The actual mining was done by Mandingo people, who lived outside the sphere of Ghana proper, but these people exchanged the gold for salt and other products they required. Also taken from the south were slaves, to be sold on northern markets. From the north, caravans brought copper, dried fruit, cowries, and other merchandise which was exchanged in Ghana and then distributed throughout the Sudan.[4]

It is easy to see that Ghana's situation was an extremely favorable one from the economic point of view, and that control of its area would yield great profits. This was possibly first recognized by immigrants from northern parts of Africa who came to settle among the Soninke (Negro) peoples and founded a dynasty. As was mentioned pre-

---

[4] J. D. Fage, *An Introduction to the History of West Africa* (Cambridge: Cambridge University Press, 1962), p. 20.

51

viously, the beginnings of the Ghana state are shrouded in mystery, and the identity of the earliest rulers is not even certain. But if the earliest kings were not Soninke, those of later centuries were. Indeed, under these kings the state appears to have thrived under strong central government and experienced at least two hundred years of relative stability. The non-Soninke dynasty was overthrown toward the end of the eighth century A.D., and Negro kings ruled until the empire began to crumble during the eleventh. Under their rule the state achieved its greatest territorial expansion, extending from Timbuktu in the east to the borders of present-day Senegal in the west, and from the headwaters of the Senegal and Niger in the south to the land of the Berbers in the north. Moreover, in the very creation of the state and in its perpetuation, the recognition of the economic advantages was a major factor. Thus, Ghana relied less on military conquest and imposition than most other African states, and in consequence it was more stable and survived longer.

The wave of Islam spreading west from the land of the Arabs eventually reached Ghana, though indirectly: the people of the northern desert, converted to a version of this faith, launched a war against pagan Ghana about 1062. Ghana did not, however, fall apart immediately after the first onslaught, as was the case in so many of the other states that existed during this period. On the contrary, the leaders and people of the empire fought stubbornly, and it was not until fourteen years later that the capital (also named Ghana) was destroyed. Even after its defeat, Ghana's momentum continued; the victorious tribes from the north had little idea how to run the country, and in 1087 a successful rebellion by the Soninke brought the state renewed independence. But the invaders had ruined the agricultural areas, and although ousted from Ghana, they continued to cut the state off from its northern trade connections. Having been the foundation of the state, the weakened economy was no longer a cohesive force, and it was not long before Ghana began to break up into various smaller kingdoms and tribal entities.

The destruction of Ghana did not end the efforts to establish states and empires in West Africa. After a relatively brief period of instability, during which the penetration by Islam continued, a new and even more impressive empire arose during the middle of the thirteenth century. This was the state of *Mali*. Like Ghana, Mali's strength depended upon the caravan routes to the north, but unlike Ghana, its area incorporated the gold-producing territories, which gave the state greater security. Its relations with the Islamic peoples of the desert and the north were good, because Mali's leaders were Moslems, the *Jihad* (Holy War) of conversion having been successful in these parts.

Many of the characteristics of Ghana were repeated in the empire of Mali. There was comparative stability, and a succession of rulers managed to hold the empire together. During the first quarter of the fourteenth century, the state reached its zenith. Territorially, it extended from Gao and the middle Niger in the east to the ocean in the west, covering the entire savanna belt, and from the Futa Jallon in the south to areas deep in the Sahara Desert. Trading caravans came from as far afield as Egypt and Morocco. The cities of Mali (Niani), about a hundred miles below present-day Bamako on the Niger River, and Timbuktu became urban centers of renown. Architectural improvements were made and great mosques constructed, an institution of higher learning was established at Timbuktu, and leaders made pilgrimages to Mecca.

But the adjutants of Mali's leaders extended the empire farther than control could be effective, and the fourteenth century saw the beginning of the end. The Tucolor of the west, the Tuaregs of the northern desert, and the Mossi of the south raided with success, and by the beginning of the fifteenth century the kings of the Songhai had also broken away. But again, the principles of state organization were not lost on those who rebelled against the weakening central authority in Mali. Other empires soon appeared.

In the region of Gao, on the middle Niger, the land and people were long subject to the rulers of Mali. When Mali fell apart, however, another state of significance, *Songhai*, arose in this area. Songhai was located farther to the east than either Ghana or Mali, so that its influence in the far west was probably less. But the tradition of greatness of the central city continued, as Gao replaced the town of Mali, which itself had taken over from the town of Ghana. From the environs of Gao, the leaders of Songhai set about extending the domain of the state, which by the early sixteenth century encompassed the lands of the Hausa in the east almost as far as Bornu, in the north extended to the very margins of Morocco, in the west almost to the ocean, and in the south well into the forests. Only in the south did some of the Mossi states manage to hold their own against the Songhai armies. Meanwhile, trade and agriculture flourished, and the heart of the empire during the first quarter of the sixteenth century experienced stability and order.

Songhai, however, suffered from intrafamily rivalries for the leadership and from competition among the various generals of the successful armies. These were the seeds of weakness which during the later 1500's, began to affect the state. By 1600, Moroccan invaders from the north captured the salt mines, while internal rebellions fragmented the empire. But Songhai had continued to spread Islam among those peoples it had subverted, it had continued to keep close ties with the Arab world of Islam, and its effects were felt long after it fell.

Viewing the sequence from a spatial perspective, it is notable that Mali arose well to the south and somewhat east of Ghana, and that Songhai subsequently developed east of Mali. These shifts had several causes and consequences. The general easterly migration of the core areas may have been related to the events taking place in North Africa, where the center of power moved from Morocco to Tunis during the same period. Doubtless, the invasion of Ghana and the breakup of the westerly trade routes led to a search for new, necessarily more eastern crossings of the Sahara. Mali's more southerly location rendered it less vulnerable to the onslaughts of the desert peoples whose raids had been fatal to Ghana, and Mali, being Moslem whereas Ghana was pagan, naturally had many ties to the east. This factor no doubt also played a role in the rise of Songhai. Since Gao lay

some seven hundred miles downstream on the Niger from Mali, goods began to move along the Niger trade route to Timbuktu and Gao, and even beyond, and the whole orientation of the region was more and more toward the central Sahara and the eastern parts of the north.

With the invasion of Songhai by the Moroccans and the ensuing chaos, the center of African power shifted southward, toward the region between the forests and the steppe in the elbow of the Niger River. There, some smaller but remarkably stable political entities, known as the Mossi-Dagomba states, survived until the Europeans entered the scene in numbers. In the far east, between Songhai and Lake Chad, the kingdoms of the Hausa and the state of Bornu also had some organization and stability. Possibly, the Cushitic influences played an indirect role there. Much later, these Hausa kingdoms were overthrown by the rising group of Fulani, who had come from the west to live in Hausaland and brought with them a strict adherence to Islam. This was another Holy War and had important repercussions all through the West African savanna belt.

Other West African States

The sequence described above is, of course, a very generalized one. Many states about which something is known—and probably others about which little or nothing has been learned—have not been included in the story of the complex political transitions in West Africa. It is even more difficult to comprehend the political changes going on at the same time in the Guinea area, the region between the savanna-steppe of the north and the coast.

For a variety of reasons, some of the political ideas of Ghana, Mali, and Songhai were carried southward. Defeated leaders sought refuge in the south, and the invasion of aggressive northern tribes sent whole populations migrating in that direction. Nor were war and revolution the only causes of a shift to the south. During the two millennia of political change, this part of Africa was also undergoing environmental changes. Put most simply, the Sahara Desert was constantly becoming drier. Agriculture became increasingly difficult along the northern fringes of the savanna, and with the increasing drought in the interior, the whole of West Africa was affected, for the moister belts to the south received proportionally less rainfall.

Details of the Guinea states are even harder to obtain than those of the savanna states. After all, the ties between the Arab world and the West African countries were close, and if the Negroes themselves did not write, the Arabs did; much of what is known about Ghana, Mali, and Songhai has been gleaned from Arab writings. But the southerly states were beyond the orbit of the Arabs, and the reconstruction of their past is a far more difficult problem. When the Europeans arrived, they began to report upon the political entities, but they had been in existence long before the first whites came.

Actually, the Europeans contributed considerably to strengthening some of these southern states. While the savanna states ruled supreme, the forest people were at the mercy of slave raiders. In those days, the forests, especially the northern margins, were merely tributary areas from which products were to be extracted. The local chiefs could do very little against the powerful armies of the empires, so that their only protection was to move deeper into the forest to avoid slave raids and the cavalry of the kings. Very little forest was actually controlled by the savanna empires, for the kings' forces simply were not suited to fight in the dense bush. The great armies were effective on the savanna, on the open lands, where grazing was available for the horses, but in the dense undergrowth they ran the risk of annihilation. Armed slave-raiding and punitive parties did enter the forest, but left again with their loot. They could maintain no effective government there.

Naturally, political organization in the forest is a difficult process, and in this respect the savanna lands experienced progress first. But then the Europeans came to the coasts, built trading stations there, and demanded the same products that the caravans had so long carried north across the desert. Further-

more, they brought firearms to the people of the forest. Suddenly, these people found themselves with economic and military advantages, and from those days on, the might of the savanna empires was on the wane.

Having brought some advantages to the people of the forests, the Europeans also introduced their version of an evil long perpetrated by the Arabs: the slave trade, which led to war and chaos among the African peoples. Yet while this very practice prevailed, some of West Africa's most important Negro states thrived.

It must be remembered that many of the political ideas incorporated in the Guinea states had been introduced from the north, so that the coastal forest states were bound to have certain features in common. Generally, it is thought that the first state of this kind was at Ife, which may have arisen as early as the tenth century A.D. From Ife, ideas spread which led to the foundation of several states populated by the Yoruba people. Perhaps the best example of the type was *Oyo*, located in the north of what is today the Western Region of Nigeria, and including sections of Dahomey. Oyo, like other forest empires, probably had its beginnings along the northern fringes rather than within the forests, and was extended southward as time went on. Oyo was noteworthy for several reasons: it was among the first of such states to form, it survived for a long time, and it brought such stability to the Yoruba people that they withstood the European impact from the south for many years.

The core areas of these Yoruba states consisted of urban centers of considerable size, surrounded by a wall which usually included some farmland within its confines. Thus, the town could withstand a siege, the enclosed farmland being just sufficient to supply some food to the people seeking shelter. There was much military activity in the expansion of the Yoruba states: the leaders of Oyo, for instance, sought to incorporate not only all Yoruba people, but non-Yorubas as well. Eventually, it was this enforced tribute and strife resulting from the slave trade that caused internal fragmentation. Oyo was paramount in its region from the seventeenth century until the first decades of the nineteenth, and had been growing in significance and influence long before that.

Another offshoot of Ife was the state of *Benin*. Originally a group of states, in the fifteenth century it was consolidated by the first of a strong dynasty of kings. Benin is known, among other things, for its fabulous bronzes and other works of art, products of skills introduced from Ife. The state centered upon the city of Benin, which grew in importance with European contact and trade. Benin's merchants became the important middlemen between the whites and the Yorubas of the interior, and through the city passed pepper, cotton cloth, slaves, and beads. The power of the merchants was increased by their procurement of firearms, and Benin's armies raided farther and farther into the interior. The kingdom reached its zenith during the late sixteenth and early seventeenth centuries, but eventually the devastation of the hinterland proved fatal. Fewer products and slaves reached the capital, fewer Europeans called there, and by the end of the century the state was in decay.

The state of *Dahomey* never reached the importance of Benin or Oyo, and its consolidation was largely the result of economic conditions created by the slave trade. Dahomey was internally divided, the Europeans encouraging this division by their support of whatever parties would deliver the slaves to the coast most efficiently. From the outside, Dahomey was threatened by Oyo and encroached upon by *Ashanti*, a state of major proportions far more powerful than Dahomey. Like the kingdoms of the Yoruba, Ashanti, located in the interior of what came to be called the Gold Coast, resulted from a union of a number of states under a powerful ruler who was succeeded by equally effective kings. In this case, a common effort on the part of Akan-speaking people to prevent the invasion of competitors led to a further combined effort to throw off the yoke of tribute imposed by a state called Denkera. Thus, the Ashanti nation was forged, with headquarters in Kumasi, under the leadership of the *Asantehene*, guardian of the Golden Stool, the symbol of national unity.

Ashanti grew during the eighteenth century, and, by the beginning of the nineteenth, the empire was encroaching upon the coastal states of the Fante, where the Europeans had their forts and trading stations. Slaves and gold were exchanged for arms and ammunition. Eventually, Ashanti invaded the nominal British protectorates along the coast. The termination of the slave trade had removed one of the economic mainstays of Ashanti, and relations between the Ashanti and the British had steadily deteriorated. Ashanti's attack, which came in 1863, was not repaid until several years later, and then ineffectively. It is a measure of Ashanti resilience that the state survived the 1874 punishment inflicted by Britain and required reoccupation in 1896. In 1900, when the British governor demanded the surrender of the Golden Stool, Ashanti rose for the last time in a hopeless rebellion. Only as late as 1901 did Ashanti territory become part of a British Crown colony.

African States Elsewhere

The foregoing discussion might lead to the mistaken conclusion that West Africa was the only region in Subsaharan Africa to witness urbanization and the evolution of states. When Europeans entered other parts of Africa, they found that progress in organization had indeed been made in several areas. The Portuguese, for instance, found a flourishing state around the mouth of the Congo River, centered upon a town located near present-day San Salvador, Angola. This, the empire of *Kongo*, entered into diplomatic relations with the Portuguese and actually had permanent representatives in Lisbon and Rome, while European missionaries proselytized among the subjects of the state. In East Africa, on the shores of Lake Victoria, the BaGanda people had organized themselves politically and economically, and in what is present-day Uganda, several feudal states were in existence before the Europeans arrived. *Buganda* was, and remains today, a core area in East Africa.

Southern, Central, and Eastern Africa continue to pose historical problems, for in

Zimbabwe, Southern Rhodesia: The Temple. One of Africa's great remaining mysteries is Zimbabwe, which is but the largest and best-constructed of an entire series of ruins extending from the northern Transvaal in South Africa into Rhodesia. Zimbabwe has been attributed to Arab invaders and African inhabitants, and guesses about the ruins' age have varied widely. Even radio-carbon dating (done on pieces of wood found enclosed in the stone walls) has not produced figures beyond dispute. Apparently, however, at least three distinct building periods took place, the first possibly during the eleventh century A.D. The building styles vary somewhat, and it is thought that the last period of construction may have come as late as the seventeenth or eighteenth century. The structures are attributed most commonly to the Mashona people, who mined gold on the Rhodesian plateau and came in contact with the Portuguese when their kingdom was well organized. The illustration here was taken at eye level, providing some idea of the height of the wall. The walls are immensely thick (over 10 feet in places) and enclose other structures (such as the famed conical tower, hidden by the wall shown here) whose function is not clearly understood. "Temple" may be a misnomer, but that is what this oval-shaped enclosure in the valley at Zimbabwe is called.

the efforts to unravel the past there, reliance has to be placed on far less satisfactory sources of evidence than those available for West Africa. Obviously, some major developments took place on the Southern Rhodesian Plateau, but the real origin of the great buildings of Zimbabwe is still far from certain. Yet trade went on between the peoples of the plateau and the coast, and powerful rulers were produced by the African peoples. The military might of the Zulu empire, centered upon Natal but possessing a huge sphere of influence across the plateau interior, at one time was probably second to none in all of Subsaharan Africa. Evidence of whole former empires may yet lie undiscovered. Much work remains to be done in this area.

Zimbabwe, Southern Rhodesia: The Acropolis. Hundreds of feet above the temple and its surrounding buildings, in an almost impregnable position atop a granite hill, is the so-called acropolis. Entrances into the acropolis are so narrow that only one man at a time can pass through the corridor leading to the interior; for this reason, the acropolis has been thought to be a fortress against attack. Among the questions immediately presenting themselves, of course, is that of water supply: How did the occupants manage to supply themselves with water while besieged? Because of this and other features of the acropolis, its function as a fort has lately been doubted. One peculiarity of the whole area in which Zimbabwe stands is its vegetation. When the entire Southern Rhodesian Plateau is parched and gray in the long, dry winter, the grass and trees at Zimbabwe are green. This was probably so when the site was chosen by the original builders. Zimbabwe has been occupied by Africans who built huts within the walled enclosures, the remains of which have been discovered. Did these hut dwellers work on the further construction of the great city? Many questions about the ruins are yet to be answered. The detail of the acropolis shown here illustrates how the builders used the boulders already present to increase the height of the walls of the structure.

The Impact of Europe

The historical sequence of European contact with Africa provides support for the recognition of Subsaharan Africa as a separate, individual region, for the differences from contemporary events in the north are many. The Moors were being pushed out of the Iberian Peninsula back to North Africa, and the Portuguese and Spanish, because of the close proximity of North Africa to their own countries, could wage the campaign with relative ease. But in order to reach West, Southern, and East Africa, the Portuguese had to set sail, arriving first in small numbers and in a few isolated places. Portuguese navigators first made contact with West Africa, arriving there in the first half of the fifteenth century; in the early 1440's, the first West African slaves were brought to the Iberian Peninsula. In the West, the Portuguese carried on what the Arabs had initiated in the East: a profitable traffic in slaves, for many centuries Africa's major export product.

The fifteenth and sixteenth centuries in Africa may well be called Portugal's centuries, although they were not only Portugal's. It was the Portuguese, however, who first rounded the Cape of Good Hope and sailed past the tip of Africa into the Indian Ocean,

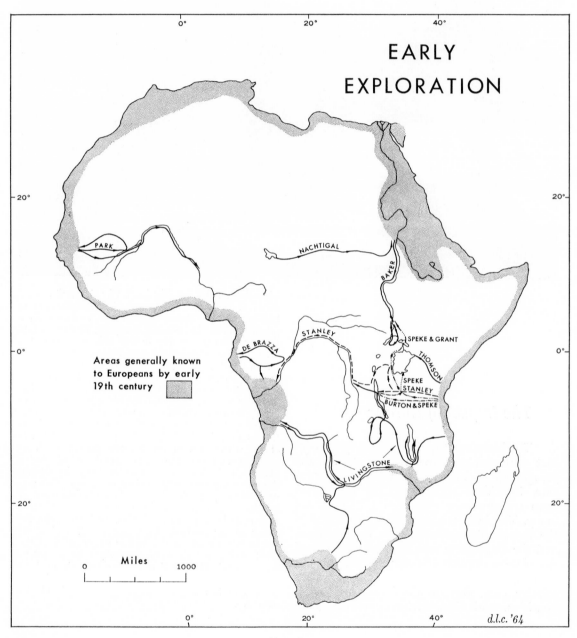

EARLY EXPLORATION

Areas generally known to Europeans by early 19th century

Miles

d.l.c. '64

Map 9

settling along the east coast and disputing possession of the lands of the east with the Arabs. Although some individual explorers penetrated far inland, the Portuguese settlements were mainly peripheral. The city of Benguela, Angola, dates from this period, as does Lourenço Marques, Moçambique, although settlement on Delagoa Bay (Bay of Lourenço Marques) was intermittent until the eighteenth century.

Initially, the voyages of Bartholomew Diaz and Vasco Da Gama produced friendly contact with the Arabs, and it was an Arab guide who first led the Portuguese to the Indies. Soon, however, Portuguese power subjugated the Arab holdings on the East African coast and spread as far north as Arabia. By not consolidating their settlements, but maintaining real interest only in the route to the Indies, the Portuguese made the error which was eventually to lead to their defeat. As the sixteenth century drew to a close, the Portuguese Empire in Europe was declining, and the Arabs began systematically pushing the invaders from East Africa. Mombasa was beleaguered and bombed numerous times, as both sides took and lost the city repeatedly. Shortly after 1700, the Portuguese had lost all the land they once held north of Cape Delgado, the present northeastern extremity of Moçambique.

In West Africa, meanwhile, the Portuguese slave-trading stations, thriving from Senegal to Angola, also shared in the decline of Portuguese power, and Britain, the Netherlands, and France appeared on the scene. A glance at the seventeenth-century map reveals that by this time other products were being taken: in addition to the Slave Coast, the map shows a Gold Coast and an Ivory Coast. The slave trade, however, remained the most profitable of all, stimulated by the demand in the Americas. Nevertheless, few real European settlements were established. Along the coast of West Africa, there were some forts, but they were there primarily for the protection of the trade. Slave traders associated with Africans who helped carry out the capture of slaves, and thus the real penetration of Africa by the white man continued to be delayed. In tropical Africa, it was not until late in the eighteenth century that the age of exploration commenced, as the slave trade began to wane. To all intents and purposes, the accumulation of knowledge concerning interior Africa began only during the nineteenth century.

THE HOLLANDERS AT THE CAPE

Portugal yielded its power position in Europe and on the seas to Holland, which had emerged undefeated from eighty years of war with Spain. During the period of slave trading and intermittent, peripheral white settlement in tropical Africa, the Dutch established a revictualling station for their ships at a place neglected by the Portuguese, Table Bay. Founded in 1652, the settlement at the foot of Table Mountain was the first and for many decades the only European base to possess some characteristics of permanency. Out of it grew the city of Cape Town, today second in size only to Johannesburg in Subsaharan Africa.

The Dutch, failing to oust the Portuguese permanently from Benguela (Portugal's rule of its large African provinces has never been interrupted), chose the site of Cape Town mainly because it had not been taken by others, and they found themselves in possession of one of Africa's best natural harbors. In the centuries to come, it became clear that Cape Town dominated what is economically the richest part of Africa, the south, but initially the Hollanders were not interested in the colonization of the Cape. Having learned from the Portuguese the need for a revictualling station, they established one, but white immigration was actually discouraged, as it was feared that a large Cape colony would become an administrative liability. Thus Cape Town's growth was retarded, and it has been estimated that a century and a half later, in 1800, the total white population of the city and the colony which had inevitably developed was only about 25,000.

The Dutch East India Company, engaged on behalf of the Netherlands government in the trade with the Indies, introduced a number of crops to the Cape, traded with the local Hottentots for meat, and imported a large number of slaves from Madagascar, Malaysia, and even West Africa, when local

Cape-Style Farmhouse, Cape Province, South Africa. Built two centuries ago when the Cape Colony was still Dutch and in its infancy, this farmhouse illustrates the individuality that was already developing there. But at the time this house was built, only those farmers who lived close to Cape Town and paid allegiance to the government there and in Amsterdam could afford this sort of luxury. Not many miles away was the frontier, where trekkers seeking independence were moving toward the interior, carrying all they owned on wagons and herding their livestock before them. (Satour)

labor ran in short supply. The company was unable to contain the Dutch citizens who had fulfilled their tour of duty with the government as farmers or employees and who refused to return to Europe, however. Many of these white people left the environs of Cape Town and trekked into the interior, warring with Bushmen and Bantu over the lands they desired. There, before the end of the eighteenth century, whites were entering Africa's interior, and for some time the southern tip of the continent was better known than most other regions.

Like Portugal before it, Holland declined from its position as the leading sea power of Europe. After a brief temporary wardship, Britain in 1806 took permanent possession of the Cape, finding it a stagnating, backward settlement and an asset mainly as a means of preserving sea power. Britain also showed

little interest in the interior. In this hinterland of Southern Africa, meanwhile, a most significant event was taking place. Among the many Bantu peoples which had migrated southward were the Zulu, who settled in Natal. Strong leadership by a succession of chiefs who developed a degree of military organization the like of which Bantu Africa had never seen thrust the Zulu empire into prominence as the most powerful on the subcontinent. Waging war on tribal peoples in every possible direction, the Zulu decimated the African population on the plateau, defied only by the Basuto and the Swazi.

With the whites confined mainly to the Cape and the powerful Zulu concentrated in Natal, direct conflict did not seem inevitable. Events in Britain, however, resulted in a mass exodus of white Dutch settlers from the Cape into the regions over which the Zulu held

60

The Big Hole, Kimberley, Cape Province, South Africa. The buildings of the skyline of Kimberly in the background suggest the size of this, the largest manmade hole in the world. It was dug in search of diamonds and begun in 1870's. Today, far more modern methods are used to extract the stones. The hole is more than a quarter of a mile across and almost as deep and is slowly filling up with water. (Satour)

sway. The efforts of William Wilberforce, aimed at the elimination of the slave trade, were reaching the public conscience in Britain, and, in 1833, slavery was abolished throughout the British Empire, of which the Cape Colony was a part. The Dutch settlers who remained after the demise of the Dutch East India Company had shown increasing dissatisfaction with Britain's efforts to anglicize the Cape, and the termination of the practice of slavery was the last straw. So began, in 1836, the mass movement of whites, most of Dutch ancestry, onto the plateau of Southern Africa in what has become known as the Great Trek. It was the vanguard of a series of waves of white immigration, resulting in the only really large white population accumulation in all Subsaharan Africa.

The Great Trek eventually brought white and Zulu into conflict, the decisive battle being fought at Blood River in Natal, where the Zulu, although numerically greatly in the majority, were defeated. It was the desire of the Dutch ("Boers," as they were often called) to establish beyond the borders of the British Cape Colony, pastoral republics where they might retain their cultural and religious heritage. Having defeated the Zulu, the Boers seemed a step closer to their ideal, and although Britain invaded Natal and removed

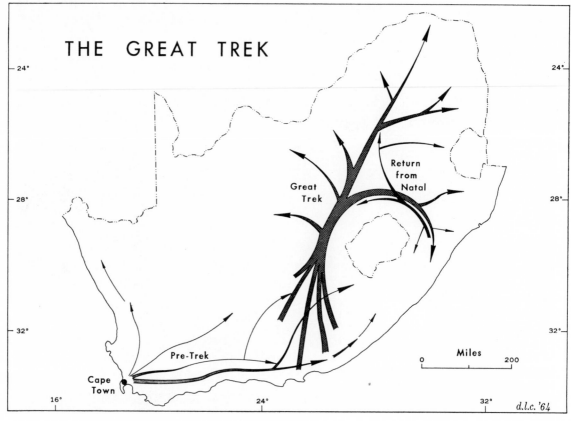

THE GREAT TREK

Map 10

the Dutch from that region, there remained the plateau itself. There, the Orange Free State Republic and the Republic of South Africa (Transvaal) were founded by independence-minded frontiersmen of Dutch origin. Although there were some border skirmishes and occasional friction with Africans, the Boer republics were recognized by Britain, and it appeared that the goal of the trekkers had been achieved.

The temporary *status quo* was disturbed in 1867 by the discovery, on the banks of one of Southern Africa's great rivers, the Orange, of diamonds. The richness of the fields and their relative accessibility brought fortune hunters not only from all parts of South Africa but also from overseas, producing a second Great Trek, this time initiated by economic causes. Kimberley became the economic capital of Southern Africa, and the building of railroads into the interior was

begun. The British annexed the diamond-iferous region to the Cape Colony, thus being enabled to administer the new city and its inhabitants. Although displeased with this action, the leaders of the Boer republics did not attempt seriously to alter it, largely in order not to threaten their continued existence.

Another mineral find, this time a much more significant one, occurred in 1884, when gold was discovered in the South African Republic near what is today the city of Johannesburg. This brought a third Great Trek, but there was no way in which the British at the Cape could annex this territory without war. The republic was unequipped for the mass of foreign intruders, and administrative chaos resulted. Johannesburg began its uncontrolled growth, within ten years reaching 100,000, while the capital, Pretoria, was eclipsed. Johannesburg became the economic capital of Southern Africa, a position which it has retained to this day. President Paul Kruger and his stubborn Afrikaner (Boer) government, resentful of the disruption created by Johannesburg's large foreign population, continually refused to cooperate in city development and denied the allocation of funds for necessary amenities. Friction between the Afrikaners and foreigners was rife. Britain, meanwhile, partly on the advice of such people as Cecil Rhodes and Dr. Leander Starr Jameson, continued to cast covetous eyes upon this rich economic prize. Troops massed on the republic's borders, and in 1899 war broke out.

In the Boer War, white faced white on a scale unprecedented in Subsaharan Africa. Britain, after some initial setbacks, at length defeated the Boers, who maintained a guerrilla campaign when defeated on the battlefield. Having finally subdued the obstinate Afrikaner opposition, the British made an effort to grant the Boers some participation in the affairs of what had once been their country. In 1910, the Union of South Africa came into being, joining the two British colonies (Cape and Natal) and the two defeated republics (Orange Free State and Transvaal). Although victorious, the British gave in to several of the Afrikaners' desires when this Union was created. One of these was the elimination from the political scene of all African and other nonwhite elements: the Union became a state ruled by an all-white electorate. Nonwhites at first retained some indirect representation, but this was subsequently discontinued. The Union survived for just over half a century, for the Afrikaners came to dominate the white electorate, and in 1948 an Afrikaner government was returned to power. It promised economic development, racial segregation, and a revival of the republic; by 1961, the three promises had all been kept, as on May 31 of that year a new Republic of South Africa came into being.

THE EXPLORERS

The developments which took place in South Africa did not mirror the sequence of events in tropical Africa. White penetration of the south came early, and numbers were comparatively large. Northward, it was long left to a few explorers to investigate the often hostile interior. Some, in spite of heroic deeds, have fallen into relative obscurity, like James Bruce, who entered what is today Ethiopia and the Sudan, following the Blue Nile to its confluence with the White Nile. Among the early explorers to achieve fame was Mungo Park, who attempted to solve the riddle of the Niger River. On many early maps, the Niger is seen to flow from east (the general vicinity of Lake Chad) to west, reaching the ocean as the Gambia. Park, in 1795, traveled up the Gambia, hoping to find an actual link with the Niger. On his first journey, he did indeed find the Niger and became aware that its flow is eastward, not west, but he was unable to follow the great river to its mouth, as he had intended. Having disproved the Gambia-Niger connection, Park in 1805 set out again in an effort to trace the Niger to its mouth which, it is thought, he believed to be the Congo mouth. The great explorer met his death in the waters of the river which was the object of his search: he drowned during a battle with tribesmen in Nigeria. Only in 1830 did Richard Lander complete Park's task and prove that the Niger flows into its delta on the Guinea Gulf.

While explorers like Hugh Clapperton, René Caillé, and Lander were traversing the western part of Subsaharan Africa, equatorial Africa remained barely touched. South of the Congo River was the Kingdom of Kongo, which was entered by a number of Portuguese from the coastal settlements during the sixteenth and seventeenth centuries, but the Katanga region was not reached until 1798, when the Portuguese explorer Lacerda penetrated it. Although there were sporadic efforts by Portuguese and Arabs to enter the interior, the real age of the explorers in equatorial Africa did not begin until the middle of the nineteenth century with the travels of the most famous of all, David Livingstone, who covered extensive areas.

Livingstone was one of the emissaries of the London Missionary Society, an organization which was very active in Southern Africa. He arrived in Cape Town in 1841 and traveled to Bechuanaland. There began his first series of traverses, and in 1849 he discovered

Lake Ngami, a part of the Makarikari-Okovango swamp and delta complex in the Kalahari Desert. Subsequently, he crossed Angola to Luanda, which he reached in 1854. The next year, he returned to the region of the upper Zambezi River, intending to follow the stream to its mouth. In the process, he discovered the stupendous falls which he named Victoria Falls, and in 1856 he succeeded in reaching the Zambezi delta.

In 1858, the second phase of Livingstone's explorations began, as he traveled up the Zambezi from its mouth, past the rapids to the Shire confluence. He then proceeded along the Shire until he reached Lake Nyasa. The lake may have been seen previously by Portuguese and Arabs, but it was Livingstone whose vivid descriptions made these areas known to the outside world.

For many years, the problem of the source of the (White) Nile had been unsolved, and Livingstone set out to find it in 1865, in his third series of traverses. This was the period during which the great explorer was lost, his fate unknown to the world for half a decade. After Henry Morton Stanley succeeded in locating Livingstone in 1871 at Ujiji on Lake Tanganyika, the two explorers together sought the origins of the Nile, traversing the area around the south end of Lake Tanganyika. Soon after Stanley's departure, in 1873, Livingstone died, weakened by malaria and other diseases.

The Nile problem was solved by John Speke, who had entered East Africa in 1857, crossed the plateau, and, with Richard Burton, discovered Lake Tanganyika in 1858. Subsequently, without Burton, Speke traversed the region about Lake Victoria, although he did not on that first journey discover the Nile outlet of the lake. In 1860, after having been taken prisoner by the BaGanda, he did locate the outlet, realizing that the question of the Nile's origin had finally been solved, unless there should be a southerly connection between Lakes Victoria and Tanganyika. Samuel Baker in 1863 placed the Nile outlet of Lake Victoria beyond doubt by traveling up the Nile through the Sudd, meeting Speke and his companion, James Grant, who were coming down the same river.

Stanley returned to Africa in 1874 and proved that the rivers west of Lake Tanganyika which he and Livingstone had seen were in the drainage basin of the Congo and could be followed to the Atlantic Ocean. It so happened that in 1876 King Leopold II of Belgium convened a meeting of geographers with knowledge of equatorial Africa, and Stanley, who reported on the nature of the Congo in the heart of the continent, impressed Leopold with the potentialities of a transportation route there. Consequently, Stanley in 1879 mounted an expedition into the Congo on behalf of the king. Obtaining concessions and treaties, within five years he accumulated for Leopold a tremendous territory which came to be known as the Congo Free State. Stanley thus changed from explorer to land hunter, and as such he played a significant role in the great struggle for Africa's territory.

THE "SCRAMBLE FOR AFRICA"

While exploration was still in progress in equatorial Africa, the struggle among European powers for possession of Africa's land— a struggle which was to lead to the colonial partition of virtually the entire subcontinent —had already begun elsewhere. As early as 1857, France and Britain came to an agreement in which France recognized Britain's sovereignty over the Gambia River and its valley, while Britain consented to France's occupance of the area around the Senegal River. Thus was the concept of "spheres of influence" born. The only territories to escape Europe's nineteenth-century invasion of Subsaharan Africa were coastal Sierra Leone, itself a British colony but established in the 1790's, with the special purpose of providing a home for freed slaves, and Liberia, founded by American interests for a similar purpose in the 1820's. Even Ethiopia, the feudal empire which had survived the upheavals of Africa over several centuries, eventually was overrun in the twentieth century by the European state last in colonial expansion, Italy.

The French were probably the first to recognize the value of a continuous, interconnected empire in Africa; in any event, the French

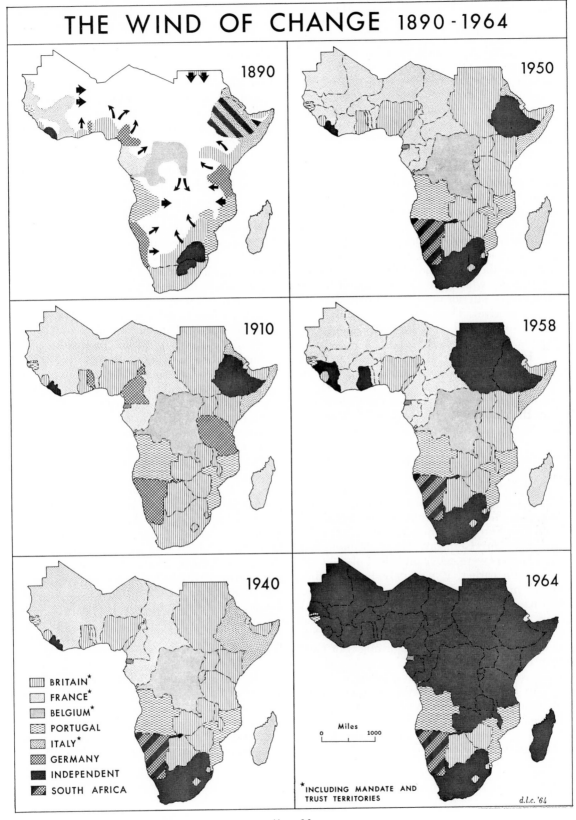

THE WIND OF CHANGE 1890-1964

1890

1950

1910

1958

1940

1964

BRITAIN*
FRANCE*
BELGIUM*
PORTUGAL
ITALY*
GERMANY
INDEPENDENT
SOUTH AFRICA

Miles
0   1000

*INCLUDING MANDATE AND
TRUST TERRITORIES

d.l.c. '64

Map 11

dream of "Africa French from Algeria to Congo" preceded the British ideal of "Africa British from the Cape to Cairo." Thus, France concentrated her efforts in West Africa and made considerable headway at an early stage. Britain continued to view her African possessions as isolated stations rather than as a contiguous empire, and then France's expansionism was temporarily halted by the war with Germany. After her 1871 defeat and some territorial loss in Europe, France, stimulated by the need for a revival of national pride and prestige, again focused her interest upon West Africa. By then, however, Germany and especially Britain were also engaged in the struggle for land in this region. Viewing with concern the spread of French power across the Sudan, the British decided to acquire the hinterland of their coastal trading stations, which, they feared, might be cut off from the interior upon which they depended for survival. Thus, Britain penetrated the interior of Sierra Leone, the Gold Coast, and Nigeria.

In the Guinea lands, it was not the French but the Africans who proved to be formidable opposition to British colonial expansion. In the interior behind the Gold Coast was the Ashanti empire, whose defiance of the British was discussed above (see p. 55).

In Nigeria, the British sphere of influence was expanded by the Royal Niger Company, formed by British trading interests and supported by the British government. Its forerunner, the United Africa Company, established in 1879, was instrumental in containing the latest European power to enter with colonialist designs, Germany. Although individual land hunters were active on behalf of the German state earlier, it was only in 1884 that Lomé on the Togoland coast was proclaimed German territory. A narrow strip of hinterland was also claimed, effectively separating the Gold Coast sphere of influence from the Nigeria region. Clearly, the major object of German claims there was the obstruction of the designs of the rival colonial powers.

In equatorial Africa, the Belgian sphere of influence was in the west, and during the first half of the nineteenth century Arab power continued to dominate the east. While Stanley was gathering treaties and concessions on behalf of the King of the Belgians, creating the Congo Free State, East Africa remained under Bantu domination in the interior and Arab hegemony in the littoral. Arab power centered on the island of Zanzibar, which had long been a focus of Arab activity. During the first half of the nineteenth century, the Sultanate of Zanzibar was associated politically with Arabia, but in 1861, shortly after the Speke-Burton explorations of the interior had begun, these ties were severed. With the opening of the Suez Canal in 1869, the sultanate attained unprecedented importance, and the sultan laid claim to large sections of the African coast. Although both Britain and Germany were somewhat interested in East Africa by this time, largely because of the reports of the explorers, the sultan's claim was recognized. Britain was less concerned with obtaining territory than with the elimination of the slave trade, and she sought good relations with the Zanzibar rulers to achieve this end. It was not until the 1880's that the British were finally successful in their efforts, and by then the sultanate had begun to crumble.

The interest shown by various European colonial powers in Africa was due to a great extent to the efforts of the explorers. The success of colonization, however, must in large measure be attributed to individuals who could also be called explorers, though less in search of truth than of gain. Stanley, an explorer at first, became such a land hunter, and some of the others became as famous as their predecessors. For Germany, Robert Flegel in West Africa (especially the fringes of the Nigeria sphere of influence) and Karl Peters in East Africa obtained concessions from local chiefs. De Brazza worked for France in the region which was to become French Equatorial Africa. For Britain, Rhodes penetrated Zambezia, later to be named after him, and obtained vast concessions. It is due to these men more than any others that the spread of European influence in various parts of Africa was rapid once it began.

As the spheres of influence of the colonial powers expanded and rival claims were made to certain parts of the continent, it became clear that a discussion of Africa's colonial partition was necessary. There was real danger of open hostilities in some areas, and in others, the local chiefs had ceded their land more than once, first to the representatives of one colonial government, then to those of another. Hence, in 1884, a conference was convened in Berlin, lasting into 1885, at which various colonial possessions were consolidated, problematic boundaries defined and delimited, and some sections of land exchanged. Some order was brought out of the political chaos into which the continent had been thrown, and the essential elements of the political map of Africa were forged.

The story of East Africa during the last decades of the nineteenth century and the beginning of the twentieth is one of rivalry and friction between Britain and Germany. In the south of this region, Karl Peters, an emissary of the German Colonization Society, traveled through what is today Tanganyika, obtaining treaties and concessions from African chiefs. Even chiefs who were already under the jurisdiction of the Zanzibar sultanate gave Peters concessions, so that by 1885 he had claimed for Germany most of the area of Tanganyika. Having become aware of his activities, the Sultan of Zanzibar objected to Peters' claims to land belonging to the sultanate, but Germany responded by sending a fleet to support them. Although the threat of naval bombardment forced the sultan to yield, there were uprisings by both Arabs and Africans in Tanganyika itself, and some years were to elapse before German power was undisputed. The Arabs rose because they feared that the slave trade would be ended by German occupation, and subsequent revolutions were sustained by Africans who had been affected by slavery but never by actual territorial subversion. Among the African peoples, the Hehe distinguished themselves by untold courage and perseverance. The last uprising was the famous "maji-maji" rebellion of 1905–6, involving most of southern Tanganyika, which was put down with great bloodshed. Germany's activities in East Africa and South West Africa, where she was involved in a bloody campaign against Herero people, are among the darkest chapters of European history in Africa, rivaling the atrocities committed in the Congo and Portuguese-Arab terror in sustaining the slave trade.

While Tanganyika came under German control, Britain was engaged in the colonization of other areas. In 1888, the British East Africa Company was created, with aims similar to those of the Royal Niger Company but with substantially less capital. Leaders of the company were aware that the BaGanda people were likely to play a dominant role in a developing East Africa, and a railroad was begun to connect Mombasa, on the Kenya coast, with Kisumu, on the shores of Lake Victoria. In 1890, the failing Sultanate of Zanzibar became a British protectorate, which included a strip on the Kenya coast but not the portion which had been claimed by Germany. Thanks to the efforts of the company, this territory in 1893 also became a part of the British sphere of influence as a protectorate.

The British East Africa Company, unlike the British South Africa Company and the Royal Niger Company, did not thrive on rich mineral finds and agricultural development. Burdened with a multitude of administrative functions which London was reluctant to take over, the company was frequently in financial difficulties, as when it was building the railroad to Uganda. Indeed, its charter was terminated in 1895, eight years before the railroad reached the shores of Lake Victoria. At the turn of the century, nevertheless, a British protectorate existed over Uganda, Kenya, and Zanzibar, and the company had made a major contribution in bringing this about.

In Southern Africa, the events leading to the formation of the Union of South Africa had occupied the center of the stage to such an extent that the huge territory of South West Africa was virtually neglected until German claims to it were substantiated by armed force. A war had long been in progress between the Hottentot and the advancing Herero, a Bantu people, and the lives of white missionaries and traders were endangered. Appealing for protection, these people failed to get support from London or Cape Town. There were a number of whites of German nationality living in South West Africa, and the German rulers took a sympathetic interest in their plight. In the 1880's, German claims in the region were expanded through the efforts of Adolph Lüderitz, and the appearance of German ships off the shores of the territory removed all doubt that Germany's presence was to be permanent. At the 1884–85 Berlin Conference, the Germans insisted upon connecting their territory with the Zambezi River, and thus the Caprivi Strip came into being, extending eastward from the northern edge of the main body of South West Africa.

One of those regions whose ownership was not settled was Zambezia, the area around the great Zambezi River, lying between Angola and Moçambique, north of the Transvaal and south of the Congo and Tanganyika. In 1886, France and Germany appear to have agreed that Portugal should extend her possessions in coastal Angola and Moçambique across the entire continent in order to link these two portions of her empire. This agreement was less an act of friendship toward Portugal than an effort to obstruct British imperialism in the south, but Rhodes and his supporters helped foil this plan. The Pioneer Column, a vanguard of white settlers equipped by Rhodes, penetrated Southern Rhodesia in 1890 and began a white immigration which was to reach sizeable proportions. The British South Africa Company obtained concessions from African chiefs, and Portuguese expansion into the interior was limited by agreement.

In the northeast of Subsaharan Africa, including the "Horn" and the Sudan, the center of the historico-geographical stage during the last decades of the nineteenth century was occupied by Britain and several powerful local rulers. Also interested in this area were France and Italy. France wished to extend her West African domain to the Red Sea and the Gulf of Aden, and Italy, having occupied coastal sections of Eritrea and Somaliland, desired the Abyssinian (Ethiopian) interior. Britain's protectorate over Egypt helped lead to British subjugation of a region which had long been the object of Egyptian expansionism, the Sudan.

The process of colonization in the northeast was only partially completed. Ethiopia was consolidated under a powerful leader, Menelik, who was also a skillful negotiator and military tactician. While the colonial powers were encroaching upon this part of Africa, Menelik himself embarked upon a program of Ethiopian expansionism, and the boundaries he pushed far beyond the limits of the Ethi-opian Plateau were eventually recognized. He defeated the Italians in battle and laid the foundations of the Ethiopian state. In the Sudan, joint British-Egyptian control was interrupted in 1881 by the Mahdist revolt, led by Muhammad Ahmad, and was not re-established until Kitchener defeated the remainder of the Dervish Army in 1898. Immediately afterward, French encroachment upon the Sudan was repudiated by a show of force, and joint British-Egyptian government of the region took effect once more.

The Twentieth Century in Subsaharan Africa

The first years of the present century in Subsaharan Africa were marked mainly by the definition and delimitation of the boundaries of colonial holdings, the establishment of governmental machinery, and the immigration of whites, as well as by economic development mainly of an exploitative nature. Germany remained embroiled in warfare in Tanganyika and South West Africa, and the Boer War reached its climax, but the wave of activity which had caused the colonial fragmentation of Subsaharan Africa in just over one decade (1879–91) was abating.

The temporary phase of relative tranquility ended with the outbreak of the First World War. Africa was severely affected, since there were hostilities on African as well as European soil. The young Union of South Africa, as part of the British Empire, was obliged to invade South West Africa. A large section of Afrikaners refused to join their British conquerors in battle against a people who had been sympathetic to the Boer side in the Boer War, and they emphasized their refusal by armed resistance. South Africa's leaders therefore were forced to put down this revolt, delaying action against German forces in South West Africa. The attack on the German colony was quickly successful, and by 1915 Germany had lost her hold over the territory.

Clashes also occurred between Britons and Germans on the border between Kenya and German East Africa soon after the outbreak of the war, but the major phase of conflict in this region came only in 1916. By 1917, the German army had been forced out of its territory and across the Rovuma River into Moçambique. The Belgians, operating from the Congo, took a major part in the hostilities. Official capitulation came early in 1918. France and Britain brought Togoland's German administration to quick surrender in 1914, and Kamerun's in 1916. One of the initial tasks of the League of Nations, therefore, was the establishment of wardships for these former German colonial areas, and the Mandate System was devised for this purpose. South West Africa was awarded to South Africa; the terms of this mandate will be discussed in detail in Chapter 6. German East Africa became a British mandate and was at this time renamed Tanganyika, while Belgium took charge of a small northwestern section, very densely populated, consisting of Ruanda and Urundi. Togoland was divided between Britain and France. Kamerun was likewise partitioned, the British section being added to Nigeria and the remainder to French Equatorial Africa. Thus ended Germany's brief but forceful entry on the colonial scene in Subsaharan Africa.

The last European power to make an effort at colonial expansion was Italy. Although possessing Eritrea and Somaliland, Italy continued to covet the interior. Her earlier defeat by the Ethiopians was avenged in 1935, when the Italians mounted a successful military campaign against them. In 1936, Ethiopia became an Italian colony. Having also obtained a section of Kenya from the British, Italy considerably enlarged her holdings in the Horn during the interwar period.

The Second World War also had its repercussions in Africa, although these were largely confined to North Africa. Like Germany several decades before, Italy lost an African empire as a result of involvement in the war: allied with Germany, the Italians were unable to protect their overseas domain. British armed forces entered Italian East Africa soon after the start of the hostilities, and by the end of 1941 Ethiopia was independent once again, with Emperor Haile Selassie restored to the throne. Unlike Germany, however, Italy was called upon to administer Somaliland once again five years after the end

of the war. This administration was terminated when Somaliland became an independent state in 1960.

Other developments took place in Subsaharan Africa during the interwar period and during the war, but they did not provide much indication of the momentous changes which were to come after 1945. There was some economic development, better communications were established, and health conditions improved as diseases were fought. In the political field, the activity was carried on mainly by the whites, who in Kenya and Southern Rhodesia managed to obtain colonial status for their territories. South Africa began to absorb South West Africa and appealed for the transfer to her jurisdiction of the High Commission Territories. Cities grew, and minerals continued to be discovered. But in terms of education and politics, Africans appeared to make little headway, and when Europe's power was restored after the Second World War, there were few observers who predicted that independence for Africa was only a few years away.

The decade of the 1950's saw developments in Subsaharan Africa as momentous as those of the decade from 1880 to 1890, but the trend was reversed. Faced by the growing forces of African nationalism, widespread political consciousness, and hostility, the colonial powers were compelled to relinquish their hold over much of their empires. The contrasts between the aims and methods of colonial administration of the various European powers became very evident during this phase of history.

THE BRITISH

Britain was the first to show some flexibility in the face of this wind of change. On paper, British colonial policy had long had as an objective the advancement of colonial peoples toward eventual self-determination. In practice, largely because of laxity and pressure by local whites, the process was much retarded, and the possibility of sovereignty was considered extremely remote, a problem for another generation. Britain did, however, foster indigenous institutions, political and cultural, and, compared with other colonial powers, educated a large number of Africans to high levels. This has been of great importance in the relatively large measure of success Britain has had in breaking her colonial ties peacefully. Although small, there was an educated African elite which, in Nigeria, for instance, was able to cope with immediate postindependence problems. Never having viewed their colonial empire as "Britain Overseas," the British were less involved in loss of face and prestige when freedom came to such states as Ghana and Nigeria. Indeed, they gained a measure of both when formerly colonial territories applied for admission into the Commonwealth. Thus, Ghana in 1957 became the first African colony to achieve complete independence, and the new state's first prime minister, Dr. Kwame Nkrumah, was an honored guest at the 1957 Commonwealth Prime Ministers' Conference.

Subsequent British achievements have been spectacular in view of the difficulties encountered. While Kenya was under the cloud of the Mau Mau aftermath, the plans were being laid for independence in Tanganyika, Nigeria, and Sierra Leone, and by the end of 1961 each of these territories had become sovereign states, taking their places in the United Nations. Problems remained to be solved elsewhere, but British policy clearly was aimed at rapid fulfillment of the Africans' desire for self-determination. Where the process was being delayed, it was often due to problems among Africans (as in Uganda) rather than between blacks and whites. This cannot be said of Kenya, nor is it true of the former Federation of Rhodesia and Nyasaland, but there, British policy is actually being obstructed by the white residents, many of whom are determined to retain as long as possible their privileged position.

The former Federation of Rhodesia and Nyasaland is a very special case, which is discussed in detail in Chapter 7. In 1953, the British government gave in to the demands of the white settlers of the Rhodesias and Nyasaland, and over bitter opposition of Africans created a federation out of three politically and racially diverse territories. Thus, the same Britain which was guiding Africans toward independence in West and East Africa dealt this aim a severe blow in Central Africa. Had

the Federation of Rhodesia and Nyasaland not been created, it is likely that Northern Rhodesia and Nyasaland would have progressed toward early independence. Federation delayed this process and rendered it more difficult, for it tied these two territories to white-dominated Southern Rhodesia. One result of this unexpected move on the part of Britain was the destruction of some of the faith which Africans had developed in British motives, and soon after it took place, troubles arose in Uganda. There, many Africans feared that an East African federation would be the next step to consolidate white domination in that region. Nonetheless, Britain went ahead with plans for Tanganyikan independence, disclaiming any intention of imposing a federal scheme in East Africa on the Rhodesian pattern.

Much of the credit for the successes of Britain must go to the Africans, who have shown, in most cases, a remarkable degree of forbearance, often in the face of real provocation. Much has been due to the exemplary behavior of such leaders as Julius Nyerere of Tanganyika, who resisted pressures toward violent action from within his own political organization and thereby risked the loss of confidence and support of some among his own people.

THE FRENCH

French reaction to the wind of change initially was very different from that of Britain. Having lost her Asian empire and waging a brutal war against Algerian Moslem rebels, France was ill-equipped to foil the aims of African nationalists in her Subsaharan empire. This empire was *France d'Outre Mer*, represented in the metropolitan parliament itself, and disengagement from it would require complete reorientation of French colonial policy. Just as France's rigidity on the matter appeared certain to provoke violent reaction, the Fourth Republic made way for De Gaulle's Fifth Republic, and France's new leader produced the concept of a "French Community." Thus, African territories which had previously been represented in Paris, and which were being integrated—some against their will—into the French state, were able, by referendum, to decide for or against further association with France in the Community. Of all the political entities in what was then French Africa, only Guinea chose complete independence outside the Community when the question was put before the people in 1958.

It should be emphasized, however, that France's problems in her former colonial empire in Subsaharan Africa are not yet over. In all countries except Guinea, France retained considerable influence, and in reality the independence of the member states of the Community is not complete. Already some of them have raised objections, since France has continued to affect major policy decisions—she had frequently directed them —for the new French-African states. But the new system, unlike that of the Fourth Republic, is flexible and allows for negotiation to prevent violent reaction.

THE BELGIANS

Unlike France, Belgium never did consider her Congo empire a part of the mother country, and there was no effort to convert Africans into Belgians. Belgium did not escape the wind of change, however, and her failure to accommodate herself to the inevitable changes plunged the territory into anarchy. Actually, the real causes for what has been called the "Congo disaster" lie in Belgian colonial policy, and events in this huge country attendant upon the achievement of statehood formed a sharp contrast to those elsewhere.

Until 1908, the King of the Belgians was the sole ruler over the Congo, and the decades of his government produced tales of terror and destruction of human life. Estimates of the toll of Leopold's rule run into the millions, the significance of which can be realized when a comparison is made to the Congo's present population of about 15 million. After 1908, policy was made according to the Colonial Charter, by which control over the Congo was vested in the Belgian parliament, specifically in the minister of colonies, advised by a council. In the Congo itself, the governor general possessed extensive executive powers, but local inhabitants, black and white, had virtually no say in the course of events affecting their country.

Belgian policy may be characterized as severely paternalistic. Although medical and social facilities for Africans, for instance, often were described as exemplary for all colonial Africa, higher education for Africans was virtually nonexistent. Opinion in Belgium was that a broad elementary education for everyone was preferable to the pyramid of education, producing an educated African elite, created in British colonies. Hence, when change came rapidly to Africa, the Congo was one of the least-prepared countries. Inevitably, there were African spokesmen, but they were inadequately educated. There was education for the masses, but to a level that was meaningless in the struggle that was to come. Belatedly, a university had been built near Leopoldville, but when independence came in the middle of 1960, the Congolese people counted only 30 university graduates.

Until the very last, Belgium continued to view the Congo's sudden drive toward self-determination as, if not a matter of generations, at least a matter of decades. Realization of what was to happen came suddenly, and too late. Extremism before independence, and the Force Publique and sectionalism afterward, developed into a crisis which reached world significance, and which has not yet ended. Only time can solve several parts of this complex problem, as leaders are needed and a disturbed economy requires support. In the south, Katanga secessionism, involving as it does one of the bases of that economy, has threatened the survival of the Congo state itself. Had Belgium been given more time and less pressure, what was envisioned in Brussels might have become reality. As the sequence of events unfolded, the failure of her brand of colonialism was evident.

THE PORTUGUESE

The Portuguese are justly described as the pioneers of European colonialism in Subsaharan Africa. Without interruption, they have held coastal stretches of Angola and Moçambique since the late fifteenth century. Modern Portuguese colonial policy, however, dates from 1933, when the Colonial Charter was established. This charter is reminiscent of that of the French Fourth Republic. Portugal's overseas territories are considered parts of metropolitan Portugal, and in recent years both Moçambique and Angola have been considered "provinces" of the homeland. Thus, while in all other parts of Subsaharan Africa the trend is toward local government and self-determination, Portuguese colonial policy remains aimed at the final, complete integration of Overseas Portugal into the Portuguese state.

Portugal is the poorest among the colonial powers in Subsaharan Africa, past and present, and her poverty is reflected in the economic stagnation and social backwardness of Portuguese Africa. Neither Angola nor Moçambique possesses political machinery in which Africans participate. African nationalism as a political force is not recognized by Portugal in her African domain. This nonrecognition is based upon the premise that all Africans in the provinces are in reality Portuguese and desire the honor of being a part of the great historical and cultural heritage that is Portugal's. African nationalism, therefore, is considered the product of rabble-rousers and agitators, a phase that will pass as have so many other crises in the four and a half centuries of Portuguese rule in Africa.

While Belgium's paternalism and failure to educate proved her downfall in the Congo, Portugal has done far less and survives in Moçambique and Angola in the 1960's. The future of Portugal in Africa, judging from the experiences of other colonial powers on the vast continent and the conditions prevailing in the last major bastion of colonialism, is not bright.

The Political Framework

Independence in Africa may extend from Dakar to Cape Guardafui, but it has not yet reached from Cairo to the Cape of Good Hope. Indeed, the political region where the wind of change has swept away colonialism ends along the southern borders of the Congo (Leopoldville) and Tanganyika, leaving 2,340,000 square miles of the continent, occu-pied by ten politico-territorial units, still to be affected. This is more than a quarter of Subsaharan Africa, but much more significant is the demographic aspect. There live well over 30 million Africans, or 15 per cent of the black African population of Subsaharan Africa, and just under 4 million whites, or 95 per cent of the total white population of the subcontinent. Thus, while the wind of change has brought political independence to a vast majority of black Africans, it has involved comparatively few whites.

Southern Africa[5] today, as perhaps never before, is dominated economically and politically by the Republic of South Africa. In the republic are concentrated the greatest wealth, the largest white population, the best communication systems, and the strongest armed forces of the continent. Governmental and political activities are virtually confined to the white sector of the population, and the country is ruled by an Afrikaner minority which is fired by a brand of nationalism no less intense and ambitious than that of the north. South Africa has witnessed an unprecedented intensification of these nationalist policies in an effort presently being made to segregate the state into racially based regions. South Africa rules supreme over South West Africa and the High Commission Territories (Basutoland, Bechuanaland, and Swaziland), having virtually integrated the former into the state as a fifth province, and dominating the latter by economic means.

African nationalism seeks to terminate the white man's rule; it demands proportional representation in government, an end to anti-black discrimination, segregation, job reservation, and crop restrictions. White nationalism is determined to preserve racial purity, maintain white rule, and protect privileges for whites by *apartheid*. The confrontation of these opposing ideologies has been prevented only by the existence of a buffer zone across the breadth of Central Africa. Consisting of the countries of the former Federation of Rhodesia and Nyasaland as the core, and the Portuguese provinces of Angola and Moçambique as the vulnerable flanks, this buffer zone

---

[5] Southern Africa in this context is that region which lies to the south of the Congo (Leopoldville) and Tanganyika.

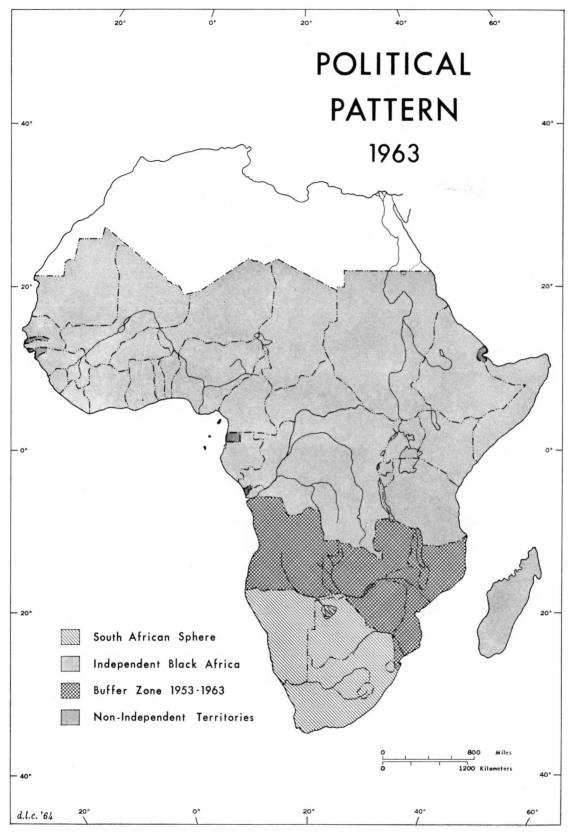

POLITICAL
PATTERN
1963

South African Sphere

Independent Black Africa

Buffer Zone 1953-1963

Non-Independent Territories

0   800   Miles

0   1200   Kilometers

d.l.c. '64

Map 12

is at present under the stress of impact from both north and south.

In Angola and Moçambique, as a result of the absence of local legislative councils and political organizations, the wind of change is bringing violence. There no channels exist into which nationalist Africans can guide their aspirations; the only road open is that of violence. When independent Africa encroached on the very borders of the Portuguese African provinces, hostilities erupted across the borders. In the Rhodesias and Nyasaland, the matter is being fought on the political plane. Africans are in a majority in the government of Nyasaland and have gained majority powers in Northern Rhodesia. In Southern Rhodesia, on the other hand, the white man has long ruled with an iron hand reminiscent of South Africa. There live a quarter of a million whites, most of them opposed to the trends prevalent in the northern segments of their country. Africans in Southern Rhodesia are agitating against disproportional land occupancy, crop restrictions, and lack of political power, but they are far less successful there than in Northern Rhodesia and Nyasaland. Nevertheless, the former Central African Federation[6] possessed a governmental mechanism which favored the whites and could be manipulated to perpetuate that privilege, but in which Africans participated at least nominally.

In Rhodesia, as in Angola and Moçambique, the proximity of independent Africa is a major factor in the present situation. White Rhodesians have shown themselves in favor of maintaining Tshombe in power in Katanga Province: an independent Katanga was itself a buffer between the Congo central government and the federation. Nyasaland Africans talk of a realignment of their country with East Africa. In the buffer zone, therefore, the impact of independent Africa may have one of two consequences. The politico-territorial units, as they exist today, may be fragmented. The disruption of the federa-

tion was long a primary aim of Africans within and outside of the state. Moçambique may well not survive the onslaught as a political entity. The other possibility is that Africans will indeed take over the governments of the territories involved, without their actual regional fragmentation. Whatever happens, the destruction of the buffer zone will be the result: either it will be absorbed completely into black Africa, or it will be divided between black and white Africa. With its disappearance, a new politico-geographic evolution will begin.

These, then, are the "three Africas": In the north, black nationalist independent Africa, in the south, white nationalist South Africa's sphere of influence, separated by the buffer zone across south-central Subsaharan Africa.

CONTRASTS

Southern Africa during the past three centuries has been the scene of two sequences of change. The first of these, the arrival and penetration of the interior by the white man, reached its culmination during the nineteenth century. The Great Trek of Afrikaners and the Pioneer Column of Rhodes heralded a migration which was essentially northward from southern and southeastern coastal regions and which halted only at the Zambezi River. The second sequence has not yet reached its climax: it is the wind of change, sustained by Africans rather than whites. Opposed to the white man's ways not only in terms of ideology, the changes wrought by Africans are directed toward the very south from which the European invaders once spread.

Both winds of change encountered impediments. The Great Trek, which took Afrikaners from the fertile Cape to the South African Highveld, resulted from cultural conflicts at the Cape, but the main body of settlers did not travel beyond the Limpopo River. Rhodes, who recognized the possibilities of the lands that lay beyond, succeeded in obtaining for Britain the bulk of what is today Southern Rhodesia, but his Pioneer Column did not cross the Zambezi River. Indeed, the Zambezi has had great influence

[6] Initially, the name Central African Federation was used most commonly. Subsequently, the country was known mainly as the Federation of Rhodesia and Nyasaland, in part because of the name of the former French state in equatorial Africa, the Central African Republic.

in the history of the Rhodesias as a dividing line between vastly different conditions. Northern Rhodesia and Nyasaland, lying to the north of the great river, were not conquered as were the Zulu of South Africa and the Matabele of Southern Rhodesia. Rather, missionaries and traders penetrated there, interested not in the alienation of land, but in the elimination of slavery. For many years after Southern Rhodesia's Africans had succumbed to the powers of the white man, there was insignificant white settlement and little white landownership to the north of the Zambezi. African tribal organization was preserved, and both Nyasaland and Northern Rhodesia became protectorates, while the whites of Southern Rhodesia, calling for greater local influence, succeeded in obtaining colonial status for their territory. Even though the discovery of copper on the Copperbelt led to some subsequent increase in white immigration and some land expropriation, particularly along the railroad constructed into Northern Rhodesia, the political status of this territory did not change.

The differences between the regions north and south of the Zambezi, which evolved from the very beginning of white penetration there, intensified as time went on. While Southern Rhodesia experienced industrial development and the growth of large urban centers, resulting in discriminatory legal measures to protect white privileges, social problems in the cities, and racial friction, the north, although not free from these evils, suffered to a far lesser degree. Southern Rhodesia came to resemble South Africa in several important respects, while Northern Rhodesia and Nyasaland were comparable to British West and East Africa. This fact was never lost on Africans living north of the Zambezi, who for two generations have been conscious of their comparative good fortune.

It is likely that the Zambezi would have become the boundary between black independent Africa and white South Africa had Southern Rhodesian whites in the 1920's not voted to remain separated politically from the Union of South Africa, and later joined with their neighbors across the Zambezi over the virtually unanimous objections of Africans everywhere in the proposed federation. This federation consisted of two units which had protectorate status, implying support for the Africans' aspirations, and one which had colonial status, meaning power for the white man and retention of the *status quo*. Two units have experienced relatively harmonious racial relations, the third cannot boast this. Two northern territories have only a quarter of the white population of the entire former federation. White power is concentrated in the south, as are economic development, crop restrictions, segregation, urbanization, and land alienation. There is no claim that these conditions are completely absent in the north, but they have historically been less prominent.

According to its architects, two advantages of the federal arrangement were to be the greater participation of the relatively poor north in the economic progress of the south, and the lesser dependence of Northern Rhodesia upon copper and its fluctuating world price. Political advantages, Africans were quick to point out, would accrue to the whites, who would be able to support each other more strongly with the country unified. Yet, when the federal parliament was convened, there were seats for Africans alongside those for whites; they were few, but unlike South Africa, there was actual interracial government. In addition, each of the three political units in the federal state retained its own government, providing Africans with two avenues for progress, the representative bodies of their individual countries as well as the government of the federation. Federation has been repudiated by the Africans, but it has had one very important positive effect. The whites who appealed to Britain to implement the federal plan also had to make concessions on multiracial government, and Southern Rhodesia's capital became the seat of the federal parliament, where Africans could argue their case. The result appears to be that Southern Rhodesian whites, unlike Southern African whites, have begun to produce a body of moderates who recognize that increased African power is inevitable in the countries forced into the now-defunct federation. Had there been no federation, and had Northern Rhodesia and Nyasaland followed Tanganyika's way and Southern Rhodesia that of South Africa, this awareness might never

75

have developed. It may come to be of crucial importance in the years that lie ahead.

Portuguese Moçambique and Angola have remained almost completely isolated from the two waves of change described previously. Nowhere is the term "Africa of the past" better exemplified than in economically stagnating, politically medieval, socially backward Portuguese Africa. Moçambique and Angola differ vitally from both independent black Africa of the north and the white republic of the south. Although there is local government, Africans are not represented, and the suggestion that black Africans should represent black African interests is inconceivable —the only interests are Portuguese, not black or white. Under the dictatorial rule of the state of which they are considered integral parts, Angola and Moçambique are even less prepared to meet the wind of change than South Africa. This is due to the complete absence of an educated African elite, African participation in governmental activities, or avenues of expression for the few politically conscious Africans.

Yet Portuguese Africa is not rigidly segregated, and the Portuguese European citizenry perhaps harbors fewer racist emotions than do whites elsewhere in Southern Africa. Unlike South Africa, Portuguese Africa possesses a system whereby Africans can gain virtual equality with whites. Known as the *assimilado* system, it permits black Africans who can fulfill a series of requirements and qualifications to become full citizens of Portugal. The effect of the system is less important than the very fact of its existence. Only some thousands of Africans have succeeded in attaining assimilado status, but they have been accepted by the Portuguese citizenry in a manner unique in Southern Africa.

Unfortunately, what has been done will prove to be too little and too late. In Moçambique, as in the former federation, the Zambezi River divides a remote north, sparsely populated by whites, from a southern sector where the significant urban centers and the bulk of the whites are found. Again, there are historical reasons for this, ranging from the conflict with the Arabs in the north to the wealth derived from the handling of imports and exports for the plateau interior in the south. Again, strongly contrasting lands are united in a single political unit, but in Moçambique there does not appear to be a mechanism for the absorption of the wind of change, as there was in the federation. With the vast majority of the African population not politically conscious, there appears little hope that events there will differ from those presently occurring in northern Angola. The province of Angola has found itself with a larger white population, but adjacent to the more militant Congo, whence the turbulence accompanying the wind of change has spilled into its territory. Whatever Portuguese military strength, however, the real vulnerability of these flanks of the buffer zone lies in the political vacuum existing there—something which cannot be said of the Congo or Tanganyika on the one hand, or South Africa on the other.

THE FUTURE

Southern Rhodesia and the Portuguese provinces in Southern Africa, Angola and Moçambique, face the surge of African nationalism emanating from the north, and the reactions to this initial thrust are varied. At the same time, these territories bound South Africa and its sphere of influence. In separating these two ideological opposites, the countries of the changing buffer zone display a variety of internal conditions ranging from those characteristic of the north to those resembling the white south. These conditions are fashioned partly by the pressures from beyond the borders, and they are changing. If the politico-territorial units of the buffer zone survive the stresses which will accompany the inevitable changes to come, then black Africa will have penetrated the white man's stronghold, and the Zambezi may again become a boundary marker in the processes of change in Southern Africa. This time, the change comes from the north. In this manner, the buffer zone would cease to play its separating role, and a new political map of the subcontinent would be shaped. Whether it is absorbed or fragmented, however, the buffer zone as it presently exists is a subject worthy of the political geographer's attention.

FRAMEWORK FOR DISCUSSION

West Africa

Northeast

Equatorial Africa

Southern Africa

0   800   Miles
0   1200   Kilometers

d.l.c. '64

Map 13

Part 2

SOUTHERN AFRICA

4

THE REPUBLIC OF SOUTH AFRICA:

SOCIOGEOGRAPHICAL ASPECTS OF

A WESTERN OUTPOST

IN TERMS OF RESOURCES, South Africa is the richest country in Subsaharan Africa. The diversified resource base includes gold and diamonds, iron ore and good-quality coal, alloys and copper, as well as soils of above-average quality and adequate water supplies over extensive regions. South Africa has become Africa's best-developed country in economic terms, possessing a sizeable iron and steel industry, plants for the conversion of coal into oil, and a number of industrial establishments far exceeding the total for all other African countries combined. Good railroad and road networks, the best in Africa, have been developed; electricity supply is plentiful; and South Africa's large cities are the largest urban centers in Africa south of the Sahara.

South Africa's population resources, too, are varied. Every continent has contributed to the complex demography of this large (472,-500 square miles) country. The arrival of the various component groups was not simultaneous, but each has made its specific contribution to the development of the state. Today, the country displays an almost incredible patchwork of races, languages, religions, customs, and modes of living. The spectacular progress made in the economic sphere in certain regions is in sharp contrast to the tribal backwardness in others.[1]

South Africa today is engaged in a unique experiment in multiracial development—an experiment which is being imposed upon the majority Bantu and other nonwhite groups by the white population. Ultimately, a federation of racial states is envisaged in which the problems of multiracialism are to be solved by separation on a territorial basis. It involves the definition, delimitation, and demarcation of anthropo-geographic boundaries imposed upon a pre-existing cultural landscape. Economic conditions are to be changed, industries relocated, markets affected. South Africa has become a laboratory for the political and economic geographer seeking to predict the consequences of this singular attempt to solve the local version of a worldwide problem.

In this chapter, an effort is made to present these developments in a geographical perspective without losing sight of the fact that they have their roots in a combination of unusual historical circumstances. Whatever the consequences, the changes will have far-reaching significance for Africa.

Regions and Races:
the Search for Nationhood

South Africa's population of about 16 million consists of four major racial groups. Two-thirds of the total is Bantu, who are divided into numerous tribal peoples. Although these peoples mingle in the urban areas and on the fringes of their tribal territories, each

---

[1] For a detailed description of the former union, see J. H. Wellington, *Southern Africa* (2 vols. Cambridge: Cambridge University Press, 1955). A later compendium is that of M. Cole, *South Africa* (New York: Dutton, 1961).

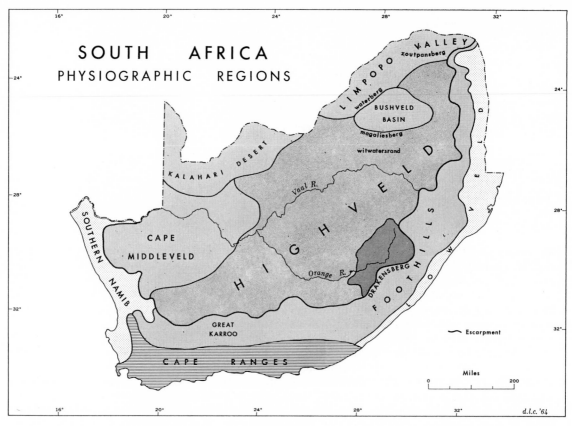

SOUTH AFRICA
PHYSIOGRAPHIC REGIONS

Map 14

African people is associated with a specific area. Thus, the Zulu are concentrated in the heart of the province of Natal, the Xhosa in the Transkei (eastern Cape), and the Venda in the northern Transvaal. The Xhosa people were the first to confront the advancing whites in the eastern Cape, where the rich valley of the Great Fish River was the scene of a series of wars between pastoralists. The Zulu rose to power when they found strong leadership in Natal, and to them the distribution pattern of Africans on the plateau is largely due. The Zulu might was broken by the white invaders, but the Zulu nation survives today. Since the Bantu entered South Africa from the north, it is not surprising that the Bantu population of the country shows a concentration in northern regions and along the coasts. On the plateau, they faced the Bushmen and the Hottentots, and later the white man. Along the foot of the Great Escarpment, the coastal

belt afforded easier migration routes, and there the Bantu penetrated farthest to the south in large numbers. Today, 10½ million Bantu remain distributed in a manner reflecting the state of affairs when the white man first gained power throughout the south, with the exception of the urban centers. South Africa's cities have drawn hundreds of thousands of Bantu from the tribal territories, and they have acted as agents of detribalization. The bulk of the African population, nevertheless, remains contained in its separate tribal territories.

The white man has been responsible for introducing to South Africa, along with his own culture, the remaining two racial groups, the "Coloreds" and the Asiatics.[2] In 1652,

---

[2] The term "Colored" is applied to persons of mixed race in South Africa. Black people are referred to as Bantu or Africans.

Cape Town, Table Mountain, and the Cape Peninsula. Facing south, this picture illustrates the urban sprawl about the foot of the westernmost outlier of the Cape Ranges. The heart of the city is immediately in front of Table Mountain, and was formerly on the shore. The empty area between the harbor and the built-up area is reclaimed land, into which the central business district is now expanding. Although protected to some extent, the harbor in Table Bay often receives the full onslaught of storms, which at times suspend all activity in the port. (Satour)

Cape Town was founded by the Dutch, but the small white settlement experienced labor troubles. The governor, Van Riebeeck, requested permission to import slaves, and within the first decade of white occupation of the Cape, slaves began to arrive from other parts of Africa as well as from Malaya and the Indies. While the Dutch in the seventeenth century found the local Hottentots an undesirable labor force and imported slaves, the British in the nineteenth century found the Zulu in Natal equally unwilling to work on sugar plantations and resorted to importing indentured labor from India. Thus, chronologically, the Africans came first to South Africa (Bushmen, Hottentots, Bantu), followed by the whites. Soon after the arrival of the first permanent white settlers, the importion of slaves began, and intermarriage of whites with slaves and (in some cases) with Hottentots produced the first Colored people. Finally, two centuries after the arrival of the whites and the beginnings of the Colored people, the Asiatics first entered Natal. A brief consideration of these minority groups follows.

Although numerically comprising only one-fifth of the South African population, the whites dominate virtually every aspect of life in South Africa. Their European ancestry is mainly Dutch and British, although Dutch characteristics appear to have faded more among today's majority group, the Afrikaners, than British characteristics have among English-speaking whites. There is, in addition, some French blood in the South African white population, derived from the first Huguenot religious refugees and their successors, and, of course, practically every other European nationality is represented. Among the white immigrants, the Afrikaners have separated themselves most completely from their European heritage. They identify themselves as intensely with Africa as do black Africans; they are fiercely proud of their language, which has evolved from Dutch and has a unique flavor today, and do not think of any part of Europe as their racial or cultural homeland. The English-speaking South Africans, on the other hand, have not relinquished their ties with Britain, do not display the undivided allegiance to South Africa of the Afrikaners, and consider themselves Europeans first and foremost. There are exceptions, naturally, but the sentiments among whites are mostly divided along these lines. An appreciation of this is indispensable to the analysis of the Afrikaners' efforts to consolidate their position in this outpost.

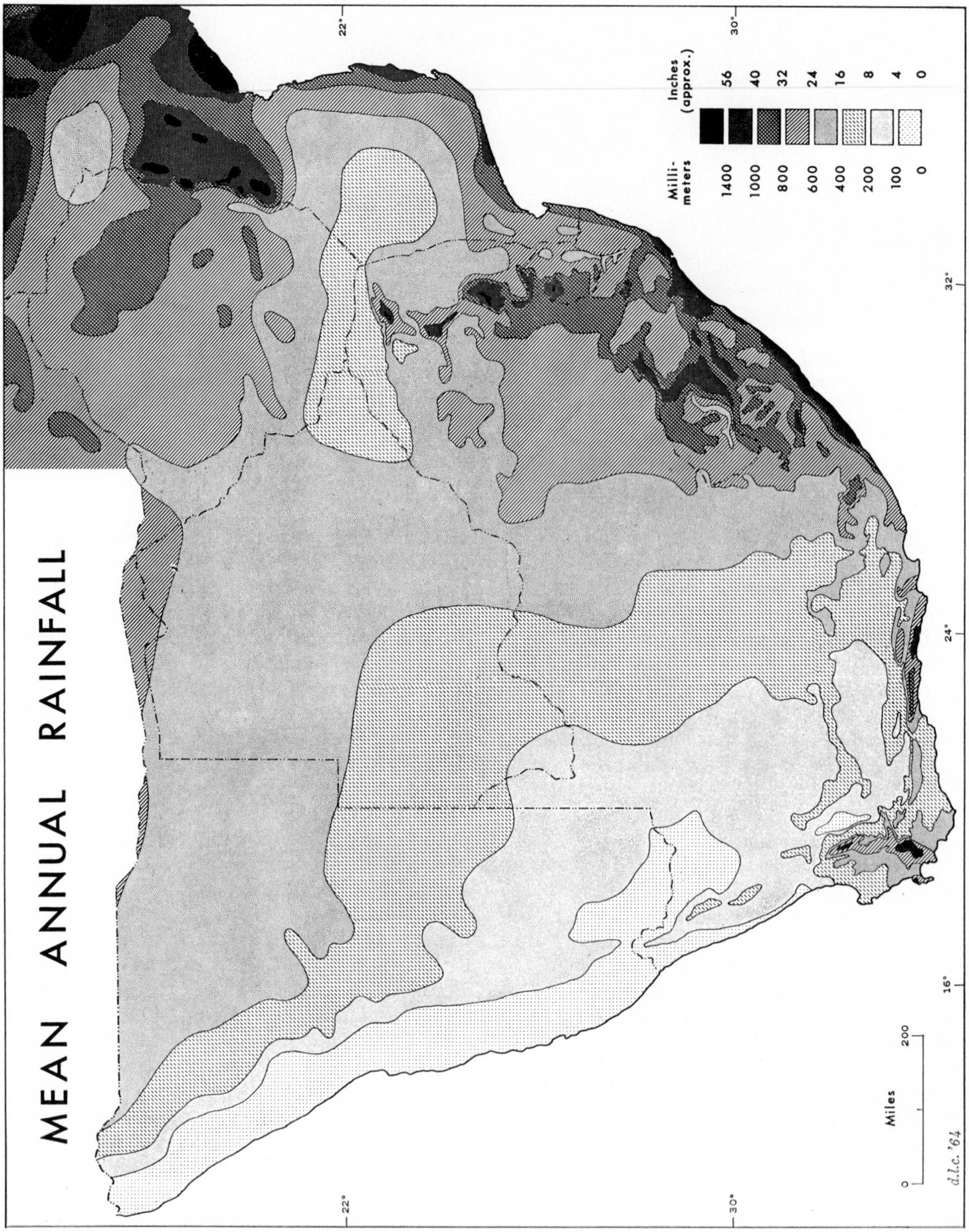
MEAN ANNUAL RAINFALL
Milli-meters
Inches (approx.)
1400 56
1000 40
800 32
600 24
400 16
200 8
100 4
0 0
22°
30°
32°
24°
16°
Miles
0
200
d.l.c. '64

Map 15

White Farmers in South Africa. South Africa produces a wide variety of crops, including many kinds of fruit, cereals, and meats. No single African country can match this output. Two unusual types of farming are illustrated here. At the right, white farmers discuss the pear harvest for the year (note Colored men doing the picking) on a farm located in the Cape Province. Above, a white farmer, assisted by a Colored helper, clips the feathers of an ostrich on a farm near Oudtshoorn, also in the Cape Province. (Satour)

Vineyards near Paarl, Cape Province, South Africa. The Huguenots who came to South Africa in the late 1600's contributed, among other things, their skills of farming under Mediterranean conditions. Largely owing to them and their successors, South Africa today has a rich annual harvest of grapes and produces excellent wines and liquors which are exported all over the world. Shown here are vineyards on a Cape farm in one of the fertile valleys lying between the Cape Ranges, one of which can be seen in the distance. (Satour)

AGRICULTURAL REGIONS

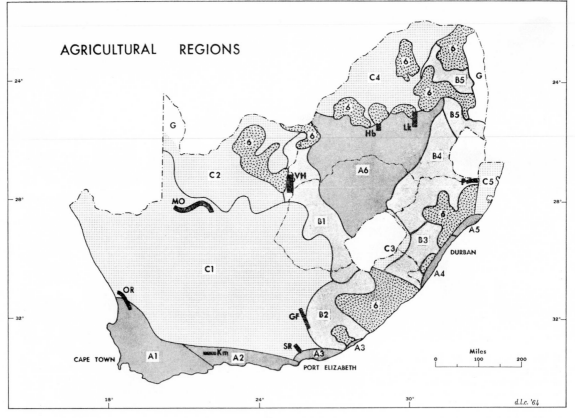

Map 16

A. INTENSIVE
1. *Southwestern Cape,* mainly in lowlands: Deciduous fruit (apples, peaches, apricots, pears, citrus fruit, vines, wheat, other cereals; sheep, dairying; timber (pine).
2. *Southern Cape Coastlands:* Citrus fruit, deciduous fruit (apples); dairying, lucerne, ostriches; timber (pine, indigenous).
3. *Eastern Cape Coastlands:* Citrus fruit, pineapples, chicory, maize, dairying.
4. *Natal Coast:* Dominantly sugar; subtropical fruits (bananas, pineapples, litchis, mangoes).
5. *Zululand Coast:* Sugar and timber (gum).
6. *Northern Orange Free State and Southern Transvaal:* Maize, cattle, sheep, dairying.

B. SEMI-INTENSIVE
1. *Western Orange Free State and Northeastern Cape:* Transition zone: maize, sheep, cattle, dairying.
2. *Eastern Cape Interior:* Sheep, dairying, cattle, citrus fruit.
3. *Natal Midlands and East Griqualand:* Timber (wattle especially, and pine), dairying.
4. *Northern Natal, Eastern Orange Free State, Southeastern Transvaal:* Maize, cattle, dairying, sheep, timber (mainly wattle).
5. *Eastern Transvaal:* Timber (wattle, gum, pine), vegetables, citrus fruit, subtropical fruits (pawpaws, bananas).

6. *Main Native Areas:* Cattle, maize, subsistence economy.

C. EXTENSIVE
1. *Karroo:* Sheep, goats.
2. *Northern Cape:* Cattle ranching.
3. *Drakensberg Foothills:* Cattle, sheep.
4. *Northern Transvaal:* Cattle ranching.
5. *Northern Zululand Coast:* Largely native areas —cattle, maize, subsistence economy; projected sugar, cotton, timber (pine).

D. IRRIGATED AREAS
OR—Olifants River: Lucerne, winter cereals, citrus fruits, vines.
MO—Middle Orange: Cotton, lucerne, wheat.
Km—Kamanassie: Lucerne, tobacco, wheat, vines.
GF—Great Fish: Lucerne, citrus fruit.
VH—Vaal Hartz: Lucerne, groundnuts, potatoes, peas, tobacco, wheat, some cotton.
Lk—Loskop: Wheat, tobacco, groundnuts, citrus fruit.
SR—Sundays River: Citrus fruit, lucerne.
Hb—Hartebeestpoort: Tobacco, fodder crops, vegetables, wheat, citrus fruit.
P—Pongola: Sugar, some cotton.
G—Game Reserves.

From a map prepared by the author in collaboration with O. Williams and B. S. Young. First published in "A Map of the Main Agricultural Regions of South Africa," *Journal for Geography,* I, No. 7 (1960), 46.

Ironically, it was not the Afrikaners who brought to the interior of South Africa the modern ways of life which they view with such pride today. The nineteenth-century Dutch wished to escape from British overlordship at the Cape, and they entered the interior with the intent of establishing pastoral republics, ranching cattle and sheep. Thus, they became known as *Boers* (a Dutch word literally meaning "farmer"), and their economic mode of life resembled more the Africans' than that which was developing in Europe. The discovery of diamonds near the confluence of the Orange and the Vaal rivers, and the subsequent discovery of gold along the Witwatersrand, drew thousands of white immigrants who brought with them capital, technical skills, and the knowledge of Europe's progress in the Industrial Revolution. Opposed bitterly by the Boers, these people infiltrated the interior republics and founded cities such as Kimberley and Johannesburg, exploiting resources which could not have been exploited by pastoralists. Against the Boers' will, the isolation of the interior came to an end, as railroads penetrated the highlands, roads were built, and urbanization gained momentum.

After their defeat in the Boer War, the Afrikaners were to participate in the economic progress of their country—progress which was initiated by recent immigrants from Europe. The level of their participation rose constantly, and Afrikaners in due course began to attain positions of power. The ratio of rural to urban dwellers among Afrikaners changed continuously in favor of the latter. In the early days of the union, it may have been true to say that the vast majority of Afrikaners still lived on the land, and the bulk of the English-speaking people and other immigrants resided in the growing cities. Today, the Afrikaner is as much an urban dweller as is his English-speaking contemporary. Constant increases in the percentages of urbanized Africans, Coloreds, and Asiatics are recorded in Table I.

Even though the whites are concentrated in the urban centers and have brought mining techniques, industrial establishments, and an alien mode of life to this part of the continent, this does not mean that the majority of the

TABLE I

PERCENTAGE OF POPULATION GROUPS IN URBAN CENTERS, SOUTH AFRICA, 1911–1961

Year	Africans	Whites	Coloreds	Asiatics	Total
1911	12.6	51.6	–	–	24.7
1921	14.0	59.6	51.9	60.7	27.9
1936	18.4	68.0	56.9	70.8	32.4
1946	23.7	74.5	60.9	71.3	38.4
1951	27.2	78.4	64.7	77.5	42.6
1961 (est.)	36.4	84.1	66.9	88.5	50.9

Source: Derived from data in *Union Statistics for Fifty Years* (Bureau of Census and Statistics, Pretoria, 1960), p. A–10.

rural areas are owned and farmed by Africans. There are approximately 300 million acres of land in South Africa; in 1957, whites held over 215 million acres, comprising well over 100,000 farms. When these figures are related to the relative sizes of the population groups involved, some indication of the densities of population in the Bantu Areas can be gained. Naturally, not all the land is of the same quality, and much of the African land is of good agricultural value. But South Africa's vast spaces are largely in the hands of whites.

Beside urbanization and industrialization, the whites brought to South Africa new crops and modern agricultural methods. On the good soils of the Cape, Natal, and eastern Transvaal, large plantation farms produce grapes, apples, bananas, and citrus fruits. On the plateau, cattle and corn are important products. Although hampered to some extent by rainfall deficiency and variability, soils which include good but also very poor areas, and, over large regions, a danger of winter frosts, South African agriculture nevertheless grows a wide variety of products and is generally far ahead of its nearest African competitors in terms of yields. Soil erosion and desert encroachment must be combated and irrigation promoted for continued progress. Efforts are being made to achieve these aims. Possessing the requirements for these practices and also owning most of the land, the whites are responsible for most of what has been accomplished.

A Shepherd and His Flock, Cape Province, South Africa. South Africa ranks among the first five wool producers in the world, and much comes from the Cape Province. Here, sheep are being driven to another pasture by an African shepherd. Typical eastern Cape scenery can be seen beyond. (South African Railways)

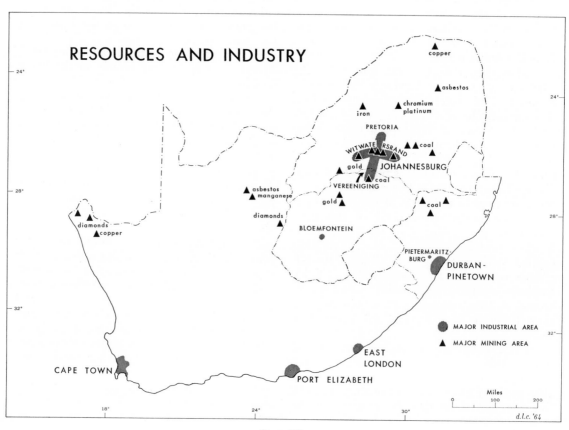

RESOURCES AND INDUSTRY

copper

asbestos

chromium
platinum

iron

PRETORIA

WITWATERSRAND

coal

gold   JOHANNESBURG

coal

VEREENIGING

asbestos
manganese

gold

coal

diamonds

BLOEMFONTEIN

diamonds
copper

PIETERMARITZ-
BURG

DURBAN-
PINETOWN

● MAJOR INDUSTRIAL AREA

▲ MAJOR MINING AREA

CAPE TOWN

EAST
LONDON

PORT ELIZABETH

Miles
0   100   200

d.l.c. '64

Map 17

Cattle Being Herded to Slaughter, Orange Free State, South Africa. The cool plateau Highveld is suitable for cattle ranching, although the winter drought is a recurrent problem and occasionally causes severe losses. The uncompromising scenery of the Orange Free State is well illustrated here, and the corrugated dirt road gives evidence that the drought is on. A mesa can be seen in the distance; these *koppies* are usually supported by dolerite sills. Also visible is a field of corn, the stable crop for the majority of South Africa's population. (Satour)

The Colored (mixed) population of South Africa, although numbering only about ½ million, constitutes the majority sector in the entire western Cape, including the city of Cape Town.[3] Several historical factors have been involved in bringing about this concentration of Coloreds in the southwest. The term "Colored" includes not only persons of mixed white and African blood, but also Malay people, who have remained remarkably distinct racially for many generations. Intermarriage with the early slaves began to produce these mulattoes, who in addition to white blood might have Hottentot, black slave, or perhaps Asiatic blood also. The Hottentots

also intermarried with the slaves, so that the numbers of the new Colored community soon attained significance. All this took place, however, while the western Cape was the only region of Southern Africa that was permanently settled and organized by whites. Cape Town was the only real town, and the Coloreds worked there and on the farms in the surrounding areas.

When the white man finally invaded other parts of Southern Africa, the Colored did not participate. That element in the white population which desired to trek onto the plateau was opposed to what it considered miscegenation. The racist elitism that was developing among these Afrikaners belied the fact that mixed marriages at the Cape had been producing Colored offspring for generations, and that people of Dutch extraction—who were now the core of the Afrikaner group—had participated actively in this process. Indeed,

[3] For details of distribution, occupations, religions, etc., of the Colored population, see K. M. Buchanan and N. Hurwitz, "The 'Colored' Community in the Union of South Africa," *Economic Geography*, XL, No. 3 (July, 1950), 397–414.

it has been estimated that two out of every three whites in South Africa carry some Colored genes.[4]

Although mixed marriages are now prohibited by law in South Africa, the Colored community continues to expand. The birth rate is very high (47.0 per thousand in 1958, compared to 24.5 for whites in the same year), but the death rate is also high at 16.9 per thousand, giving an annual increase of just over 3 per cent. By contrast, the death rate for whites is only 8.6 per thousand, the annual rate of increase being just under 1.6 per cent—only about half that of the Colored community, but considerably higher than the average in western European countries.

Like their white contemporaries, the Colored people speak either Afrikaans or English, but Afrikaans predominates (89 per cent in 1958). This fact attests to their early association with the Dutch people of the Cape, even though the Dutch never integrated the Colored community with their own. About 30 per cent of the Colored churchgoing population attends the Dutch Reformed churches, about one-third attend English churches, and about 70,000 (5 per cent) practice the Islamic faith. In view of the segregationist philosophies of the Dutch churches, the number of Colored adhering to them is remarkable. Islam is most prevalent in Cape Town, where it is carried on by the Malay community as it has been for centuries.

The economic condition of the Colored minority is not good. Various avenues of employment are closed to Colored persons by law, and a sizeable portion of the community has always lived in destitution. Cape Town's worst squalor is in the Colored slums, for the Colored have participated in the move to the cities that has marked all South Africa for several decades. The Colored cannot compete successfully with the skilled European (if he is not barred from such competition by law), and he loses jobs in the unskilled field to Africans, who work for less. Material advancement among the Colored people has therefore been painfully slow, and it is to this that much of their apparent apathy must be ascribed.

_____
[4] Wellington, *op. cit.*, II, 237.

A *Vessel of the Cape Snoek-Fishing Fleet, South Africa.* Many Colored people have successfully turned to fishing as their occupation. Shown off the Cape coast, this boat is returning to port with a catch that may be sold to a canning factory or by the fishermen themselves on the town market. (South African Information Service)

In Cape Town, the Colored have maintained themselves in only a few industries, including stevedoring, textile work, bricklaying, and furniture building. Still, there are presently more Coloreds in industrial occupations (mostly general labor) than in agriculture, and the difference is growing, despite the problems they face in the city.

Among the Colored, a small elite is currently developing, consisting of a few successful professional people, teachers, and administrators. This elite has not yet begun to function as a unit in support of Colored causes, but it is growing and may attain significance from this point of view. It is evidence of the severe social stratification which exists in the Colored community, based frankly on somatic characteristics. The great majority of the elite are of light skin color, the middle group is literally of medium skin color with clear evidence of white blood, while the lowest class is made up of individuals only barely dis-

Asian Girls Working on the Sugar Plantations, Natal, South Africa. Initially, the Asians who came to South Africa were brought as indentured laborers to work on the sugar estates, as the Zulu did not wish to work there, and slavery had been abolished. Comparatively few Asians now remain on the sugar fields, and Africans have become the major labor force there. During harvest time, however, these Asian girls are earning a few extra shillings by cutting cane. (South African Information Service)

tinguishable from Africans.[5] This class consciousness even within the Colored minority has played an important role in the general failure of the community as a whole to gain in influence in South African affairs.

While the Colored may claim some ethnic affinity with Africa, the Asiatic, like the European, is a real intruder on the African scene. In South Africa today there are about a half-million Asiatics, concentrated in Natal. Of course, both the Colored and the Asiatics are scattered in parts of the country other than their region of concentration, but in both cases the core agglomerations dwarf other settlements. The concentration of Asiatics in Natal has been the result of the events of only one century. In 1860, the first group of indentured Indian laborers arrived for work on the sugar plantations. The practice was to continue, at first almost exclusively by the

[5] S. Patterson, *Colour and Culture in South Africa* (London: Routledge & Kegan Paul, 1953).

importation of this labor, later with the added factor of nonlabor immigrants, for a half-century, until the South African government, alarmed at the increase in the number of Asiatics, stopped the process in 1913.

By this date, however, the Asiatic population of the country was about 150,000. Most Indians whose period of indentured labor had expired declined the free passage back to India and remained to develop market gardens near the cities. Wealthy merchants had immigrated and were establishing successful commercial enterprises in competition with the whites. In Durban, Asiatics were impressing their unmistakable stamp on urban development, and today, over one-third of this city's total population is Asiatic.

Since 1913, the increase in the total Asiatic population has been rapid. The birth rate has dropped somewhat over the past three decades, but remains 30.8 per thousand (1958), while the death rate is only 8.2, so that the annual increase is of the order of

2.26 per cent. The South African government, in efforts to stem this tide, has attempted to implement several repatriation schemes, but the vast majority of the Asiatics in South Africa have recognized their material advantages and have remained there. One reason for the government's eagerness to repatriate Asiatics in large numbers lies in their changing occupations. No longer are they found solely in the sugar fields and the market gardens surrounding the towns. They have joined in the trek to the cities, and nearly 90 per cent are now in the urban centers, leaving only few in agriculture, where the labor now is performed by Africans.

In the cities, the Asiatics have reaped the harvest of their diligence as they did on the land in the past. Many are successful and wealthy businessmen, and there are large numbers of Asiatics in textile work, the building trades, and the transport industry. Some have achieved wealth and property, and competition with the whites continues in the higher echelons, while competition with Africans occurs in the unskilled, low-paid areas. White and African resentment against the Asiatics has been expressed in outbursts of rioting in Durban.

The great majority of South Africa's Asiatics are Indians, and about 70 per cent of these are Hindu. They continue to speak a variety of Indian languages and separate themselves from the 20 per cent who are Moslems, many of whom have moved to the Transvaal.[6] The high birth rate (despite the fact that during importation the ratio of men to women was kept heavily in favor of the former), the divisions within the community reminiscent of the caste system, the alien religions in a Christian country, and the failure of the Asiatics to adopt adequate sanitary practices has separated them from the ruling whites, who feel justified in treating the Indian little better than the African. As a result, numerous discriminatory acts have been passed in parliament, efforts are being made

to restrict Asiatic land ownership in cities, and no steps are being taken to give the Asiatic direct representation in the South African government. Unlike the Colored, the Asiatics have allies on the world scene, and India and Pakistan have repeatedly appealed for United Nations consideration of the treatment of Indians and Pakistani in South Africa. In response, the South African government has offered ever greater incentives for repatriation, including cash grants in addition to free passage, but no large-scale exodus has resulted. Hence, it is assumed that the Asiatic does not suffer excessively from his treatment at the hands of the white rulers, and no remedial steps have been taken as desired by India and Pakistan.

A Nation Divided

This, then, is the South African nation, although few would assert that South Africa's peoples are indeed a nation in any sense of the word. The question is how a nation thus fragmented can evolve along desirable lines. The Brazilian answer has been integration, and although not completely successful, this example is often quoted as one where failure has been averted. The South African response has been along completely opposite lines. Asserting that integration leads to cultural and moral decay as well as to racial pollution, the white ruling minority has produced a blueprint of separate living for the sectors of the South African population which is at present being implemented.[7] It is a plan which has no rival anywhere in the world and is considered a unique solution to a unique problem. Although admittedly intensifying the divisive factors between South Africa's peoples, it will, according to its architects, lead to political independence for each sector while leading toward economic interdependence.[8] The South African state, therefore, is

[6] Asiatics are prohibited by law from taking up residence in the Orange Free State. See K. M. Buchanan and N. Hurwitz, "The Asiatic Immigrant Community in the Union of South Africa," *Geographical Review*, XXXIX, No. 3 (July, 1949), 445.

[7] H. J. de Blij, *Africa South* (Evanston, Ill.: Northwestern University Press, 1962), p. 247.
[8] H. F. Verwoerd, Prime Minister of South Africa, at news conference, April 2, 1961, in London, England.

African Mineworker Drilling in a Gold Mine, Johannesburg, Transvaal, South Africa. Hundreds of thousands of Africans have been attracted to the city of Johannesburg alone, where many have found work in the mines. Workers have come from as far afield as Swaziland, Moçambique, and even Nyasaland. Many have stayed in the city for decades, and have become urbanized and detribalized. They know no other life than that the wage earner in the city. (Satour)

African Residents of Johannesburg, South Africa. Many Africans in South Africa have succeeded in the cities and are comparatively well off. These men may be employees of a mining concern, clerks, or holidaying domestic servants. Along with every resident of South Africa, these people are affected by the Bantustan project now being carried out. (Satour)

envisaged as developing along lines similar to that of the British Commonwealth.[9] There will not be a federation and therefore no central government, but a group of adjacent, racially based units, each internally independent politically.

The goal of the blueprint for separate development is the preservation of Western culture in the South African outpost. The mingling of white, Asiatic, and Bantu cultures is deemed undesirable, and thus each must be provided with his own "homelands" in which cultural development may take place without a threat to its purity. Obviously, this involves the relocation of hundreds of thousands of people who have for centuries been thrown together by the forces of economic development, urbanization, and mutual need. A complete reorientation of the South African economy, massive relocation of industry, and alterations to the transport network are among the major problems facing the state in consequence of the regional form of *apartheid*.

The ultimate test of the philosophy of separate development will be its economic consequences. As a nonfragmented unit, South Africa during the past fifty years has experienced rapid and almost uninterrupted economic progress. The net national income of the union in 1912 was $370 million, and in subsequent years the gold price helped reduce fluctuations even during the worldwide depression of the early thirties. In 1937 the NNI was over $1 billion, and in 1962 it approached $6 billion.[10] South Africa's 16 million people produce one-fifth of the total income for the entire African continent, and South Africa accounts for 20 per cent of the annual international trade of all Africa. These are impressive figures, but they may be affected negatively by the strait jacket of separate development. The unpopularity of *apartheid* in world public opinion has led to

[9] *Ibid.* There remain a number of apparent contradictions in the scheme. The most obvious is that involving economic interdependence. The white areas would probably be economically independent from the black states, but the latter would depend upon the white state for certain important commodities as well as for an outlet for the labor force.
[10] *Union Statistics for Fifty Years* (Pretoria: Bureau of Census and Statistics, 1960), p. S-3.

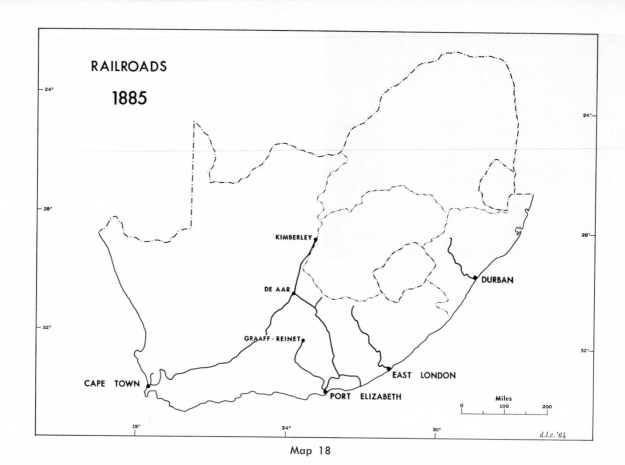

RAILROADS

1885

KIMBERLEY

DE AAR

DURBAN

GRAAFF - REINET

CAPE TOWN

EAST LONDON

PORT ELIZABETH

Miles
0   100   200

d.l.c. '64

Map 18

RAILROADS

1900

PIETERSBURG

PRETORIA

to L.M.

JOHANNESBURG

VRYBURG

KIMBERLEY

BLOEMFONTEIN

DE AAR

DURBAN

GRAAFF-
REINET

CAPE TOWN

EAST LONDON

PORT ELIZABETH

Miles
0   100   200

d.l.c. '64

Map 19

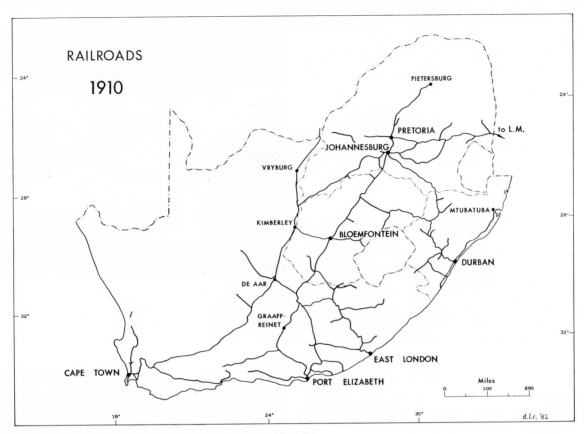

RAILROADS

1910

PIETERSBURG

PRETORIA

JOHANNESBURG

to L.M.

VRYBURG

MTUBATUBA

KIMBERLEY

BLOEMFONTEIN

DE AAR

DURBAN

GRAAFF-
REINET

EAST LONDON

CAPE TOWN

PORT ELIZABETH

Miles
0   100   200

d.l.c. '64

Map 20

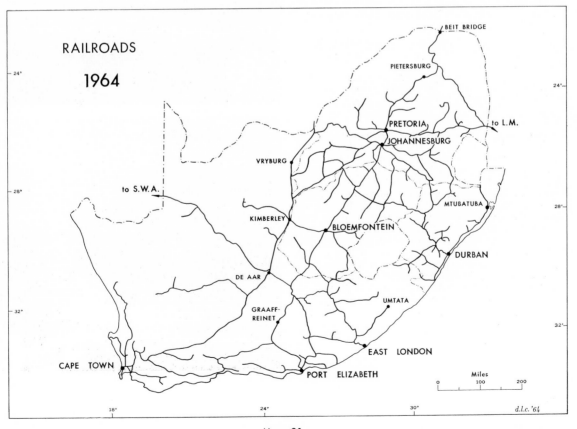

RAILROADS

1964

BEIT BRIDGE

PIETERSBURG

PRETORIA

JOHANNESBURG

to L.M.

VRYBURG

to S.W.A.

MTUBATUBA

KIMBERLEY

BLOEMFONTEIN

DE AAR

DURBAN

GRAAFF-
REINET

UMTATA

EAST LONDON

CAPE TOWN

PORT ELIZABETH

Miles
0   100   200

d.l.c. '64

Map 21

efforts to establish a boycott against South African goods. Internally, the reorganization of the state will be a costly process. And finally, the supreme test is likely to involve the degree of economic viability of the Bantu homelands (Bantustans) and the ability of mining and industry to maintain progress through a changing labor situation.

Reversals in Prevalent Trends

Among the most significant trends to accompany South Africa's path toward leadership of the African economic scene have been the growth of urban centers and the expansion of the manufacturing sector of the economy. Urbanization was first stimulated by mining, but the contribution of mining to the national income has declined in favor of manufacturing and even agriculture. Yet the cities continued to grow, and Johannesburg, once based entirely on mining, now has over 60 per cent of its white employed population engaged in professional, administrative, and commercial activities.[11] After an early phase dominated by agriculture, the South African economy between 1929 and 1943 was sustained mainly by mining as the most important single contributor. Since 1943, how-

---

[11] T. J. D. Fair and E. W. N. Mallows, "The Southern Transvaal," *The Town Planning Review,* XXX, No. 2 (July, 1959), 125–38.

Three South African Ports. The South African coast line, like the coast line of the entire continent, supplies few sites for port development. In addition to Cape Town, the ports of Durban (top), East London (middle), and Port Elizabeth (below) serve the interior. Largest is Durban, whose quays, modern customs facilities, and railroad yards are illustrated here. Note the impressive skyline in the distance. East London's artificial harbor has been built in the mouth of the Buffalo River. Port Elizabeth does not enjoy the benefit of a well-protected natural harbor, but artificial piers have created a fine port. Of the three, Durban handles by far the greatest amount of trade and the bulk of that of the Witwatersrand. Port Elizabeth is next in importance, and East London's port is mainly of regional significance. (Durban Publicity Association and Satour)

ever, manufacturing has taken the lead, now contributing as much as mining and agriculture combined. These manufacturing industries have not relied only upon overseas markets; indeed, their success is largely a reflection of the increased capacity of the South African market. Even though their respective shares were disproportionate, Africans, Coloreds, and Asiatics benefited from the economic progress of the country as well as the whites. Thus, a multiracial market with constantly increasing purchasing power developed, and any interference with this trend is likely to have severe negative consequences for South Africa's thriving economy.

Urbanization in South Africa has advanced further than in any other part of Subsaharan Africa, and Johannesburg, Cape Town, and Durban have no rivals in terms of size on the subcontinent. As break-in-bulk places, the cities on the coasts benefited by the progress of mining and industry on the plateau, and Port Elizabeth and East London vie with Cape Town and Durban for the trade of the interior. On the Highveld, the Witwatersrand became the core of the entire country. Further gold discoveries were made and towns sprang up east and west from Johannesburg, so that a lengthy urbanized belt developed. North of Johannesburg, Pretoria prospered as the country's administrative center, and southward, Vereeniging on the Vaal River benefited from ample water supply and the proximity of coal deposits. The southern Transvaal thus became the hub of all South Africa, with an east-west manufacturing and mining axis and a north-south administrative and transportation axis. Johannesburg alone has over 1,100,000 inhabitants today, but the two axes of the southern Transvaal include over one-quarter of the population of the entire country. A megalopolis is developing there.

In the urban centers of South Africa, and

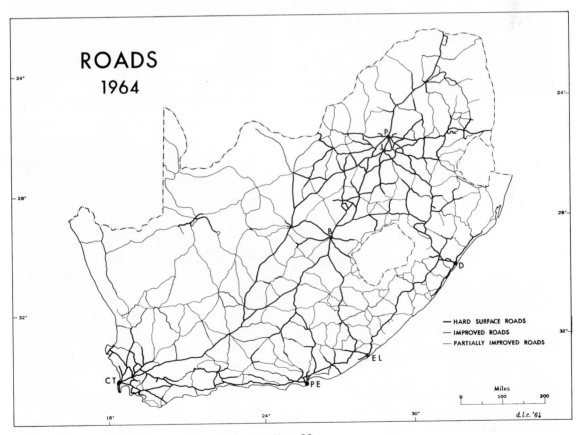

Map 22

Modern Transportation in South Africa. No country in Africa has as good a transportation system as South Africa. Excellent bridges (top, left) have been constructed across many gorges and other physical impediments to fast road connections. Many hundreds of miles of roads have been asphalted. Four-lane highways are beginning to make their appearance (below, left), and one now connects Pietermaritzburg with Durban, Natal. The railroad network has also been steadily expanded and improved, and an increasing mileage is being electrified. Johannesburg (below, right) has the country's busiest central station. Fast trains connect the major cities of the country, such as the famed "Blue Train," between Johannesburg and Cape Town (below). (Satour and South African Information Service)

Bloemfontein, Orange Free State, South Africa. The old capital of the former Orange Free State Republic is now the capital of a province of the South African Republic. Although among interior South Africa's oldest towns, Bloemfontein does not rank among the largest, as this illustration of the heart of the central business district shows. With the discovery of gold in the Free State, however, faster growh may lie ahead. Bloemfonein is a university town and retains its strong Afrikaner nationalist flavor. (Satour)

especially on the Witwatersrand, the representatives of the racial sectors of the population have long been thrown together in the common economic effort. In spite of residential segregation and job restrictions based on race, the fortunes of black and white in South Africa have become inextricably mixed. The urban centers, from Cape Town (the first city) and Kimberley (the first mining town) to Johannesburg and Durban, have attracted the capital investment and skills of foreigners and the muscle of the African. Together, they achieved South Africa's economic progress, most dramatically reflected in the urban sprawl and high-rise core of the Golden City. Johannesburg became the continent's financial capital, overseas investors displayed much confidence in South Africa's future, and every sector of the economy blossomed. In 1912, total employment in industry is estimated to have been under 100,000; in 1962, it approached 1 million.

The four industrialized regions of South Africa are the Witwatersrand, the Durban-Pinetown area, the region around Cape Town, and the area of Port Elizabeth. Mining stimulated these industries in large measure. The manufacture of explosives became a major industry on the Witwatersrand, and the need

for mining boots stimulated the footwear manufacturing of Port Elizabeth and Durban. The need for coal and electricity increased constantly. An iron and steel industry was established at Pretoria, with a subsidiary plant near Vereeniging. A further step toward self-sufficiency was taken with the construction of the world's largest oil-from-coal plant in the northern Orange Free State.

As the urban centers grew, so did the market for agricultural products. No longer a subsistence pastoralism, South African agriculture produced a vast variety of specialized fruits and vegetables, a higher corn yield per acre than anywhere else on the subcontinent, wheat, a variety of other cereals, and sugar. Near the cities, market gardening and intensive agriculture developed. But whether around the cities or in the vast interior, the bulk of the labor was carried on by Africans under the direction of white landowners.

Thus, the African for decades was leaving his tribal homeland for city, mine, and farm. As elsewhere in Africa, detribalization was proceeding apace, and in the cities could be found a permanently settled African population which was as solidly urban—though poorer—as its white counterpart. Nevertheless, there remained parts of South Africa which were recognizably tribal in nature. Zululand, in Natal, and the Transkei, in the eastern Cape, although affected by the steady stream of emigrants, changed but little as South Africa progressed. Subsistence agriculture, poor soil management, and diseased cattle characterized these and other "native reserves," and the exodus was the result of local conditions as much as of the attraction of the cities and mines of the white man.

The blueprint of separate development for South Africa's racial groups involves the relocation of hundreds of thousands of Africans in their tribal homelands—a unique form of retribalization, the "purifying" of the white areas as far as possible, and the establishment of cooperating states reserved for specific racial groups. It involves the reversal of a number of the trends enumerated above. Many Africans are being moved from the urbanized areas, and the permanent urban

black population is being replaced by a temporary migrant population. This is checking the influx of Africans into the cities, and it is removing from the urban areas a sizeable African middle class which was in process of developing. The result, at least during the transition period, is a shortage of unskilled labor for mines, manufacturing establishments, and commerce, and farms and homes are also beginning to feel the effects of the new policy.[12]

[12] The plan for separate development was drawn up by a group of scientists appointed by the South African government in 1948, known as the Tomlinson Commission. In October, 1954, this commission produced a report consisting of 51 chapters comprising 3,755 pages, 598 tables, and 66 large-scale maps, advocating a form of regional racial separation. An abbreviated edition was published later under the title *Summary of the Report of the Commission for the Socio-Economic Development of the Bantu Areas Within the Union of South Africa* (Pretoria: Government Printer, 1955).

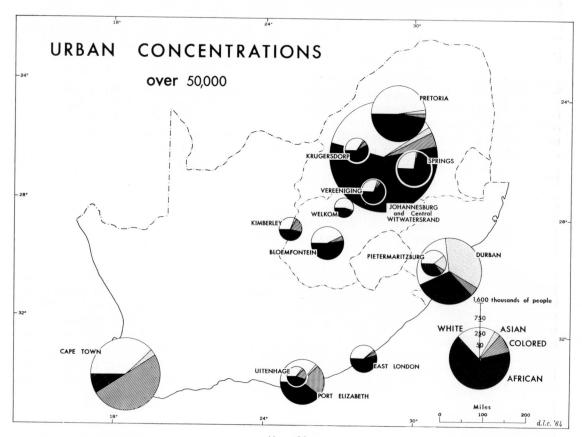

Map 23

Pretoria, Administrative Capital of the Republic of South Africa. In contrast to Bloemfontein, Pretoria, the old capital of the South African (Transvaal) Republic, has grown into one of South Africa's major cities. This photograph was taken from the headquarters of government, the Union Building, and shows the central business district with its many modern and tall structures. In the far distance on the right is the steel plant of ISCOR, the major industry of the city. (Satour)

Any appraisal of the effects upon a state of regional fragmentation must involve a consideration of the degree of participation in the common economic effort of each of the population sectors to be separated. Since the results of this process are being felt today, it is necessary to view the labor situation before the publication of the Tomlinson Report. The last industrial classification prior to this event was that of 1951 (see Table II).

In 1951, out of a total Bantu population of 8,535,000, 2,312,000 were resident in the urban centers and 2,590,000 on white farms. A total of 57.4 per cent of the Africans in the country thus lived in the white areas, where they outnumbered the whites by about 5 to 3.[13] Table II shows that, in the same year, nearly 68 per cent of the economically active persons in South Africa were Africans, excluding the subsistence farmers in the African reserves. The implications of separate development as far as they affect labor, there-

---

[13] D. H. Houghton, "Economic Dangers of Separate Bantu Development," *Optima,* IX, No. 4 (December, 1959), 188.

TABLE II

POPULATION OF SOUTH AFRICA:
INDUSTRIAL CLASSIFICATION, 1951
(THOUSANDS)

	Africans	Whites	Coloreds	Asiatics	Total
Agriculture, etc.	1,253	145	98	13	1,509
Mining	449	57	4	1	511
Manufacturing	227	183	70	22	502
Construction	132	67	39	2	240
Electricity, etc.	17	7	2	–	26
Commerce	101	179	25	23	328
Transport, Communications	73	113	14	2	202
Services	741	204	111	17	1,073
Inadequately described, registered unemployed	118	28	42	14	202
Totals	3,111	983	405	94	4,593

Source: Derived from data in *Union Statistics for Fifty Years.*

fore, would be such that upon immediate implementation, the white areas would be deprived of virtually the entire labor force in the case of farming (8 out of every 10 laborers) and mining (9 out of every 10 workers), and nearly half of it in the case of manufacturing (9 out of every 20 employees). These figures illustrate the degree to which economic integration has taken place in South Africa, and they affect only the Africans. The extent of nonwhite participation in the South African economy is even more strikingly illustrated when figures for Coloreds and Asiatics are also included.

Reorientation toward separate development, therefore, must be a gradual process, and this is what the South African government envisages. The question is whether, even though gradual, separation of the races will be permitted at all by the economy, or whether markets, resource dissemination, and entrepreneurship will be so inhibited by fragmentation that the favorable trends of the past will be reversed.

Much will depend upon developments within the Bantustans, where for centuries little change has taken place. The sudden increases in population which these areas will experience as a result of Bantu relocation will require rapid economic growth. The carrying capacity of the lands must be improved, there must be scope for labor in industry, and vast quantities of capital will be required. South Africa is prepared to pay the price of racial separation, but what is required may be too much for the state to carry. The Bantu Areas, out of which the Bantustans of today are being forged, are African reserves mainly because they provided little in the way of resources; hence, they were left out of the main stream of economic progress prevalent in the white areas. Land occupance remained wasteful, erosion of soils was rampant, crop yields were low, and it has been estimated that the productivity of the Bantu Areas has actually declined during the past 50 years. What these areas exported was labor, and although they will be able to continue to do so on a migrant basis, the total resident population will expand to an unprecedented extent at a time when the first steps toward economic development have yet to be taken.

In Subsaharan Africa, as Stamp has pointed out with reference to Tanganyika's infamous peanut scheme, the lesson of time has been to make haste slowly. South Africa's Bantustan plan requires, among other things, that the size of an economically viable landholding within the Bantu Areas be known. Industrial development and urbanization will not take place overnight, so that the initial mainstay of the growing black population must be productive farming. This means the reversal of a long-prevalent trend rather than the acceleration of one already extant. However, the Tomlinson Commission, rather than awaiting local improvements in farming methods, proposed a complete reorganization of farming in the Bantu Areas in the following terms:

In terms of the present standard of Bantu production, a farming family in the Bantu Areas requires, on the average, 111 acres of land to make a gross annual income of $196.00. This is the average size of a farm unit and gross income of all farmers, including those on irrigation schemes and on sugar farms, as well as those in the mixed farming and pastoral regions. On this basis, the Bantu Areas can carry about 307,000 farming families or about 51 per cent of the population as recorded in the 1951 census. To open the way to efficient agricultural development of the Bantu Areas, approximately half of the present population will, therefore, have to be removed eventually from the agricultural land, and will have to find a living outside of agriculture in other primary, and in the secondary and tertiary spheres of economic activity.[14]

By 1981, it is envisaged that the Bantu Areas will be able to carry 9 million people, of whom 2 million will depend upon the earnings of migrant laborers. In order to achieve this, the Bantustans will annually have to provide jobs for 20,000 persons in secondary industries and an additional 30,000 persons in commerce and tertiary activities, while undergoing agricultural reorganization. During the years prior to racial separation on the Tomlinson Commission's recommenda-

---

[14]*Summary of the Report of the Commission for the Socio-Economic Development of the Bantu Areas Within the Union of South Africa*, p. 114.

tions, the average annual increase in jobs as specified above was just over 300, which gives some idea of the scale upon which economic change will have to take place.

Perhaps the most sweeping changes, affecting not only the interiors of the Bantustans but also the other parts of South Africa, involve the industrial development of the Bantu Areas. South Africans who were in agreement with the blueprint of separate development as long as it concerned the relocation of Africans in their own reserves and the improvement of subsistence agriculture, ceased to be complacent when plans were made for the industrial development of these regions. Objections came mainly on two grounds: that the artificial infusion of capital and the protection these new industries would receive would lead to "unfair competition" (the industries in the Bantu Areas having the advantage over those elsewhere), and that the location of industries anywhere but in those places determined by purely economic factors would be folly. The first objection is an indication of the failure of the South African manufacturer to heed the government's warning that sacrifices must be made in the interests of racial purity. As Wellington said, such good intentions go by the board when the purse strings are affected, and the South African businessman is no exception. The fears of unfair competition are, in addition, not well founded, for the degree of development of industry projected by the commission is unattainable, if recent trends are any guide. The second criticism is one espoused by most economists, who fear the fragmentation of South Africa's integrated economy and the costs involved in the artificial development of industrial areas inadequately supported by resources, local capital, and entrepreneurship. In other words, the state's savings must be employed at a time when the entire economy is facing the adverse effects of the project and international boycotts. Although these effects are seen as temporary, there are fears that the impact will be so severe that a new upward swing may never come. The South African government considers the risk worth taking, since the goal is the survival of the white community's cultural heritage and racial identity.

Bantu Areas and the Distribution of Resources

If economic development in the Bantu Areas is to be accelerated, these regions must be provided with a sizeable share of the South African resource base. Their location is such that all important mineralized regions lie beyond their borders. In 1952, when South Africa received $465 million for her mineral production, only $13 million was for minerals produced in the Bantu Areas. The large areas of the Transkei, Ciskei, and Zululand have produced insignificant amounts of coal, iron, and titanium, the total value in 1952 being less than $25,000. There are deposits of nickel, copper, and marble, but on a national scale they are of little importance. The Bantu Areas of the plateau are better endowed, having small deposits of copper, platinum, asbestos, lead, gold, iron, and diamonds. In terms of mineral production, however, the Bantu Areas cannot be expected to attain much importance within the period envisaged by the Tomlinson Commission as leading toward a degree of self-sufficiency.

The absence of large mineral deposits within Bantu Areas is a natural consequence of the white man's exploitation of South Africa's resources. Indeed, those areas which are today Bantu Areas are specifically those in which the white man, mainly from this point of view, had little or no interest. The plateau has produced the bulk of South Africa's minerals, including gold, coal, iron ore, platinum, diamonds, asbestos, and manganese. The bulk of the value of mineral production in South Africa comes from the gold fields and has ever since gold was discovered in quantity on the Witwatersrand. In 1946, an extension of the Witwatersrand fields was discovered in the Orange Free State, and the new field has led to a modern gold rush and an unprecedented increase in the value of South Africa's gold production. In 1960, it was three times that of the next ten most important minerals.

The plateau, in addition, has produced iron ore and coal, on the basis of which South

Africa established an iron and steel industry. The first plant was built at Pretoria, favorably located between the iron ores of the central and western Transvaal and the coal of the eastern Transvaal, and later the coal of the Orange Free State came to be used at the new steel mills near Vereeniging. The large quantities of coal permitted the establishment of large power plants near the cities, and electricity supply has not been a major problem in South Africa as it has been in so many other parts of the continent.

Other minerals—chrome and platinum are mainly derived from a basin in the south-central Transvaal called the Bushveld Basin—are found almost without exception in South Africa's white areas. South Africa leads the world in the production not only of gold but also of diamonds and platinum, and in addition is the leading supplier of certain grades of chrome ore and asbestos. Her production

of coal, which by value is the second mineral (before diamonds, asbestos, and copper), is the largest in the Southern Hemisphere. But because of the fact that capital, mechanization, and skills were required when mineral exploitation began, South Africa's mineral resource base is maldistributed today between the white and Bantu Areas. And since South Africa's progress for long was almost completely a reflection of the successes of the mining industry, it is not surprising that the Bantu Areas lagged while the white areas advanced. This maldistribution of mineral resources means that there are no possibilities for the development of primary industries in the Bantu Areas today, and the opportunities for secondary industries are limited. In white South Africa, much of the stimulus for the development of secondary industries was derived from mining. This vital stimulus is virtually absent in the Bantu Areas.

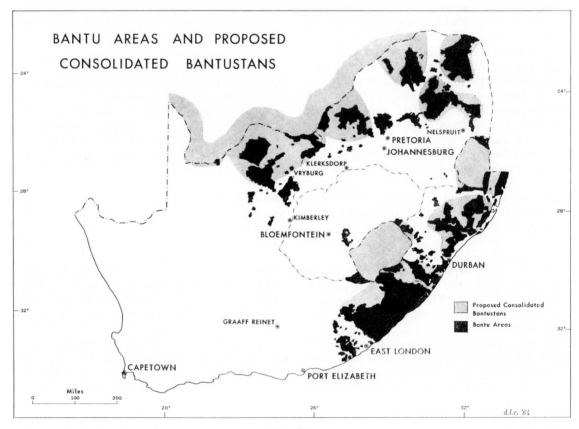

Map 24

Bantu enterprises in the Bantu Areas. There is hope that textile industries (based in part on wool from Cape sheep), wood pulp, rayon, and paper industries (based upon afforestations), and some chemical industries will develop over short periods. Plans are being prepared for the extension of the national transportation network into the Bantu Areas, and water and electric power will be made more available. These stimuli, it is hoped, will overcome the inherently negative characteristics of the Bantu Areas and lead to a mobilization of Bantu capital, the rise of Bantu entrepreneurs, and the economic viability of South Africa's Bantustans.

Bantu Areas and Urbanization

Cities and towns, geographers have often said, are the result of and response to a region's needs. As might be expected from the vigorous economic development of South Africa, there has been more urbanization there than anywhere else on the subcontinent. Conversely, the Bantu Areas, lagging in so many ways, have not produced any major urban centers. The South African government, recognizing the need for a reduction of population pressure on the land, is artificially establishing urban centers throughout the Bantu Areas. Several dozen such "towns" are being erected, some with regard for the needs of the developing region, others apparently quite arbitrarily, with little chance of survival. This is one of the unique aspects of the Tomlinson Commission's plan: it is an experiment in forced urbanization the like of which the world has never seen.

South Africa's "white" cities have attracted hundreds of thousands of Africans, and the urbanized African population of these places has been an ever increasing problem to city and government officials. Mines and industries drew these Bantu to the urban centers, where they became a permanently resident sector of the population, a situation which the South African government deems undesirable, since it hampers the effectiveness of control, leads to overcrowding of the black suburbs (all South African cities are of course residentially segregated), and above all, causes racial mixing and loss of cultural identity. One part of the Bantustan scheme is the removal of this permanent African city population and its replacement by a migrant population of temporary labor. Those urbanized Africans who are sent back to their homelands must be provided with urban areas there, since they cannot all live off the land. Hence the major goal of urbanization in the Bantu Areas.

Johannesburg is South Africa's largest city, and its problems are symptomatic if not entirely representative of the country's multi-racial urban centers. The two major population sectors are the African (about 640,000) and the white (360,000), with a variety of minority groups numbering less than 50,000. Ever since 1886, Johannesburg has drawn more Africans than any other urban center in South Africa, so that a third-generation African urbanized population now exists there. It is this permanent urban African population sector which the Bantustan plan seeks to relocate in the proposed urban centers in the Bantu Areas. It will be replaced by a migrant population, and only the white population will have the right of permanent residence in the "white" cities.

The main problems to be solved by this scheme are those of control over influx of Africans into the urban centers and limitation of urban sprawl of low-class African suburbs. Johannesburg's African population (like that of Pretoria, Germiston, and other cities) has long increased faster than housing could be provided, and conditions in the city's "shanty-town" suburbs were among the worst forms of urban squalor in the world. To be sure, the cities have their share of poor-class white suburbs, but the major solution for the prevalent urban decay was considered to lie in the repatriation of Africans. This process is now in progress, the initial result being a scarcity of labor for domestic and commercial purposes.

Johannesburg exemplifies several of the characteristics of South Africa's urban centers. Its areal extent is vast, covering perhaps four times as much territory as a European city of comparable size. Its core and central business district are congested and small compared to the entire urban region. Vertical development

Subsaharan Africa's Largest City: Johannesburg, South Africa. The only city in Subsaharan Africa with over a million inhabitants and the economic capital of Africa, Johannesburg's downtown area is congested and skyscraper-studded. Its skyline and character are constantly changing, as mining is giving way to industry and business. In the foreground is the new railroad station, and in the far distance some of the mine dumps can be recognized. (Satour)

is considerable and comparable to that of any American city of similar population. The city's functional zones, as a result of the decline of mining and the growth of industry, are inter-digitated, although the residential areas are strictly segregated according to race. Unlike the cities of Portuguese and former French Africa, the civic and administrative buildings of South Africa's cities are dispersed throughout the central city. This is one of the points of contrast between the urban places of British-influenced Africa and those of the remainder of the continent.[16]

In many ways, Johannesburg is unique, being not only the largest South African city, but also the heart of the country's most intensely industrialized area and the financial capital. East and west of Johannesburg, along the outcrop of the gold-bearing reefs of the Witwatersrand, a string of mining towns has sprung up, and their urban areas are merging

into a South African megalopolis. Johannesburg's northern boundary is within sight of expanding Pretoria, the country's administrative capital and most rapidly growing city. Southward lies the lifeblood of the industrialized Southern Transvaal—the Vaal River and the water supplies of Vaal Dam. There also lie Vereeniging, the new iron and steel plants, and, in the Orange Free State, the newly developing mines and industries. The Johannesburg area, therefore, has been the focal point of mining, industry, communications, commerce, financial affairs, and administration in South Africa. The city has received a succession of stimuli which have kept it in the forefront of rapidly urbanizing South Africa.

The other cities of white South Africa from which Africans will be repatriated include the two major ports, Cape Town, whose population is mainly Colored and white, with Africans an insignificant minority, and Durban, where whites, Africans, and Asiatics live in approximately equal numbers. In Cape Town, historically the most remote city from the advancing Bantu, perhaps 60,000 Africans

[16] For some comparisons, see H. J. de Blij, "The Functional Structure and Central Business District of Lourenço Marques, Moçambique," *Economic Geography*, XXXVIII, No. 1 (January, 1962), 56–77.

Views in the Transkei Bantu Homeland, the First Bantustan. The Transkei is possibly least poorly endowed with resources among the projected Bantustans. It contains some well-watered lands and adequate pasture (top). About 100,000 acres have been afforested with pine (right). But the density of population will probably overtax the land, and there will have to be outside sources of revenue if the plan is to succeed. Urban centers are to be developed, farming intensified, communications improved. There are many other needs: schools, hospitals, doctors. The picture below shows two residents of the Transkei preparing for a social event. (Satour and South African Information Service)

109

have settled in addition to 290,000 whites and 340,000 Colored people. There, as in Johannesburg, residential areas are segregated by race. In Durban, on the other hand, the more rapidly growing African sector of the population numbers some 200,000, with an even faster-growing Indian population of similar numbers, and about 185,000 whites. Thus, of the three major cities of South Africa, Johannesburg and Durban are most deeply involved in Bantu relocation, with the situation in Cape Town hinging more on the fate of the Colored people.

In the white cities, the Bantu have no proprietary rights and few administrative powers. Reasoning that they would be able to attain these and other rights in their own urban centers, the Tomlinson Commission proposed urbanization in the Bantu Areas in the following terms:

. . . the Bantu, especially those living in the Bantu Areas, have undergone a measure of indirect urbanization, through working in the European cities frequently over a long period of time. This has given the Bantu a certain knowledge of, and familiarity with urban conditions.

Although there are no Bantu towns, there are very good reasons why they should now be established without delay. The formation of towns is an inherent part of development and this is also true in the case of the Bantu Areas. Moreover, urban development is necessary for the proper organization of agriculture. For instance, it has already become evident that about 300,000 families or more than 1½ million persons will have to abandon Bantu agriculture, in order to give those who remain, the opportunity of making a living out of the land without resorting to periodic spells of work elsewhere. These people can only make their way to urban areas.[17]

What are to be the economic bases for urbanization in the Bantu Areas? The commission, though aware that a city must satisfy certain needs, stated that "any urban concentration creates its own bases . . .," adding that white industries, located near the borders of the

Bantu Areas, will provide one of the required stimuli. In actuality, South Africa, wishing to end the influx of Africans into urban centers which cannot contain them, seeks to divert this stream into areas where such urban development, irrespective of its future capacity for absorption, must yet take place. The expectation is that urbanization, rather than succeeding progress in other fields, will be contemporaneous with the general reorganization in agriculture and industry planned for the Bantu Areas.

The reorganization of the South African state is one of the unique aspects of present-day Africa, meriting attention no less than does the success of the wind of change elsewhere. Whatever the moral implications of this form of *apartheid*, it cannot be denied that South Africa has become a laboratory for geographic study. The future of the new Republic will be mirrored in this effort, now in its second decade of execution. The political framework, the economic structure, human relations, and even the survival of the very state are in the balance. For South Africa, this is a period of transition. Both the process and the results are of absorbing interest, as some trends are intensified and others are fundamentally reversed. Should it be permitted to run its full course, the process of racial separation will create a state which will be unique. But even if the scheme is not carried to completion, the impact already made is ineradicable; indeed, it is the salient aspect of the political, social, and economic geography of South Africa today.

---

[17] *Summary of the Report of the Commission for the Socio-Economic Development of the Bantu Areas Within the Union of South Africa*, p. 145.

5

SOUTHERN AFRICA'S PROBLEM AREAS:

THE HIGH COMMISSION TERRITORIES

ALTHOUGH THEY ARE separate political entities today, the future status of the High Commission Territories—Basutoland, Bechuanaland, and Swaziland—is uncertain. Presently, Bechuanaland and Swaziland are British protectorates, while Basutoland is a colony. Sometimes collectively known as "the protectorates," these three countries came into existence as a result of an unusual set of historical circumstances, survived the days of union in South Africa mainly by accident, and, in isolation and comparative poverty, they face a clouded future.

The High Commission Territories have several features in common. Each is landlocked, and each bounds the Republic of South Africa. Basutoland, indeed, actually perforates South Africa and is thus completely surrounded by it. Swaziland, although nearly enclosed by the Transvaal province, has a short but crucially important boundary with Moçambique. Bechuanaland borders on South Africa and South West Africa along most of its margins, but it has a boundary with Southern Rhodesia also. Of the various neighboring countries, however, South Africa wields most influence in each of the High Commission Territories. Large numbers of laborers from the territories work in South Africa each year, and the republic is the dominant trade partner in every case. In terms of total population, there is no great variation among the territories: Basutoland is the most populous with 800,000 people, while Swaziland and Bechuanaland each are occupied by about 300,000 inhabitants. None of the High Commission Territories has any appreciable industrial development, although Swaziland with some significant mining is economically more favored than either Basutoland or Bechuanaland. Communications are poor, both internally and with the outside world. The contrasts with wealthy South Africa are strong, as living standards are low, urbanization negligible, and agriculture in need of reorganization. In fact, the High Commission Territories in many ways resemble South Africa's Bantu Areas.

On the other hand, there are important differences between the three territories. While Swaziland measures only 6,704 square miles and Basutoland 11,716, Bechuanaland is one of Africa's larger territories, covering 275,000 square miles of Kalahari steppe and swamp. Basutoland lies on the high eastern edge of the plateau and consists in large part of cold, high uplands, steep valleys, and expanses of barren rock, although the west does provide some pasture land of good quality. Swaziland lies along the Transvaal escarpment itself, covering terrain which, over 5,000 feet high in the west, descends in steps to the eastern lowlands only some hundreds of feet above sea level. Bechuanaland occupies much of the interior Kalahari Basin, and it suffers from extremes: there are vast expanses of dry, parched terrain and large marshes and swamps, resulting in a concentration of population in the more habitable east, where some adequate pasture lands occur.

With reference to the problems facing the High Commission Territories, the position in terms of known resources is most important. In this respect, the smallest of the three, Swaziland, appears best endowed. The world's fourth largest asbestos mine lies at Havelock, and there are deposits of tin, iron ore, coal, barytes, and possibly some radioactive minerals. Swaziland benefits from its location on the margin of the South African Plateau, whose mineralization extends into the area occupied by the protectorate. Basutoland, on the other hand, while also lying on the plateau, is underlain by immense thicknesses of basalt, especially in the east. Apart from some diamond finds, these basalts have not produced important mineral resources. Their height has resulted in severe erosion, and rivers lie in deep canyons. Even where lower strata are exposed, mineral resources have not been located in quantity. Bechuanaland, underlain by basalts in the north and sands elsewhere, was also thought to lack significant minerals, but recent drilling through the surface cover indicates that valuable deposits may yet be found. Mining companies have displayed an interest in the eastern part of the country, but developments are yet in an initial stage.

As might be expected, the country with the largest known mineral resource base has also attracted the largest white settlement. In both Basutoland and Bechuanaland, the white population of about 2,500 is engaged mainly in administration and government, and, particularly in Basutoland, they have few rights. In Basutoland, for example, there is no white ownership of land. In Swaziland, however, the growing white population now numbers over 10,000, and, beside administrative and governmental functions, the whites are engaged in the mining industry and commercial farming of the protectorate. They own about half of the land of the territory and produce the bulk of its exports.

The problems of the High Commission Territories are mainly of a political and economic nature. South Africa has repeatedly demanded that the administration of these areas be transferred to her, especially in view of the Tomlinson Commission's recommendations that they be made Bantustans. The High Commission Territories cannot prevent a South African takeover without the assistance of Britain. Economically, the dependence of each upon South Africa (as the major market for exports and the main outlet for excess labor) is almost complete. Thus, they are anomalies in a political scene which for decades has tended toward consolidation.

Basutoland: Soil Erosion and Economic Dependence

The enclave of Basutoland provides a study in contrasts. The empty, majestic, tundra-like eastern uplands, in places exceeding 10,000 feet in elevation, are only dozens of miles from teeming valleys and densely populated grasslands in the west. The average density of population for the entire country is 60 persons per square mile, but with perhaps two-thirds of land in steep slopes, rock outcrops, and excessive heights, this figure is meaningful only when the sharp western concentration is taken into account. Pedologically, Basutoland is one of the poorest territories in Southern Africa. Unfavorable parent material, unreliable precipitation, sparse natural vegetation, and heavy relief have combined to hamper soil development. Overgrazing and mismanagement have destroyed large portions of those regions which were best endowed, and one of the characteristics of present-day Basutoland is the large number of gullies and heavily eroded fields, fast reducing the available, usable soil acreage.

A useful way to view Basutoland is to recognize three major belts, each running northeast to southwest. In the west lie the so-called lowlands, really a misnomer, for much of this lower region is higher than the bulk of the South African Highveld. The population concentration there is reflected by the communications network, which shows a strong contrast to the empty eastern parts of the country. Although studded by mesas and buttes, this western lowland provides the best opportunities for cultivation and animal husbandry in Basutoland. In the center of the country lies a belt of foothills, whose elevations and slopes become steeper and more barren toward the east. Communications become difficult, few roads penetrate there, and pastoralism now dominates. Finally, the eastern section of the country is composed of the magnificent Drakensberg, affording only some opportunities for herding.

One asset of Basutoland is its water supply, which is rather plentiful. The Orange River rises in the colony, and the Orange and Caledon drainage systems dominate the east and west, respectively. Only during the 1960's were plans finally laid to use the headwater region for producing electricity, and the long-term lack of power has been among the impediments to development in this country. Over large parts of the east, rivers lie in deep, youthful valleys, and there the water has few other uses.

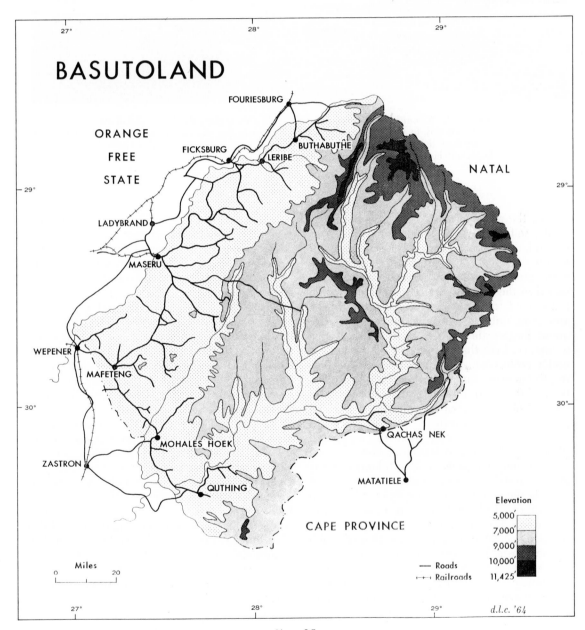

Map 25

Among the Foothills in Central Basutoland. In this region, the lower and flatter lands of the west give way to the Drakensberg mountains occupying the eastern part of the colony. Since agriculture becomes increasingly difficult as slope incidence increases, pastoralism is more important here. Overgrazing and soil erosion have scarred the landscape seriously. (Satour)

In the absence of significant mineral deposits, soil is the most important resource in Basutoland, and upon it depend practically all Basuto people. The subsistence crops are corn, grown in the lower west, and wheat, raised in the central part of the colony, which is too cold for corn. Severe droughts, frosts, and crop failures, however, have made frequent large-scale imports from South Africa necessary. Less than 9 per cent of the land is under cultivation, and the scope for expanding the acreage through irrigation is very limited. The Basuto, fortunately, have adopted a method of farming superior to that of the majority of other African peoples in Southern Africa: they have long used the ox-drawn plow in preference to the hand hoe.

Farming for profit in Basutoland consists almost entirely of raising sheep and goats, and wool is the country's major export. The sheep population of about 1½ million, in addition to an only slightly smaller total of goats and cattle, is responsible for the destruction of much of the natural vegetation and, in consequence, of the soils of the territory. The government is constantly attempting to regulate pastoralism in the colony in order to protect the soil, and some progress is now being made.

Basutoland's people constitute one of the very few population groups in Subsaharan Africa which may be called a nation, and the economic poverty of the country has been coupled with an early awakening of a form of African nationalism. The first Basuto leader, Moshesh (*c.* 1780–1870), welded the nation out of the peoples scattering before the marauding Zulu, consolidated them in the rugged mountains of the Drakensberg, and then ruled them with wisdom and cunning such as no other African leader has displayed. He successfully withstood the whites, both Boer and Briton, and guided his people into a position of strength which insured their survival long after his death. He was, however, unable to prevent the isolation of his nation, and the very isolation which once insured Basuto survival has become a great liability. One of Moshesh's aims was the establishment of a British protectorate over his country at a time when both the Cape Colony and the Orange Free State Republic sought its annexation. He eventually succeeded, and when the Union of South Africa was created, the Basuto people were permitted to remain a separate political entity.

Thus, the political awakening of the Ba-

Basuto Shepherd and his Sheep, Basutoland. The mesa-studded west of Basutoland is the home of most Basuto people, for the land there provides more opportunity than the relatively barren east. A gully is eroding the valley in the foreground. Among Basutoland's problems is the rocky nature of the soil covering much of the part of the country that has any soil at all. Note the small outcrop on which the boy is standing and the boulders near his feet and elsewhere. The shepherd wears a blanket, which is no luxury on cold winter days and nights in Basutoland. Thatched houses can be seen in the distance. (Satour)

Potters in Basutoland. Containers for all sorts of uses —large bowls for hauling water from the stream or well, ornamental jugs for sale to tourists, ceremonial pieces, and so on—are made by these skilled people. (Satour)

Grain Baskets in Basutoland. These grain baskets, containing the harvest of the villagers' lands stored for lean periods, can be seen in most Basutoland villages. Note the mud-walled, thatch-roofed house in the background and the blankets worn by the adults. (Satour)

115

Basuto Riders. Parts of Basutoland can be reached only by horse or mule, and the Basuto are skilled riders. This characteristic scene shows two blanket-wearing men on their way to visit friends. (Satour)

suto came early, and British policy restricted white settlement in the territory to administration and commerce; all land remained in the hands of the Basuto. This land, however, proved inadequate for the needs of the people, and Basuto men began to seek work on the mines of the Witwatersrand and in the Orange Free State. A permanent migration developed, and with it, the vulnerability of Basutoland grew. Basuto families depend upon the wages earned by the workers in South Africa for the payment of taxes and the purchase of imported food. Today, perhaps 130,000 Basuto males work outside of their country. Thus, the political progress of the Basuto has not been accompanied by any trends toward economic self-sufficiency. Nevertheless, the British government has yielded to Basuto demands for greater internal self-government, with the official status of the territory now being that of Crown colony. This situation, of course, is paradoxical. Basutoland, already economically dependent and isolated, is enveloped by a South Africa in which Afri-

cans are economically better situated but politically far less fortunate. South Africa is loath to contribute to the economy of a country in which political trends are contrary to those in the republic.

South Africa's sentiments were reflected by the 1963 decision to close the borders between the republic and the High Commission Territories. This move resulted from the growing concern that the territories were harboring opponents of South African policies who might in time return to the republic to resume their activities. The possibility that the High Commission Territories might become bases for guerrilla activities also contributed to the establishment of border posts and fences guarded by the South African military and police. All residents of the territories intending to work in South Africa must now have special papers in order to do so, and this is likely to impede the flow of migrants considerably. Basutoland, of course, will be hard hit by these changes, but it is also the major supporter of anti-South African activities. Mountain areas are the traditional refuges for revolutionaries, and Basutoland itself was born of the protection the highlands afforded Moshesh's men. Modern times might see the same mountain areas used in similar ways. Nor is this possible in Basutoland only. Swaziland's highlands and forests provide suitable shelter also, and South Africans well remember the problems of the British in flushing remnants of the Mau Mau out of the forests of the Aberdare Mountains of Kenya.

The future of Basutoland, like that of the other High Commission Territories, must in part depend upon its capacity to resist absorption by South Africa, or at least by its ability to withstand economic pressure by the republic. Economic development has long lagged severely. There is virtually no urban development (the capital, Maseru, is a town of only 6,000 people, mostly engaged in government and commerce), only one mile of railroad, and some 500 miles of passable roads in a country the size of Belgium. Past trends have not been favorable in spite of considerable subsidies by Britain, and the country suffers under some severe limitations. It does, on the other hand, have a growing tourist industry based upon the incomparable scenery of the north and east, and with an improvement of internal communications, this may become a big asset.

Bechuanaland: Impediments to Progress

Occupied by less than half the number of people of Basutoland, Bechuanaland's Texas-sized territory is nearly 24 times as large as the small colony. Yet in terms of economic and political advancement, Bechuanaland is by no means in a better position. While vast, it possesses few assets. Communications are poor. Urbanization and industrial development are practically nonexistent, except for towns based on administration and numbering some hundreds of people only, and a few very small mining establishments. While Basutoland suffers from its high relief and slope, Bechuanaland is gently undulating, with hardly any topographic or climatic diversification except in the east. In general, while the precipitation totals for Basutoland are higher, the two countries share an unreliability of rainfall and consequent stock losses and crop failures.

Several factors have combined to retard advancement in Bechuanaland. Most obviously, the absence of mineral resources and good conditions for agriculture have rendered the territory unattractive compared to its richer eastern neighbors. Under present conditions, the land is barely able to support a population of 350,000. Moreover, this is an area where diseases such as sleeping sickness are still not eradicated. The country is especially known for the dangers of malarial fever, for the rainfall (generally between 18 and 25 inches annually) comes during the hot season, and there is dense bush and much stagnant water in the north and west.

Unlike Basutoland, Bechuanaland is occupied by several African peoples, and there has not been the same degree of unity and political consciousness there. The dominant group, occupying the most favored, eastern part of the territory, is the Bamangwato people. Elsewhere, the Barolong, Batawana, and other Bantu peoples occupy parts of the protectorate, along with scattered Bushmen in the Kalahari area of the south and west. The Bamangwato are estimated to number about 160,000, and thus constitute somewhat less than half the total Bechuanaland population.

Bechuanaland did not participate in the rapid economic development of South Africa, Southern Rhodesia, and South West Africa, except indirectly. While the Cape was British and Southern Rhodesia was developing, the British built a railroad connecting Kimberley with Salisbury, bypassing the Boer republics. Running through Bechuanaland, the railroad has been of some benefit to the protectorate, but there are no branch lines. The main contribution of the country to the economic development taking place around it has been labor. It has been estimated that in certain years half of the total adult male population was at work in South Africa, Rhodesia, and South West Africa.[1]

---

[1] W. Fitzgerald, *Africa* (7th ed.; New York: Dutton, 1950), p. 172.

The dominant economic activity in Bechuanaland, both in terms of employment and monetary revenues, is pastoralism. Eastern Bechuanaland is a rolling hill land, with a somewhat higher precipitation than the average for the protectorate and some good grasslands. Cattle (numbering about 1½ million) are the most common domestic animals, and in a normal year the returns from cattle ranching constitute the bulk of the value of exports. Generally, South Africa buys about half of the exports of the protectorate, Northern and Southern Rhodesia taking most of the remainder.

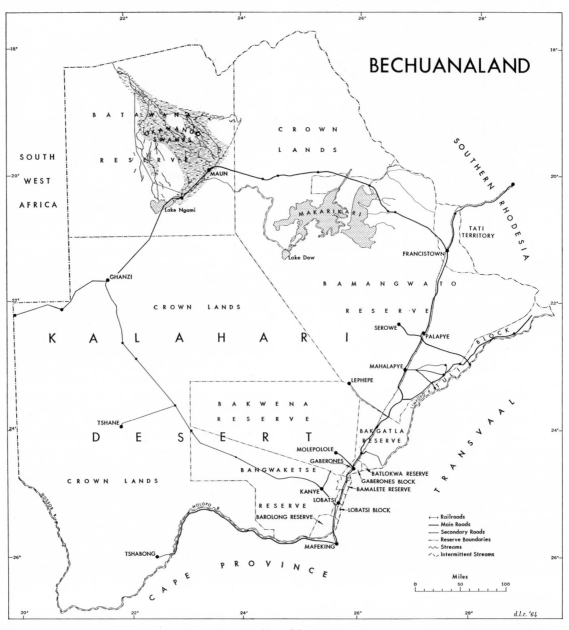

Map 26

118

In Swaziland and Basutoland, most of the progress until the present time was made in the two decades after the Second World War. During the first half of this period, however, Bechuanaland's progress was impeded by a political problem which for years deprived the Bamangwato people of recognized leadership. As a result, no decisions could be taken on concessions to mining companies interested in eastern Bechuanaland, and economic activity stagnated. This situation was a costly one for the country, especially in view of the acceleration of development elsewhere in Africa at that time.

The matter involved the chief of the Bamangwato, Seretse Khama, who immediately after the war was studying at a British university. In 1948, he married a white woman, an act which caused division among his own people and consternation in British governmental circles. The British doubted the wisdom of his return to the Bamangwato people and prevented it until 1956.[2] The Bamangwato, who reasoned that this act on the part of Britain was a show of sympathy for segregationists in South Africa, refused to come to important decisions concerning not only mining rights but also school construction, taxation, and so on, without their chief. When the matter was solved, ten valuable years had for all intents and purposes been lost. There was, however, one positive development: the Bamangwato people had become aware of the need for changes in the governmental arrangement of their country, both internally and with respect to Britain. They made known their desire for the establishment of a legislative council for the protectorate, and Britain decided to agree to certain reforms.[3]

Although the crisis involving Bamangwato leadership is over, Bechuanaland's future is not bright. The country has seen little progress, has a sparse and relatively small population which is not homogeneous, and

will require vast expenditures for significant development. The aridity is all-pervading, the dominating industry (cattle) suffers from outdated customs, excessive concentration of animals, and low-quality products, and the depletion of underground water supplies is imminent. The grazing lands are deteriorating, the potentialities for agriculture are severely limited, and the country's financial situation is bad. Necessary geological and hydrological surveys have not been carried out. There may be some possibilities for irrigated agriculture in the Tati and Tuli areas, and mineral discoveries may yet be made. Meanwhile, the territory faces the possibility of South African economic and political pressure as do Basutoland and Swaziland. Such economic development as might render it capable of survival does not appear likely in the near future.

Swaziland: Land Division and the Customs Union

Swaziland, smallest of the High Commission Territories, appears to have the greatest potential for growth. It possesses a proven resource base which has been exploited for several decades, there is some industry, and there is some climatic and pedologic diversification. Moreover, the Swazi people, although not entirely homogeneous ethnically, share a common history (including successful resistance to Zulu aggression), an attachment to and identification with Swazi territory, and a rapidly growing degree of political consciousness and desire for progress. There are about 300,000 Swazi in Swaziland proper, and in addition perhaps as many as 100,000 Swazi people, paying allegiance to the Swazi paramount chief, live beyond the borders in South Africa.

The distribution of the Swazi nation over an area far in excess of Swaziland Protectorate is a reflection of one of the major problems facing Swaziland today: the problem of land. The Swazi, although not conquered by the Zulu, were unable to prevent their powerful southern neighbors from claiming much of their territory. Subsequently, when con-

[2] J. Redfern, *Ruth and Seretse: A Very Disreputable Transaction* (London: Gollancz, 1955).

[3] This desire was expressed by white as well as African inhabitants of Bechuanaland, an indication that the Seretse Khama affair had had its effects upon both groups in the protectorate. See De Blij, *Africa South*, p. 274.

tact was made with the first white invaders, Swazi chiefs carelessly ceded away vast tracts of land in return for trivial objects. Most guilty was Chief Mbandzeni (Umbandine), who by the time of his death in 1889 had assigned the entire land of the Swazi to whites. Thus, the Swazi by the end of the nineteenth century had lost those lands they had successfully defended against the Zulu.

Having ceded their land, the Swazi, aware of their predicament in being squatters on what was once their own territory, appealed to Britain for protection. The British, realizing the problems involved, refused to

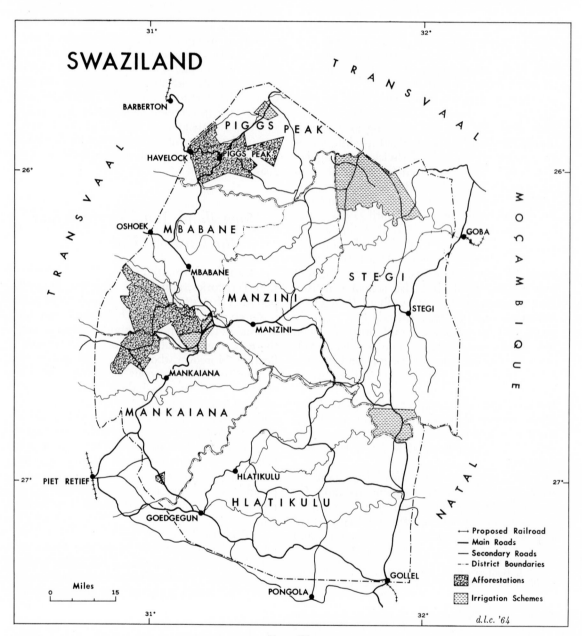

Map 27

establish a protectorate over the Swazi when the appeal was made in 1893. Indeed, Britain was concerned over events on the South African Plateau at this time, and was prepared to allow Swaziland to become a part of the South African Republic. Doubtless, this would have happened had the matter not been un-der review at the time of the outbreak of the Boer War; when the war was over, the British agreed (in 1902) to establish a protecto-rate over the Swazi. Thus, the Swaziland Protectorate came into being through a suc-cession of the sort of accidents that make history.

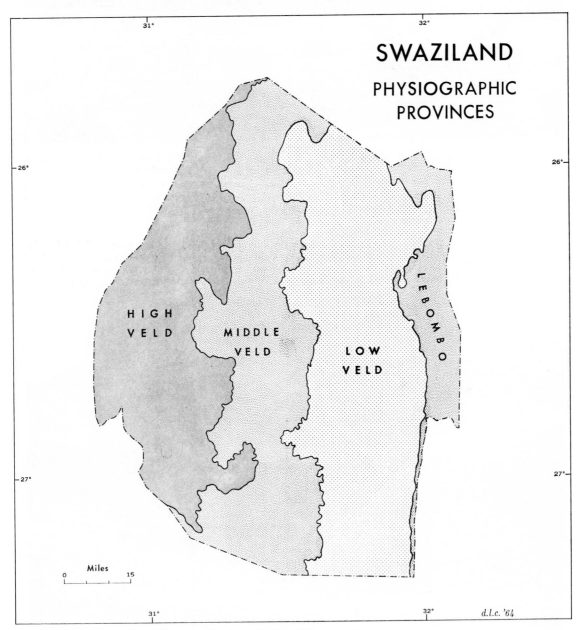

SWAZILAND
PHYSIOGRAPHIC PROVINCES

HIGH VELD

MIDDLE VELD

LOW VELD

LEBOMBO

Miles
0   15

d.l.c. '64

Map 28

View of a Village and Surrounding Landscape, Swaziland. This country, less densely populated than Basutoland and better off in terms of resources and soils, nevertheless has serious problems. Since there is a larger white landowning population than in either of the two other High Commission Territories, many Swazi live concentrated in rocky, less desirable parts of the country. (Satour)

The Highveld in Swaziland. The incomparable scenery of Swaziland is exemplified by this photograph taken among the afforestations on the slopes of the Highveld mountains. The land in this picture is owned by the Crown (the forested acres in the distance) and a white farmer, whose cattle and private forests can be seen in the right foreground. (Satour)

The establishment of the protectorate, however, did not end the land problems of the Swazi people. Whether or not under protectorate status, Swaziland had been ceded to white settlers. With the Swazi indicating their desire to remain outside a unified South Africa, it became necessary to define the international boundaries of the country. This was completed in 1907, while a specially appointed commission was attempting to unravel the complex of adjacent and overlapping concessions with the aim of returning to the Swazi people some of the land they once owned. The commission in 1907 published a plan for the partition of the territory along lines which essentially form the basis of present-day land division in Swaziland.

After the delimitation of its international boundaries, the area of Swaziland was found to be 6,704 square miles, all under concessions. The commission proposed that exactly one-third of the total land of each concession be returned to the Swazi nation, that the pieces of land thus deducted be consolidated as much as possible, and that these stretches of territory form the home of the Swazi people. The Swazi, in return for this allotment of land, were given five years (July 1, 1909, until June 30, 1914) to leave the land remaining under concession and move to their own areas. Any Swazi able to make private arrangements with the white landowners to remain on the ceded lands could do so, however. In fact, no major migration of Swazi to their own areas resulted, most being able to stay on the ceded land. The important achievement of the commission, nevertheless, was that the Swazi nation obtained tribal lands with which the people could identify themselves, on which the chief and elders could live, and where Swazi practices of land ownership, cattle and goat herding, and so on, could be maintained.

In 1914, the population of Swaziland was perhaps somewhat over 100,000, with about 1,000 white settlers, and, at that time, population pressure on the land was much less than it is today. The commission dealing with the territory's partition, in recognition of a future greater need for land, developed a mechanism by which land could be purchased from the white landowners for inclu-sion into the Swazi nation's areas, or for Crown land which at a later stage might be vested in the Swazi nation. The growth of the Swazi people outstripped the increase in available land, however. Today, with the population of Swaziland estimated to be between 250,000 and 300,000, slightly over half of Swaziland's area is in Swazi hands, the remainder being held freehold or under long lease. Thus, about 10,000 whites (and a few hundred Colored people and some Asiatics) own half of Swaziland, a manner of division which the Swazi would like to change in their favor.

The Swazi who live on the land (as against the 10 per cent who are urbanized and active in the mines) are pastoralists, and there are about 530,000 cattle in the protectorate. This, according to experts involved in the problems of Swaziland, is 100,000 more cattle than the country can hold adequately, and the annual net increase, largely due to tribal customs and economic conditions, is over 16,000.[4] In addition, Swazi own about 150,000 goats, which contribute to the overgrazing from which much of the territory suffers.

Britain has made considerable effort to improve Swazi agricultural practices, but has been faced with reluctance to adopt the proposed changes. This can be attributed to several factors, not the least important of which is similar to that experienced in Southern Rhodesia and South Africa: while much land lies apparently unused in white landholdings, Africans are loathe to improve conditions on what they have, feeling that such improvements would not be necessary if they had the white lands. In addition, there are the tribal customs which reduce the number of cattle taken each year for slaughtering, including their use as a form of currency, the prestige associated with numbers (rather than quality), and their inclusion in the usual bride price.

Nevertheless, some Swazi have accepted such principles as contour farming, fallowing, and other forms of soil conservation, and are farming for profit rather than subsistence.

---

[4] Manzini Indaba Society, *Progress and Prosperity in Swaziland* (Manzini: Shirley Press, 1962), p. 6.

Swazi Walking Along Lowveld Road, Swaziland.
Tradition continues to play an important role in the
life of most Swazi people, and the king, Sobhuza II,
is a strong traditionalist himself. These Swazi are
dressed to participate in a ceremony at a nearby
village. (Satour)

Soil Erosion in Swaziland. The Land Rover at the
top of this gully provides some idea of the size of this
scar in the soil. The gully was initiated by constant
driving of cattle back and forth from a village to a
drinking place along a hillside, and it is now out of
control, growing with each rainstorm.

There are some model farms run by Swazi
which earn as much money as do many white
farms in the protectorate. But the land initially given to the Swazi nation through the
partition of the concessions was by no means
Swaziland's best land, so that opportunities
for this sort of progress have been few. It is
considered vital that other Swazi adopt the
necessary practices to prevent the degree of
soil erosion from which large parts of Basutoland suffer, and British technicians are constantly working to effect these changes. The
dreaded cattle disease, East Coast fever, has
been virtually eliminated by the enforcement
of regular dipping of all cattle.

An added problem for Swaziland is the
use of Swazi territory by white landowners
for purposes which are not beneficial to the
protectorate. For instance, while whites and
Africans own about 35,000 head of sheep
within Swaziland, white landowners move
about 150,000 head into the area from the
Transvaal each winter for grazing purposes.[5]

[5] *Offisiële Jaarboek van die Unie van Suid-Afri-
ka, 1956–57* (Pretoria: Staatsdrukker, 1958), p. 963.

This practice, and absentee land ownership, are detrimental to any region and especially to one where pressure upon the land is already considerable.

Swaziland's major revenues have always come from the white lands and from the mines. One reason for the early demand for Swazi concessions was the discovery of gold in the northwest, where the Barberton Mountain Land extends into the protectorate. Gold has long since ceased to make a contribution to the economy, but the subsequent discovery of asbestos proved of far greater importance. One of the world's four largest asbestos mines, developed at Havelock, has long contributed the bulk of the value of Swaziland's exports ($17 million in 1960). Both tin and barytes have figured prominently among the exports. Additional discoveries of coal deposits and a large, high-grade, iron ore field have been made, and exploitation of these is to begin in 1964. One reason for slow development has been the transport problem: Swaziland until 1964 did not have a railroad, and plans for connecting the interior of the protectorate to the coast are only now being executed. The new railroad connects the iron deposits at Bomvu (on the Transvaal border) to Lourenço Marques. Japan has purchased 1,200,000 tons of ore per year for a period of ten years. The railway is likely to use Swaziland's coal reserves, as it passes within a few miles of the coalfields at Mpaka. Its total length will be 137 miles. The asbestos mine at Havelock is connected to the railhead at Barberton by one of the world's longest overhead conveyor systems.

Major attention has recently focused upon the changes in agriculture in the white areas. The Great Usutu River, meandering through the eastern lowveld of the territory, has lent itself to irrigation in a region which has pedologically and climatically been found suited for the cultivation of sugar.[6] Great afforestations have been developed in the high and rainy west, and the effect on the industrial pattern is the establishment of

sugar mills and a large wood-pulp factory, in addition to a number of smaller concerns. Cotton, pineapples, and tobacco are grown for profit, and a real revolution may be in store for agriculture with the improvement of internal communications, an expected increase in urbanization, and improved connections with the outside world.

One reason this progress has lagged lies in an economic arrangement referred to as the Customs Union between South Africa and Swaziland. When, in 1909, Swaziland chose to remain outside the projected Union of South Africa, an economic arrangement was agreed upon which was to tie Swaziland almost inextricably into the South African economic framework. In fact, this system had been in operation since 1904, but it was formalized at the time of union in South Africa. Prior to this time, the British had negotiated with the Portuguese about the building of a railroad from Lourenço Marques into Swaziland via Goba, and the Portuguese had actually constructed their section of the railroad as part of an agreement. The Customs Union, however, determined that all goods leaving Swaziland for any outside market would have to travel through South African territory and be transported by South African carriers. Thus, the Portuguese railroad could not function, and the British never constructed their part of it. This created a considerable amount of resentment in Lisbon and Lourenço Marques, but it was not until the 1960's that work on the connection was finally begun, and by then political developments had terminated the union status of South Africa.

Thus, the short boundary between Swaziland and Moçambique, long a barrier to exports, has finally begun to play the vital role a glance at any map suggests it should. The heart of Swaziland, via the railroad now under construction, will be less than 80 miles from the port of Lourenço Marques, and spectacular developments are predicted upon its completion. Swaziland, in effect, will finally avail itself of an opportunity which has long been blocked by the Customs Union. In addition to the stipulations concerning the movement of goods, South Africa also controls the sales of Swazi export products in the former union: for instance, the Swazi

_____

[6] For details concerning the physiography of Swaziland see H. J. de Blij, "The Concept of the Physiographic Province Applied to Swaziland," *Journal for Geography*, I, No. 7 (September, 1960), 7–20.

The Barberton Mountain Land, Swaziland. In the extreme northwest of Swaziland lies the gold-mining area which drew the first diggers to this part of Southern Africa. The gold region was centered upon Barberton in the Transvaal. Today, the Mountain Land produces mainly asbestos, and the gold production has dwindled to virtually nothing. Shown here is the relief in the Mountain Land, typical of the descent from the plateau Highveld to the lower areas in the east.

Havelock Mine, Swaziland. The fourth largest asbestos mine in the world lies in Swaziland's Mountain Land, producing by far the greatest part of the country's mineral revenue. Part of the workings are shown here. The ore is carried by overhead cableway to the railhead at Barberton in the Transvaal.

The Market at Mbabane, Swaziland. Mbabane is the small capital of the protectorate, with most of the residents engaged in administration or business. Most of the tourists visiting the country pass through the town, and many Swazi earn a living by selling their handcraft products at the local market. Baskets, wooden bowls, reed mats, and shields with spears are among the items sold here.

are not permitted to sell cattle in South Africa other than a limited number for slaughter. Weight regulations affecting the cattle that may be exported are such that sales are very few. This is one major reason why the cattle population of Swaziland is growing rapidly, and it is a demonstration of South Africa's power to blockade a High Commission Territory at will. Aware that survival depends, as in Basutoland and Bechuanaland, upon economic development, the Swazilanders are now setting out a new course of action in the hope of achieving greater strength. Unlike Basutoland, this territory is not surrounded by South Africa, and unlike Bechuanaland, it is not without a resource base. It has real opportunities, which have lain dormant for a long time. Swaziland appears to be on the threshold of a period of growth toward economic viability.

Nonetheless, major problems remain. A large sector of the Swazi adult male population must seek work outside the protectorate —mainly in the Johannesburg mines—and an end to this migration would be almost as disastrous for Swaziland as it would for Basutoland or Bechuanaland. Although there are some small industries in Swaziland, urbanization has not progressed far: the capital, Mbabane, and the second town, Manzini, each have about 7,000 people. Communications may improve, but at present they are inadequate. The South African government operates a bus service within the protectorate as part of the South African railroad network, and in consequence it controls communications. There are some small African private bus companies, but there is no competition for the South African service, a termination of which could cripple the territory. A hard surface, all-weather road is being built from the Transvaal border via Mbabane and Manzini toward the Portuguese border near Goba, but progress is slow, and all other roads in the territory have dirt surfaces. Stretches are impassable during the wet season, during which farms and even villages may be temporarily isolated.

Another, entirely different problem involves the nature of the white population of Swaziland, which is fast changing. One of the effects of the customs agreement (and similar arrangements between South Africa and the other High Commission Territories) is that there are no border formalities, and thus it is possible for a South African to take up residence in Swaziland without really emigrating; he merely registers his presence in the territory at a police station. Recently, the white population has grown rapidly with the arrival of large numbers of South Africans who have taken a hand in the agricultural development of areas such as the sugar fields at Big Bend on the Great Usutu River. Indeed, the Afrikaans-speaking white population of parts of southern Swaziland already outnumbers the English; and these new arrivals are landowners, as they cannot be in Basutoland. This is one of Swaziland's real liabilities in view of the opposing trends in South Africa on the one hand and the High Commission Territories on the other. Although they bring capital and certain skills to Swaziland, these immigrants follow social practices which are frequently at odds with those espoused by the representatives of the British government. The result, it is feared, may be similar to the division of the South African white population, introducing into Swaziland a situation which has never prevailed in a High Commission Territory.

South African Claims

The Union of South Africa was established by the South Africa Act of 1909. Section 151 of this Act states:

. . . *The King, with the advice of the Privy Council, may, on addresses from the Houses of Parliament of the Union, transfer to the Union the government of any territories, other than the territories administered by the British South Africa Company, belonging to or under the protection of His Majesty, and inhabited wholly or in part by natives, and upon such transfer the Governor General may undertake the government of such ter-*

ritory upon the terms and conditions embodied in the Schedule of this Act.[7]

Clearly, at that time, the possibility of eventual transfer was envisaged, and as early as 1913, South African Prime Minister Louis Botha wrote to Lord Gladstone, then High Commissioner for South Africa, that Swaziland and Bechuanaland must be incorporated "at the earliest possible date." Subsequently, Prime Ministers Jan Hertzog and J. C. Smuts both pressed for the transfer, and it appears likely that they would have been successful had not the Second World War interrupted the negotiations. After 1948, Prime Minister Daniel Malan reopened the issue, but by then, *apartheid* had begun to increase in South Africa, and the union and the High Commission Territories were moving in socially divergent directions. In 1954, the South African government actually went so far as to pass a resolution as follows:

This House resolves that the transfer to the Union of the government of Basutoland and the protectorates of Bechuanaland and Swaziland, to be administered in accordance with the terms and conditions embodied in the Schedule of the South Africa Act of 1909, or such other terms and conditions as may be agreed upon between the two governments concerned, should take place as soon as possible.

The motion was rejected in Britain, and the last major effort to effect transfer came at the 1956 Commonwealth Prime Ministers' Conference, where the idea was once again negated. The British government indicated that transfer was no longer a matter "between the two governments concerned," but one in which the African peoples would have the final voice. Especially since 1948, there has never been any doubt regarding the sentiments of these people.

The basis for South Africa's claims was broadened by the inclusion of the High Commission Territories in the Bantustan scheme. The Tomlinson Commission proposed to make

[7] *Basutoland, the Bechuanaland Protectorate and Swaziland, History of Discussions with the Union of South Africa 1909–1939* (London: Her Majesty's Stationery Office, 1952), p. 118.

SOUTHERN AFRICA'S PROBLEM AREAS: THE HIGH COMMISSION TERRITORIES

the territories Bantu Areas, in the hope that Britain would agree to the transfer on these grounds. Britain, however, felt that the Tomlinson Commission, in including the High Commission Territories in its report, had gone beyond its frame of reference, and the suggestion served more to stiffen than to relax British opposition to incorporation of the territories in South Africa. Chief Sobhuza II and his Swazi people, like the Basuto and the peoples of Bechuanaland, depend upon British support for the retention of their identity on the troubled Southern African scene.[8] There are signs that Britain intends to protect that identity, but the future of the High Commission Territories, economic as well as political, remains uncertain.

---

[8] Reports have been made of secret negotiations between Chief Sobhuza and the South African government involving a land exchange in the south, near the Pongola irrigation scheme, around the town of Gollel (Golela). See E. S. Munger, *Swaziland: the Tribe and the Country,* American Universities Field Staff, Report No. 2 (1962), X, 15.

6

SOUTH WEST AFRICA: POLITICAL GEOGRAPHY OF A COVETED PRIZE

SOUTH WEST AFRICA, like the High Commission Territories, forms a part of what may be called the South African sphere of influence. In fact, South Africa has administered South West Africa under the terms of a League of Nations Mandate dating from 1919, and the vast (317,725 square miles) territory has virtually become a fifth province of the republic.

Prior to the assumption of control by South Africa, the territory formed part of the German colonial empire in Africa. Germany had begun to lay claim to sections of South West Africa from about 1883, but fierce opposition from the Hottentot and Herero peoples prevented the pacification of the area until as late as 1907, when the Hottentots capitulated. Germany took possession of the region while attention in Southern Africa focused upon the plateau, the diamonds, and the gold, and while Britain could not be persuaded to extend her influence over the western deserts. During her brief tenure, while fielding one of the largest armies ever to enter Southern Africa, Germany attempted to develop the colony by investing heavily in modern communications, an artificial harbor, mines, and ranches. Diamonds were discovered along the coast, and some real progress was made, although the Germans never were able to eradicate the impression made by what has been referred to as "colonization by the Mauser."

When South Africa defeated the German South West African army north of the capital, Windhoek, and the union subsequently came to rule South West Africa, the colony still remained one of Southern Africa's least attractive regions for settlement and investment. The white population was small, there seemed to be little opportunity for development, and the area was far from the economic heart of the south. What the Germans had achieved appeared to be entirely artificial, not based upon the promise of the territory itself. From South Africa's point of view, perhaps the greatest advantage of ownership of the former colony was the expansion of her power over additional territory extending from the Orange River to the Zambezi.

The Terms of the Mandate

The nature of the League of Nations Mandate under whose terms the government of South West Africa was transferred to the Union of South Africa is of great significance in the present situation. The territory was classified as a Class C Mandate, which meant that it was to be administered as an integral part of the governing state. One of the architects of the Mandate System of the League of Nations was a prime minister of South Africa, J. C. Smuts, who was active until 1948 in constant efforts to incorporate South West Africa in the union. According to the Mandate of 1919, South West Africa was officially transferred to "His Britannic Majesty,"

130

Namutoni, Ethosha Pan Game Reserve, South West Africa. Germany's armies could not subdue the African inhabitants of South West Africa without a major campaign of terror. One of the relics of those days is illustrated here, although the fortress of Namutoni now serves a more peaceful function as a rest camp in a game reserve. (Satour)

to be governed on his behalf by the neighboring union, which then paid allegiance to the British Crown.

Several developments since 1919 have lent added significance to the terms of the original Mandate. First, when the League of Nations was dissolved, other states which had accepted Mandates after the First World War continued to administer their respective territories under the new terms of the Trusteeship Council of the United Nations. South Africa, on the other hand, refused to place South West Africa under the Trusteeship System, and instead tightened its grip on the territory. The League of Nations had determined that the wishes and petitions of the local inhabitants of Mandate territories should be transmitted to the League, that their interests should be protected, and that annual reports on conditions in the region should be properly conveyed. The union had long failed in its duties in these respects, and

since 1945 has also refused to comply with the rules of the Trusteeship Council. Knowledge about conditions within the territory became less over the years, as until 1962 the South African government refused to allow United Nations representatives to visit the area.

The means by which the South African government sought to incorporate South West Africa in the union have been many and varied. In 1946, the government produced a "petition" signed by 208,850 Africans, in addition to a majority of the whites in the territory, appealing to the United Nations to permit the final inclusion of South West Africa in South Africa.[1] The petition was rejected by the United Nations, where it was realized that the literacy percentage of the

[1] H. J. de Blij, "Notes on the Geography of South West Africa," *The Journal of Geography,* LVII, No. 7 (October, 1958), 340.

African population (then about 430,000) was so low that the number of signatures could not possibly reflect the desires of a people who were aware of the meaning of the document. Meanwhile, the South African government, led by the victorious Afrikaner nationalist majority of 1948, began to perpetrate in South West Africa the practices of *apartheid* which were being legalized in South Africa. Hence, in 1949, the General Assembly of the United Nations placed the matter before the International Court of Justice in The Hague, Netherlands, requesting an opinion on several aspects of the issue.

The International Court judged that South Africa was at fault in not submitting

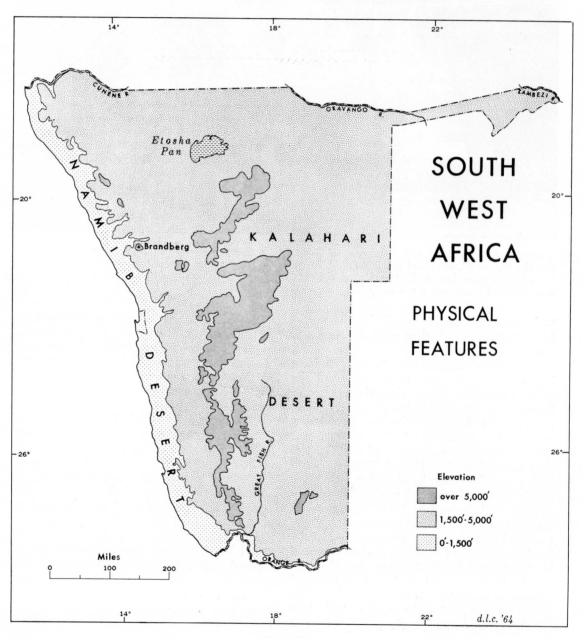

Map 29

petitions and reports on South West Africa to the United Nations. In addition, it stated that South Africa was not, without permission from the United Nations, allowed to change the political status of the territory. Finally, the court ruled (by the narrowest possible margin, 8 votes to 6), that South Africa was at no time legally required to place South West Africa under the Trusteeship System.[2] The decision without question strengthened South Africa's hand in the debate. In the first place, no decisions of the International Court of Justice are binding, and the major question of the relations of South West Africa with the United Nations had, for all intents and purposes, been decided in favor of South Africa. The union, therefore, continued to intensify its policies of racial segregation within the territory and its political integration with the South African state as a virtual fifth province. Appeals from within the region went unreported and unheeded.

In 1960, an event occurred which had a major effect upon the South West African issue. In May of that year, South Africa became a republic and left the British Commonwealth at the moment of its birth. Hence, however nominal British rule in the union of the 1950's may have been, South Africa now officially ceased to recognize the British monarch as the titular head of state. Immediately, the question arose, Had South Africa also abdicated its position in South West Africa? Since the territory was, according to the South African government, still ruled under the terms of the 1919 League of Nations Mandate, and that Mandate was in favor of "His Britannic Majesty," now no longer recognized by South Africa, did the Mandate revert to Britain? In 1962, for the first time in history, the South African government relented in its refusal to allow United Nations representatives to visit South West Africa, and this gesture may well be related to the new situation. At the same time, a preliminary suggestion was put forward by the government that the partition of South West Africa—rather along Bantustan lines—should be considered as a permanent solution by the United Nations. Objections came immediately from white residents in the territory and from United Nations officials, in whose opinion the only acceptable move would be the transfer of the entire territory to United Nations jurisdiction.

A Coveted Prize

The tenacity with which South Africa is defending her position in South West Africa is indicative of the usefulness of this area as an integral part of the South African state. Nevertheless, what South Africa acquired in 1919 was a region which appeared to be a real liability: it was vast, largely desert and steppe, sparsely populated, and expensive to organize and govern even after the attempts made by the Germans to develop it.

South West Africa in 1919 meant something very different from what it means today. There were those who in the early days referred to its acquisition as "Smuts's folly," and it did seem that, apart from some revenues from diamond production, it could contribute little to a fast-developing, wealthy state. In the early 1920's, the Hottentots rose against their new rulers to be put down by armed troops and the air force, and the Herero in the north harassed the South Africans almost without interruption. South West Africa, apparently, gave far more trouble than she was worth.

The period since the Second World War has seen the evolution of a new Africa and the confrontation of ideological opposites, black and white nationalism. To the latter, fighting for a permanent place on a black continent, the possession of territory has become a matter of vital interest. South Africa's pressures on Britain for the transfer of the High Commission Territories and her refusal to yield any distance in the South West Africa question are reflections of this situation. By controlling the High Commission Territories, South Africa can prevent the development there of a form of nationalism she does not

[2] H. M. J. van Rensburg, *Die Internasionale Status van Suidwes-Afrika* (Leiden: Luctor et Emergo, 1953), p. 6.

The Kaokoveld, South West Africa. Northwestern South West Africa is among the driest and most barren sections of the entire South African sphere of influence. Only a few tufts of vegetation manage to survive among the rocky, sandy soil. Toward the interior, the picture changes as the annual rainfall increases and the soil improves somewhat, sustaining a steppe-savanna vegetation and permitting pastoralism to a limited degree. (South African Information Service)

want. By continuing to rule South West Africa, South African power is extended over a region covering Southern Africa from the Cape to the Zambezi River, a situation psychologically satisfying, politically desirable, and strategically reassuring to an expansive nationalism. A glance at any map of Southern Africa shows to what extent the possession of South West Africa increases the direct sphere of influence of the new republic.

Economically, also, the importance of South West Africa has changed greatly between 1919 and 1963. Although the existence of diamonds was known at an early stage, the real potential of the territory is only now coming to light. Copper, lead, zinc, manganese, and germanium ores are now extracted, in addition to tin, various forms of salt, and a host of other, less important minerals. The possibility of further discovery was emphasized with the recent location of a large, medium-grade, iron ore deposit which is likely to be profitable. The center of mining in the interior is Tsumeb, a rapidly growing settlement where some industrial development related to the mining industry is taking

place. A comparison of South West Africa with such political entities as Bechuanaland, Somalia, Chad, and so on, shows that this territory is better endowed with minerals than many others on the continent, and further prospecting looks promising. From this standpoint alone, South Africa's reluctance to withdraw its rule there is explicable. South West Africa is by no means as poor as it appeared forty years ago.

On the other hand, South West Africa's climatology is not encouraging. Reflecting the cold Benguela Current, the entire coastal region at the foot of the omnipresent escarpment is desert. This, the Namib Desert, is one of the driest in the world, most of it receiving less than 2 inches of rainfall annually. In general, although the rainfall increases in a northeasterly direction, the southwestern half of South West Africa receives less than 12 inches of rain each year, and reliability is low. Only the northeastern extremity, including the Caprivi Strip, enjoys an annual rainfall of over 20 inches. Eastern South West Africa merges into the Kalahari Desert, although latosols and a thorntree-

134

studded grassland make the term "steppe" more applicable to this part of the country. In general, soils are poor, and the grasslands are capable of supporting only extensive pastoralism. Agriculture under irrigation is carried on in a few valleys with artesian water. Best endowed is the central plateau, where adequate pasture lands exist, capable of supporting large numbers of cattle and karakul sheep. Compared to the South African Highveld and its eastern and southern fringe areas, however, the physiography of South West Africa is not attractive, in spite of a great deal of topographic similarity: much of the plateau lies at and over 5,000 feet, descends to the coast along a prominent escarpment, and declines into the interior Kalahari Basin as well.

By administering South West Africa, the South African government rules the 600,000 inhabitants of this vast territory. The sparseness of the population is in strong contrast to conditions in large sections of the republic itself, and its wide dispersal throughout the territory presents major problems of organization and control. In spite of its scattered population, South West Africa possesses a high mileage of railroads and roads, a system linked to that of the republic. Only the northern mining town, Tsumeb, is not yet connected to this network, which has the same gauge (3 feet 6 inches) as that of South Africa. A narrow-gauge railroad links the Windhoek–Walvis Bay line with the northern mines, but a wider-gauge line is planned. Graded dirt roads, generally passable during all seasons, connect the various towns.

Although, compared with Bechuanaland, for instance, the communications network of South West Africa is good, there remain large portions of the territory which are far from all roads and railroads. Among these isolated regions are the most densely populated areas of the country. South West Africa's population is, of course, not evenly distributed across the area. The whites, numbering over 70,000, occupy the bulk of the plateau and are concentrated in the towns there and on the coast. There are more than 4,600 ranches on the upland. The Africans (10,000 Bushmen, 30,000 Hottentots, and over 450,000

Tsumeb, South West Africa. The mining heart of northern South West Africa, Tsumeb, has grown rapidly since the Second World War. Just after the war it had but a few hundred inhabitants, and today it is South West Africa's second town after the capital, Windhoek. A good impression can be gained of the landscape in this area. Tsumeb is connected by rail to Walvis Bay, through which its ores are exported. (South African Information Service)

Aspects of Windhoek, the Capital of South West Africa. Situated on the plateau and connected by rail to the coast and to South Africa, Windhoek has become South West Africa's largest town. The capital is located amid the Auas Mountains (top). Contributions by Germany to the townscape remain in the central business district (center) among the stately homes of the suburbs. The German element in South West Africa remains strong, and continuing ties with Germany are evidenced by the fact that West Germany is South West Africa's major foreign trade partner after South Africa. The South African contribution to modern Windhoek is reflected by tall buildings and wide, asphalted avenues (below). (Satour and South African Information Service)

Bantu) are heavily concentrated in the north, although the Hottentot occupy the south and the Bushmen live along the eastern border with Bechuanaland. The northerly concentration of the Bantu reflects the historical developments associated with their arrival along migration routes from the north, their conflict with the Hottentot, and the occupation of the favored core of South West Africa by the white invaders. Most numerous of the Bantu are the Ovambo people, and perhaps best known are the Herero, whose fierce resistance against the Germans is legendary, and who have been most vocal in the political

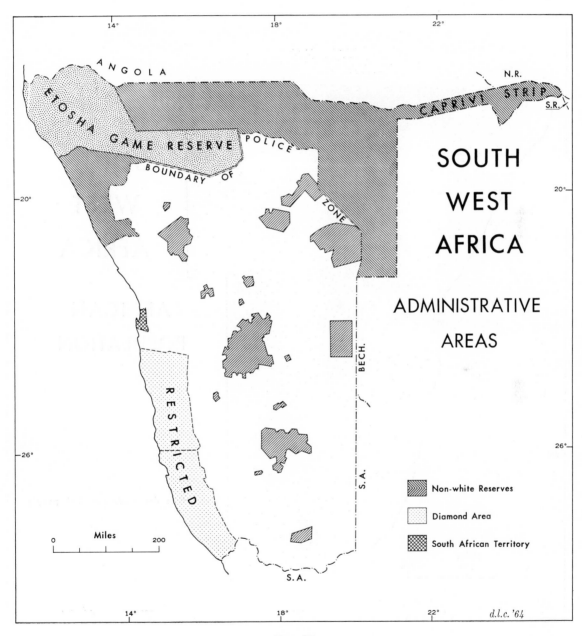

Map 30

developments affecting their country. Finally, there are over 10,000 Colored people in the territory, most of whom live and work on the ranches and in the towns of the southern plateau.

The heavy concentration of Bantu in the north, where they are farthest removed from the effectively controlled part of South West Africa, may present problems of administration for South Africa in the future. The politico-geographic organization of South West Africa is such that a first step toward partition is in effect. Officially, a boundary line exists dividing the area where the bulk of the land is in white hands (the south) from that where the Africans are concen-

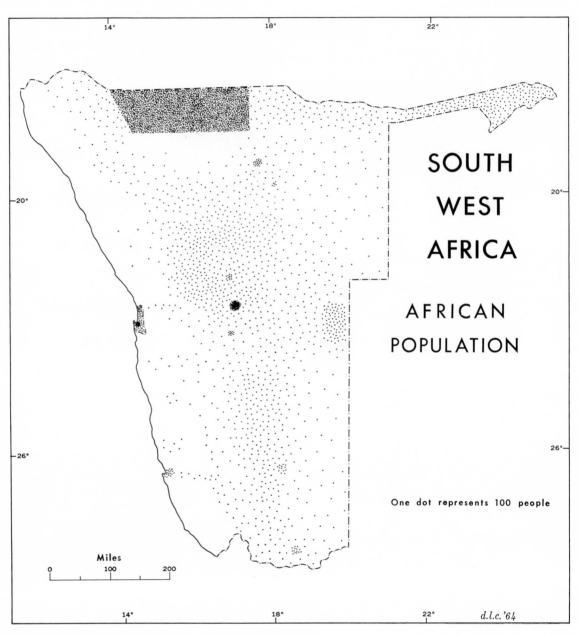

SOUTH

WEST

AFRICA

AFRICAN

POPULATION

One dot represents 100 people

Miles

0   100   200

d.l.c. '64

Map 31

trated.[3] The southern, "white" area is known as the "Police Zone," where the white man's law prevails. North of the line is the South African version of the British protectorate. There, tribal authorities have been preserved,

[3] R. F. Logan, "South West Africa," *Focus,* XI, No. 3 (November, 1960).

land alienation is prevented, and white-black contact is officially confined to a few missionaries, traders, and government liaison officers. Agriculture is the only possible pursuit in the north, and many of the African men seek work in the white Police Zone.

Northern South West Africa is possibly the one region which, although under South

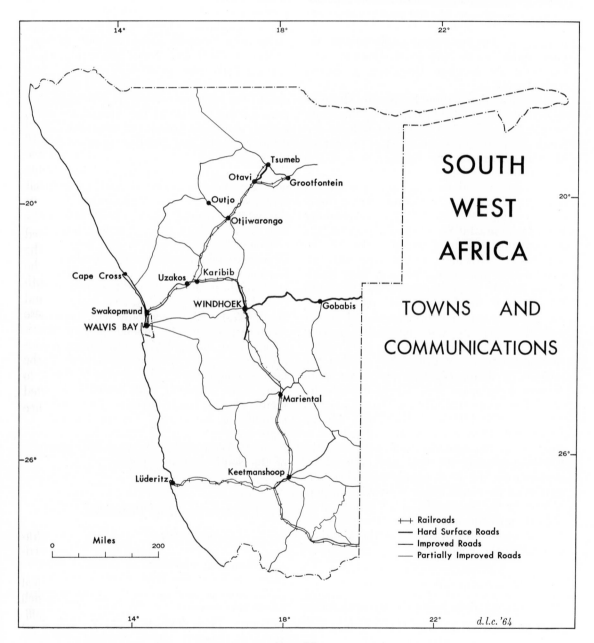

Map 32

African control, lies outside what may be termed the effective national territory of the republic.[4] Throughout the remainder of South Africa, communications are such that men and equipment for the enforcement of law can be rapidly moved wherever the need arises. Northern South West Africa, however, is isolated. Although the Police Zone area is twice as large as the African region (the respective figures are 212,000 square miles and 106,000 square miles), the Colorado-size north remains by far the largest really remote region under South African domination. Significantly, its northern boundary is shared with Angola.

Political domination by South Africa is as desirable to most, but not all, of the white people in South West Africa as it is to the South African government. Most numerous are the Afrikaners, who number over 40,000 and are active in all spheres of life, especially administration and farming. South West Africa retains a distinctly German flavor, however, through the 20,000 German-speaking whites who inhabit the towns and also engage in ranching. To the German sector of the population, Afrikaner control, opposed bitterly in 1915, has been a blessing. After South Africa herself, West Germany ranks as South West Africa's top foreign trade partner, and the ties between the former colonial power and the Mandate are constantly growing stronger. In addition, there is an English-speaking minority of over 7,000, so that the territory is thoroughly trilingual. The South African government feels a responsibility toward this white minority and has given it a voice in both houses of the South African Parliament. Thus, elections are carried out as they are in the republic itself, with only the whites possessing the vote and only whites representing the local population. This integration of the white South West African population in the South African electorate is an indication of the shared cause: the perpetuation of South African control in the Mandate, at least in the Police Zone.

---

[4] This statement does not imply the negation of South West Africa's international status as a Mandate. The integration of the territory in the South African sphere of influence is such that, effectively, South West Africa has become South African territory, however.

Apartheid in South West Africa has had some negative consequences, however, and voices have been raised among the whites of the territory against the implementation of any Bantustan plan there. The major reason for this is economic: prospecting in South West Africa may well discover mineral deposits in areas which, without foreknowledge of the geology, could carelessly be made into Bantustans and thus be permanently lost to white exploitation. Opposition has come especially from Tsumeb, closest to the northern border of the Police Zone, where important mineral finds were made only recently. The opposition to regional *apartheid*, therefore, should not be misconstrued as a sudden concern for the welfare of the African majority, but a sentiment based on economics in a country where the frontier spirit still survives.

South Africa covets South West Africa not only because mineral and agricultural resources exist in the Mandate or because the white minority there needs protection. The South African state, it is felt, has made considerable investment in the region, has organized its economy and developed its transportation network, and now deserves the fruits of these efforts. In addition, it is argued that the precarious agricultural sector of the South West African economy will render the territory permanently dependent upon South Africa, and that political independence and economic dependence are antithetical. These factors, coupled with the desires of the resident white minority, the security requirements of the South African state, and the inability of the United Nations seriously to influence the course of events, have created in South West Africa a virtual fifth province of the South African republic.

Economics and Political Geography

Economic viability, as political geographers studying the High Commission Territories have pointed out, is the prime requirement for survival in the face of political pressure. This does not imply that such survival depends upon absolute self-sufficiency, but absolute dependence upon the foreign state which is attempting to intensify its degree of control is fatal. This is the major reason for the failure of the decolonization process in the so-called independent countries of the French Community in Subsaharan Africa, and the effects of real decolonization in spite of such dependence are well illustrated by Guinea.

South West Africa's economy depends on three major sources: minerals (mainly diamonds), agricultural products (mainly karakul pelts), and fish (lobster, pilchard, and so on). These and other products have brought a certain prosperity to the Mandate, although the majority of its inhabitants are still engaged in a subsistence form of agriculture, and the economy depends almost entirely on markets outside its borders. The value of the mineral resource base is inestimable, since diamonds, accounting for about one-third of the income for all exports, can be sold on the world market and need not depend upon South African outlets. To a lesser extent, this is true also of the more voluminous ores of copper, lead, and so on. Minerals constitute well over half the value of South West Africa's annual exports.

Both agriculture and fishing depend heavily on the South African market, and both industries have been developed with the aid of South African capital. Sheep and cattle ranching are the major agricultural occupations, and only the products of sheep ranching, karakul pelts, produce significant revenues on overseas markets. Cattle on the hoof, meat, and butter are sold in South Africa almost exclusively. The South West African fishing industry sells canned lobster in many parts of the world, but most other products go to the republic.[5] In addition to canned fish, the industry produces fishmeal, fresh fish, and fertilizer. These products all go to South Africa, and the South African government is attempting to encourage the home consumption of fresh fish. Obviously, the sale of fresh and frozen products depends entirely on the nearby market. In addition, it should be emphasized that the South Afri-

can Railroads are responsible for all transportation of the products of the South West African economy. Thus, any isolation of the Mandate from the republic at the present time would be a fatal blow to the economy of the former.

While it is vulnerable to the whims of outside markets and the maintenance of communications depends on an outside power, South West Africa internally faces the perpetual threat of droughts which can cripple the agricultural sector of the economy, require imports of subsistence grains from South Africa, and create serious conditions in the north. At such times, which are relatively frequent due to the high variability of precipitation, the Mandate's dependence upon South Africa is clearly illustrated. Returns from the Karakul industry are drastically reduced, cattle die in great numbers and meat sales to the republic dwindle, and costly imports are necessary. In the present situation, such imports obviously come from South Africa, but in the event of closure of this avenue, the territory would be hard put to find a source for its most urgent needs. From the politico-geographic point of view, this aspect of the dependence of South West Africa upon South Africa is the most serious: when the economy prospers, it does so on the basis of South African markets. When it fails, it requires South African support. Nevertheless, unlike many other African countries, South West Africa normally has a favorable trade balance, and while this is so, it remains an asset to the republic.

Two Anomalies

The politico-geographic map of South West Africa includes two peculiarities. On the coast, opposite the capital, is the territory's main harbor, Walvis Bay. Technically, this town and its immediate environs (totalling 400 square miles) form a part of South Africa's Cape Province and not of South West Africa. It is, therefore, an exclave of South Africa, and was established as such in 1878, when the governor of the Cape, in response to appeals from white settlers in the region, annexed this small area to protect British

[5] H. J. de Blij, "The Sea Fishing Industry of South Africa," *Journal of Geography*, LVII, No. 3 (March, 1958), 135.

141

interests. The Germans then developed the port of Swakopmund, just 26 miles northward by railroad. Walvis Bay, however, possesses indisputably the better natural harbor, and after the South African takeover, its port was rapidly developed. Swakopmund was neglected and eventually closed.

Thus, the bulk of South West Africa's ocean trade leaves the country through a port which is not a part of the Mandate. For many years, Walvis Bay remained administered from the Cape, but recently the administration of the town was handed over to South West African authorities. Undoubtedly, any change in South West Africa's status would cause this situation to be reversed, since Walvis Bay (population 5,000) remains legitimately a part of the republic. Thus, South West Africa faces the problem of not possessing the area and facilities of the major port serving her interior, while transportation is also in South African hands.

A second peculiarity of South West Africa lies in its shape. Compact and largely delimited by geometric boundaries, the regularity of its outline is broken by a proruption for the existence of which there would appear to be little reason. Known as the Caprivi Strip, it was the result of negotiations between Germany and Britain. The Germans desired access to the Zambezi River, and in 1890 signed an agreement which stated that the corridor would lead from the Protectorate of South West Africa to the Zambezi River along a passage which would at no point be less than 20 English miles in width. Thus was created one of the liabilities of the politico-geographic scene of Southern Africa. The strip bounds Angola, Northern and Southern Rhodesia, and Bechuanaland and cuts through terrain which is physically rather uniform. It is far from the developed areas of Southern Africa, yet it is by no means sparsely populated compared to the remainder of South West Africa. Living there and in the surrounding countries are mainly Ovambo people, and today the area is a part of the Africans' lands beyond the Police Zone. Isolated and desolate, its present significance is negligible. No mineral resources have been located, "access to the Zambezi" has been meaningless, and it sustains the precarious

form of agriculture that marks other parts of northern South West Africa.

In the event of political change, however, the strip may attain unprecedented significance. As a part of the South African sphere of influence, it carries South African rule to the heart of south-central Africa, helps surround Bechuanaland on all but one side, and, in addition, separates Bechuanaland from Northern Rhodesia. Thus, South Africa and Southern Rhodesia virtually envelop all High Commission Territories, and the Caprivi Strip closes an avenue of penetration leading from Northern Rhodesia, where African political consciousness has been great in recent years, to Bechuanaland, where trends have also been opposite to those prevalent in South Africa. Although the least effectively ruled today, the Caprivi Strip may become one of the republic's most prized territorial possessions.

7

THE BUFFER ZONE: THE FAILURE OF FEDERAL PARTNERSHIP IN RHODESIA AND NYASALAND

BEYOND THE SOUTH AFRICAN SPHERE of influence, and separating it from black independent Africa, lies what has been called the buffer zone, consisting until 1963 of the Federation of Rhodesia and Nyasaland and the Portuguese provinces of Angola and Moçambique. The territory of the former federation constitutes the heart of this region, including some of Subsaharan Africa's most favored parts. There lie the riches of the Great Dyke, the minerals of the Copperbelt, the farmlands of Nyasaland (now called Malawi) and the Southern Rhodesian plateau, the coalfields of Wankie, the vast iron ore deposits of Que Que, and the waters of great rivers such as the Zambezi, the Kafue, and the Shire. Of course, the region has its share of excessively dry land, such as that of the western interior, and swampy and malarial parts, like those around Lake Bangweulu. This is an area of contrasts, and these opposites are not confined to its economic and physical geography. Historically and politically, also, there has always been great diversity.

In 1953, unification was imposed upon the two protectorates of Northern Rhodesia and Nyasaland and the self-governing colony of Southern Rhodesia. This difference in status of the component parts of the federation reflected a vital contrast in their historical development: Southern Rhodesia, like South Africa, was invaded and conquered by the advancing white man. Northern Rho-

desia (now known as Zambia) and Nyasaland, protected by distance and apparent environmental hostility from large-scale invasion, remained virtually uninfluenced by the white man, and when whites did enter, they came as missionaries, traders, hunters, and as opponents of the slave trade. Although there was fighting in Nyasaland, it was not against the African population in general. War was waged by the British against Portuguese and Arab slave traders, and against those local African chiefs who assisted the traders. Once slave trading had been eliminated, however, Nyasaland and Northern Rhodesia, having become protectorates, remained almost entirely in African hands. African tribal authorities were protected, extensive land alienation was prevented, and those regions in Rhodesia which lay north of the Zambezi River had set out on a path which differed greatly from that of strife-torn Southern Rhodesia.[1] Since then, the differences on either side of the Zambezi have intensified, although the discovery of copper and other minerals on the Copperbelt drew a sizeable white settler population to Northern Rho-

---

[1] The regions now known as the Rhodesias before the turn of the present century were called Zambezia, after the great river in whose catchment basin they largely lie. Cecil John Rhodes's contribution to the white occupation of the area was recognized in 1895 by the official change of name from Zambezia to Rhodesia.

desia. The imposition of federation in 1953 took place in spite of these historical and political contrasts and was justified on the basis of economic necessity. Indeed, it came as the result of pressure on the British government by the white minority in the colony of Southern Rhodesia.

The Zambezi River

The influence of the great Zambezi on events in the Rhodesias has been considerable, from the arrival of the first white settlers to the present. Near Livingstone, in the southernmost portion of Northern Rhodesia, the river plunges over the Victoria Falls, there to enter the gorges and canyons of its middle course. The Zambezi Valley, from Victoria Falls to near Zumbo on the border with Moçambique, is remote, hot, deep, densely bushed, and disease-ridden.

The first coordinated body of settlers to arrive in Southern Rhodesia was the so-called Pioneer Column, a group of some 190 whites paid and fitted out by Cecil Rhodes, who left Rhodes's farm near Kimberley in May, 1890. The Pioneer Column had been preceded by other whites, who had collected concessions from Southern Rhodesia's Matabele and Mashona peoples, but there was no real "trek" until two years after Zambezia had been proclaimed a British sphere of influence. Under orders to establish fortifications and to raise the British flag on the Southern Rhodesian Plateau, the Pioneer Column reached the site of the capital of the former federation, Salisbury, in September, 1890, and built a fort there.

The region which was the immediate object of Rhodes's attention, Southern Rhodesia, forms the divide area between the Zambezi River in the north and the Limpopo River in the south. The Limpopo came to be the limit of Boer hegemony, just as the Zambezi retarded the invasion of whites into northern parts of Rhodesia. To the west of the Limpopo lay Bechuanaland, soon to become a British protectorate, and on the north the Boers would have had to cross the Zoutpansberg as well as the wide Limpopo Val-

ley to enter Rhodesia. The Pioneer Column occupied the heart of Southern Rhodesia, after traveling through Bechuanaland, thus avoiding a crossing of the Limpopo.

Rhodes had been effective in establishing the British South Africa Company, which obtained mineral and trade concessions from African chiefs and which was responsible for government and commerce in Zambezia. The Pioneer Column consisted of representatives of this company. The Matabele and Mashona, who had been engaged in intertribal warfare before the arrival of the white settlers, found themselves in combat with their new enemy, and by 1897 the company possessed all their lands.

North of the Zambezi, however, developments came far more slowly. The desirability of the Southern Rhodesian Plateau was immediately evident to the arriving settlers, and the discovery of minerals, including gold, on the Great Dyke confirmed the wisdom of its annexation. But little was known about Northern Rhodesia for many years to come. Although the company was responsible for the administration of these northern territories, known until 1911 as Barotseland (Northwestern Rhodesia) and Northeastern Rhodesia, the Paramount Chief of the Barotse was left in control of his territory and people, and similar arrangements were made in the east. In Nyasaland, meanwhile, missionary activity and opposition to the slave trade were successful, and in 1891 a protectorate was proclaimed there.

Thus, from the very beginning, white rule to the south of the Zambezi River was complete and direct, while to the north it long remained indirect and much less effective. Although communications were rapidly established within Southern Rhodesia, the Zambezi was bridged in only one place, Victoria Falls, in 1904. Bulawayo had been connected by rail to Kimberley (and Cape Town) in 1897, and Salisbury was linked to Beira by 1899. Contact with the remote north was made either via the railroad across the Zambezi at Victoria Falls or by ferry at Chirundu, but otherwise there were no links between the two flanks of the Zambezi catchment area along 500 miles of the river's course. Northern Rhodesia and Southern Rhodesia, therefore, developed in large measure in isolation from each other, and initial contrasts grew stronger as time went on.

The barrier created by the Zambezi Valley became especially significant after the discovery of copper and other minerals on the Copperbelt. The mine at Broken Hill began production as early as 1902 (although the full extent of the deposits was recognized only much later), and communications and power supply presented immediate problems. The railroad linking the cities of the Copperbelt

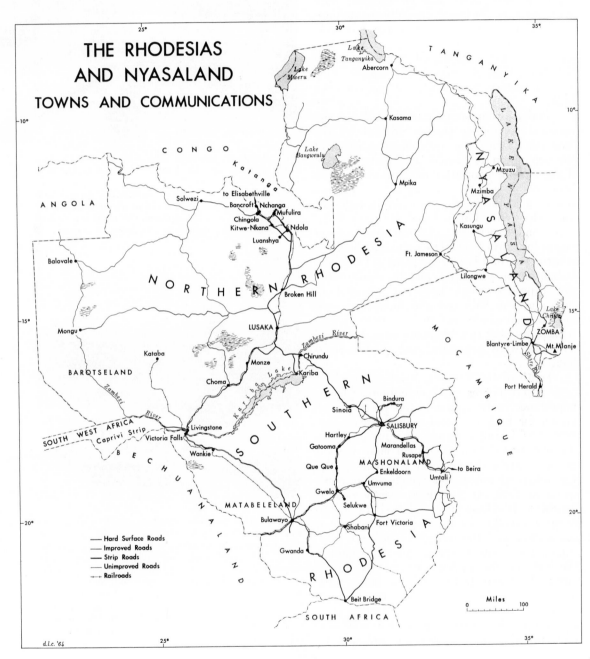

Map 33

to the port of Beira is a tortuous one about twice the length of the direct distance between the two locations. The distance to Cape Town is so great as to make bulk shipments uneconomical; thus much of the export load goes through Angola. Moreover, the Copperbelt depended upon coal from Wankie to supply it with power, and the Rhodesia Railways were in continual difficulty in attempting to cope with the country's increased coal requirements. Although a railroad was projected to link Lusaka directly with Sinoia and Salisbury, thus eliminating the lengthy loop around Victoria Falls bridge, it has not been built.

Perhaps more important than the actual physical barrier to contact created by the Zambezi River is the psychological effect of the separation it caused. In Southern Rhodesia, development after the turn of the century was rapid. Mining and agriculture attracted a continuing flow of white immigrants, and, along the Great Dyke between Bulawayo and Salisbury, industrial development began in a string of towns, culminating in the construction of a large steel plant at Que Que. Urbanization was rapid, and the South African experience was largely duplicated in such places as Salisbury and Bulawayo: residential segregation was the practice, squalid African housing developments were built, restrictions were necessary, and serious problems arose.

South of the Zambezi River lie the best agricultural regions (with exceptions of lesser importance in Nyasaland), and products are grown for both the local and overseas markets. The lucrative nature of agriculture on the plateau led to a permanent land division between Africans and whites known as the Land Apportionment Act, which was promulgated in 1930. At this time, exactly half of Southern Rhodesia was allotted to white farmers, one-third was set aside for African occupation, and the remainder was not allocated. The white lands in general occupied the core of the plateau around the major cities, the Great Dyke, and the better soils and moister parts of the colony. The fringing African lands were of such quality that subsistence farming (corn cultivation and pastoralism) was the only possible practice. In

Strip Road in Southern Rhodesia. Rhodesia's strip roads do not make for comfortable driving, but they do provide sure passage on a hard surface over long distances, even during the rains. Of course, these roads are much cheaper to construct than full-width asphalt roads, and the government chose to expand the road mileage rapidly in this low-cost manner.

Road Sign in Southern Rhodesia. Such warnings as this are necessary in areas where elephants and other big animals still roam in spite of man's encroachment. This photograph was taken near Kariba, and the dirt road in the foreground was constructed for the purpose of moving equipment and materials into the Kariba Gorge for the building of the dam. The burnt veld in this picture is characteristic of late winter on the plateau; the grass has dried for months, and the slightest spark sets it alight, sometimes with serious consequences.

146

A White Farm in Southern Rhodesia. The central part of the Southern Rhodesian Plateau was largely allotted to the white colonists by the Land Apportionment Act of 1930. Magnificent ranches, estates, and plantations arose as a result of suitable climate and soils for the cultivation of a variety of crops and the raising of cattle. This particular farm is located near Salisbury. (United Nations)

Cutting Hay on a Southern Rhodesian Farm. African laborers work on a white farm near Salisbury. The flatness of the land permits mechanized agriculture, in strong contrast to many of the African areas, where the plots of land are smaller, the population pressure greater, unused land at a minimum, and slope incidence higher. (United Nations)

addition, Africans were prohibited from growing certain cash crops.

These conditions are very reminiscent of those existing in South Africa, a fact which has never been lost on Africans in Northern Rhodesia and Nyasaland. The different positions of white settlers in a colony (Southern Rhodesia) and in a protectorate (Northern Rhodesia and Nyasaland) were well understood and appreciated there, and Africans constantly expressed concern that the vast powers of the white man in the south might be extended over the two protectorates north of the Zambezi. Initially, however, even the whites were not interested in such an arrangement, since Northern Rhodesia and Nyasaland were considered to be vast and poverty-stricken regions whose government was a costly affair better left in London's charge.

Voices in favor of unification were initially raised by whites in Northern as well as Southern Rhodesia, when the first major boom occurred to the north of the Zambezi with the recognition of the extent of mineralization on the Copperbelt. By then, the white population south of the Zambezi was far greater than that to the north, and the difference has existed ever since. Presently, the white population of Southern Rhodesia is about 240,000, while that of Northern Rhodesia is some 80,000. As a result, Northern Rhodesia and Nyasaland never did experience the degree of urbanization of the south and were spared, except on the developing Copperbelt, the associated problems. Active African opposition to unification was immediate, and frequent appeals were made by local leaders to London to prevent the formation of any federation or unitary state in Rhodesia. Some land alienation took place along the railroad leading from Southern Rhodesia to the Copperbelt, and, of course, on the Copperbelt itself, and it was feared that a Land Apportionment Act would also be applied to Northern Rhodesia and Nyasaland should unification come about.

The Zambezi, in addition to separating areas which are strongly contrasted historically and politically, also divides Rhodesia into two parts which are physiographically very unlike. Pedologically and climatologically, Northern Rhodesia is not as well fa-

147

vored as the south, which is blessed by relatively high elevations just within the tropics. The area around Salisbury receives between 30 and 40 inches of rainfall annually, and although substantial sections of Northern Rhodesia receive as much or more, the moderate temperatures of Southern Rhodesia render this area more suitable for farming. The driest parts of Southern Rhodesia lie in the Zambezi Valley itself and in the extreme south and west, and, in the valley, high temperatures reduce the effectiveness of the limited amount of rain that does fall. In general, Southern Rhodesia, well endowed with nutritious grasses, is moistest in the east, where the colony is at its greatest elevation, and the Great Escarpment plays its orographic role in rain formation. There lie many of Southern Rhodesia's best farmlands.

Lacking the elevation and divide character of Southern Rhodesia, the north is hotter, more poorly drained, and less well endowed in terms of soils, nutritious vegetation, and good farmlands. This is the transition region from highland Southern Africa to lowland Central Africa, for to the north of the catchment area of the Zambezi lies that of the Congo River. Extensive swamplands occur in various parts of Northern Rhodesia, such as the Lukanga Swamp in the Kafue drainage basin and those in the north around Lake Bangweulu. Northern Rhodesia becomes very moist in the north and east, where parts receive over 60 inches of rain annually. With the exception of some small favored sections, Northern Rhodesia has sustained only a subsistence form of agriculture.

In reality forming the eastern edge of Northern Rhodesia, Nyasaland is physiographically more diversified and generally better endowed than its neighbor. By far the smallest entity in the temporary federation, its 46,000 square miles include 9,000 square miles of the surface waters of Lake Nyasa. Nyasaland in effect forms the western flank and a section of the upland of the rift valley that created Lake Nyasa, and erosion has carved a varied topography from the fault scarp. In addition, some volcanics have been extruded, and Nyasaland's soils are generally better than those of most other parts of the northern federation. The alluvial soils along the lake

shore have long sustained a dense African population, as have those of the river valleys.[2] Nyasaland is moister than most other parts of the federation, the Mount Mlanje area near the border with Moçambique receiving between 90 and 100 inches of rain annually. Although Nyasaland possesses only one-thirteenth of the land area of the former federation, it has about one-third of its total population of some 9 million.

A study of the economic geography of the former federation also reveals strong contrasts between the lands separated by the Zambezi. Indeed, it was the economic justification on which the British government based the creation of the federation in 1953. The argument was that federation would benefit each component from an economic point of view, providing a better balance, greater diversification, and a wider resource base for the economic effort of the new state. Since unification has failed and was largely the result of temporary political and economic conditions, the three countries are here considered separately, indicating the conditions which suggested federation as a desirable step.

South of the Zambezi: Southern Rhodesia

Southern Rhodesia has always had the most diversified economy of the three federated units. Agricultural as well as mineral products rank among the top exports, and it is the only region where the beginnings of a local market have developed and where some industrialization has taken place. The rapidly growing urban centers stimulated the cattle and dairy industries, while corn is the staple food for the African majority, numbering some 2¾ million. On the white farms and ranches on the plateau, cattle and corn are the most important products for the local markets, and they are sometimes exported to other parts of Africa as well.

Although corn was the pioneer crop of

---

[2] F. Dixey, "The Distribution of Population in Nyasaland," *Geographical Review*, XVIII (1928), 274–90.

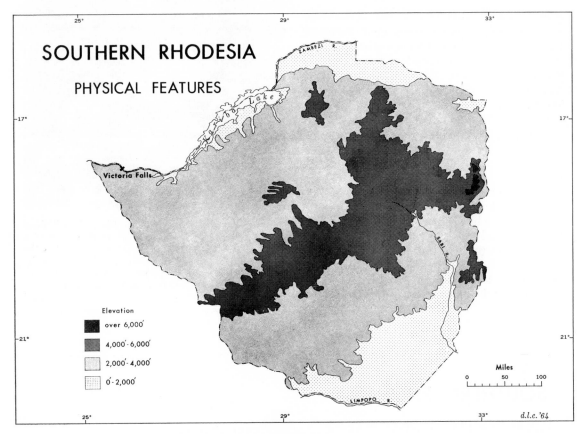

SOUTHERN RHODESIA

PHYSICAL FEATURES

Elevation

- over 6,000'
- 4,000'-6,000'
- 2,000'-4,000'
- 0'-2,000'

Miles
0   50   100

d.l.c. '64

Map 34

Southern Rhodesia, the suitability of the colony for other, more valuable crops was soon realized. Tobacco was introduced in 1910, and it has become the leading export product, with rapidly expanding acreages. Over 200 million pounds of Virginia tobacco are now produced annually, of which over half is purchased by British buyers. Revenues from the crop amount to about 40 per cent of the annual total for all exports. In the Sabi River valley, cotton is grown with some success, recent yields having exceeded 2 million pounds, and in the east, tea production is steadily growing. Self-sufficiency in sugar was achieved in 1962, and the growing of vegetables was encouraged by heavy duties on imports. Although there are periodic meat shortages in Southern Rhodesia, the colony is self-sufficient in milk and other dairy products. Citrus fruits are raised largely for the local market, although some are exported.

Peanuts are grown extensively by Africans. The great majority of Southern Rhodesia's cash crops are grown by white farmers, and for a long time there were legal restrictions upon the growing of cash crops by Africans. African farmers do produce about one-third of the Turkish tobacco, but, in general, the African farmlands are used only for subsistence agriculture and pastoralism, partly because they are the least favored in the colony, partly because they are densely populated and cannot sustain large numbers of people and support cash crops as well.[3]

Southern Rhodesia's mineral production is varied, and gold, asbestos, and chrome rank after tobacco as the country's major ex-

[3] The 1960 production of Turkish tobacco in Southern Rhodesia was just over 2 million pounds, of which 1,400,000 pounds were produced by 120 white growers and 600,000 pounds by 4,417 African farmers.

149

ports. There is no Witwatersrand in Southern Rhodesia, but in many years gold, extracted from a large number of mines scattered over much of the colony, produced one-third of the export revenue. Its relative importance has declined, especially since the Second World War. Along the Great Dyke, asbestos and chrome have long been mined, and there are copper, beryl (the largest proven beryl deposit in the world lies just east of Fort Victoria), and a number of other minerals for export.

Southern Rhodesia is fortunate in possessing the large coal deposits of Wankie. It is this coal which alone supplied power for the mines and industries before hydroelectric power came to be utilized. Coal production is likely to decline as more hydroelectric power becomes available, but in the peak year, 1959, nearly 4 million short tons were mined. Near Que Que, iron ores and local limestone

Tobacco Production in Southern Rhodesia. All three of the territories formerly united in the Federation of Rhodesia and Nyasaland produce tobacco, but the emphasis in Southern Rhodesia, which produces by far the largest crop each year, is on greater production per acre and on higher quality. A stand such as that illustrated here is second to none. (Federal Information Department, Southern Rhodesia)

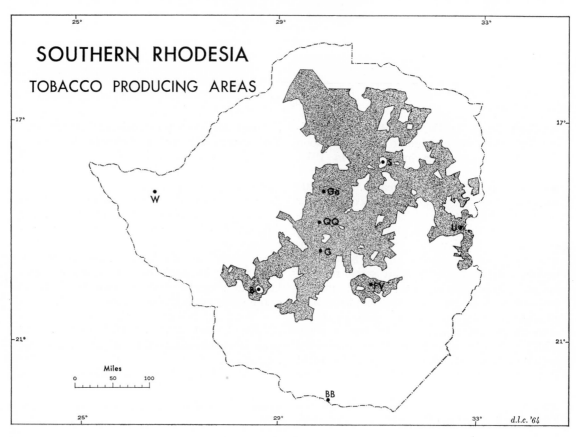

Map 35

and dolomite are used in the country's iron and steel plants, which use coal from the Wankie colliery.

Industrial development in Southern Rhodesia, especially during the decade following the end of the Second World War, was very rapid. Subsequently, political crises and increased competition combined to retard the growth of manufacturing, but expansion has continued, if at a slower rate. Net industrial output in the colony quadrupled between 1946 and 1956, and metal manufacturing industries accounted for the highest output. A large new steel plant has been built at Redcliff, near Que Que. Products for local consumption are made, such as metal doors, steel tubes, rails, and the like. Local use of the deposits of chrome ore is made at the large ferroalloys plant at Gwelo.

Industries based on tobacco and cotton have developed, mainly in Salisbury and Ga-

tooma, respectively. The textile industry has benefited from a doubling of import duty on clothing made in South Africa. The clothing industry is centered in Bulawayo. Other industries founded upon agricultural products are the manufacture of beverages, the refining of sugar (at Salisbury, Bulawayo, and Ndola), the treatment of forest products, the milling of paper, and the like. Compared with other territories of Subsaharan Africa (with the single exception of South Africa), the development of manufacturing in Southern Rhodesia is far advanced. Employment in industry has trebled since the end of the war, and additional industries such as car-assembly plants, breweries, and an oil refinery are under construction. Although on a smaller scale, industrialization and urbanization in Southern Rhodesia resemble those of South Africa. In brief, the economy of the colony is quite well diversified, the purchasing power

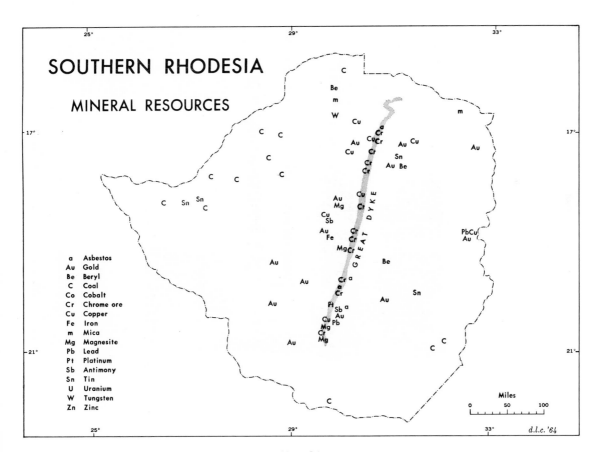

Map 36

Salisbury, Capital of Southern Rhodesia. Formerly the capital of the ill-fated federation, Salisbury remains the seat of government, financial headquarters, and chief city of Southern Rhodesia. Shown here are the central business district with its spectacular vertical development and the surrounding "middle zone" of factories, warehouses, and some residences. The confidence which inspired this postwar building boom has largely disappeared, as Southern Rhodesia's leadership in the federation failed, and the future of the colony is in doubt.

Modern Buildings and Six-Lane Avenue, Salisbury, Southern Rhodesia. The central business districts of Salisbury and Bulawayo are modern in every aspect, the majority of the tall structures having been built since the Second World War.

An "Improved" Dirt Road in Northern Rhodesia. Most of Africa's roads are still of this quality or less. This good, wide, graded road leads through the dry country of eastern Barotseland. The Baobab tree occurs throughout Southern Africa north of the Tropic of Capricorn. Note the dry, dense bush country.

of the local market is growing, and but for the political problems that have developed, the economy of Southern Rhodesia would appear to have the elements necessary for a bright future.

North of the Zambezi: Northern Rhodesia (Zambia)

Northern Rhodesia's economy depends almost entirely upon copper mining and the price of copper on the world market. Corn is the staple crop for African farmers, as it is in the south, and the only commercial crop of any significance is tobacco. Compared to the total production of Southern Rhodesia, the top yield of 9 million pounds is insignificant; it is only about one-third of the annual tobacco production of Nyasaland. Other than

tobacco, a few thousand pounds of soybeans, sugar cane, and wheat are produced each year. Around the cities of the Copperbelt, some vegetable-growing has developed, but as yet there is nothing in Northern Rhodesia's agricultural pattern to compare to that existing south of the Zambezi. In the extreme south, around Livingstone, some good stands of teak and mahogany occur, and some sawmilling has developed.

The Copperbelt, rather like the Great Dyke and the Witwatersrand, is an island of economic activity. Northern Rhodesia is one of the world's largest copper producers, and copper accounts for about 88 per cent of the protectorate's annual export revenues. One of the characteristics of the Copperbelt mining industry has been the constant increase in local refinery capacity. In 1943, 213,000 tons of blister copper and 68,000 tons of electrolytic copper were exported; in 1960, the figures were 167,000 and 400,000 tons, respectively.

In addition to copper, the Copperbelt produces zinc, lead, and cobalt, but the returns from these minerals are negligible compared to those from copper. Zinc and lead together constitute less than 10 per cent of the value of all exports.

Thus, whereas Salisbury (300,000) and Bulawayo (200,000) have a considerable amount of secondary industry, the cities on the Copperbelt are mining towns. Ndola, Kitwe, and Chingola are among the urban places which have drawn the bulk of the white population that has come to the protectorate, and elsewhere only the capital, Lusaka (95,000), is of similar size. As the population totals show, there is no urbanization on the scale that there is in Southern Rhodesia. Apart from those industries directly connected with the mining operations, manufacturing in Northern Rhodesia has developed hardly at all. There is a sugar refinery at Ndola and a chemical plant is being developed at Lusaka. The contrasts between the regions north and south of the Zambezi in terms of industrial development are well illustrated by the fact that 85 per cent of the value of the gross output of all federal industries was produced in Southern Rhodesia.

153

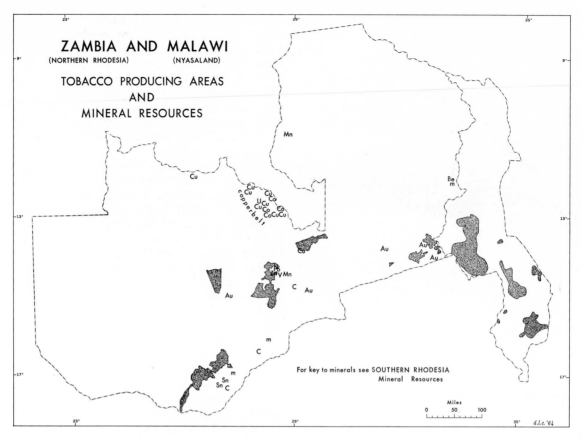

Map 37

With lagging agricultural development and little industry, Northern Rhodesia depends almost completely upon the exploitation of its copper.

Nyasaland (Malawi)

While Northern Rhodesia relies upon minerals, Nyasaland is an almost entirely agricultural country. Its comparatively good soils and adequate precipitation are its only real assets. Population on the agricultural land is dense, but there are a number of large, white-owned plantations. The most important crop, tobacco, accounts for about two-thirds of the value for all exports, and no restrictions are placed upon African participation in this effort. There are over 75,000 registered African tobacco farmers in the protectorate. Nyasaland's second cash crop is tea, which is grown mainly on the white farmers' estates in the south. A total of about 30,000 acres under tea produce a rapidly rising revenue, most of the exports going to the United Kingdom. The third important cash crop is cotton, which is also grown mainly in the Southern Province. Although the income from this crop is yet small, increased yields may be expected, now that Nyasaland's suitability for raising cotton has been established.

A large variety of other crops are grown in Nyasaland, most of local importance only. Corn and rice are the staples, and coffee and cocoa have shown promise. As elsewhere in the region, peanuts are grown extensively. African cultivation of bananas is increasing, and the demand in Southern Rhodesia for potatoes has stimulated this crop.

Mining, industrial development, and ur-

Tea Production in Nyasaland (Malawi). Tea is one of the chief exports of Nyasaland and has been produced mainly on large white-owned estates. The tea gardens shown here lie on the slopes of Mount Mlanje (background). (Federal Information Department, Southern Rhodesia)

Lake Nyasa, Nyasaland (Malawi). Portions of the Zambezi River, Lake Nyasa, Lake Bangweulu, the Luapula River, and the Chambeshi River are navigable and extensively used for water transport in the area of the Rhodesias and Nyasaland. Shown here is Monkey Bay on Lake Nyasa, with two lake steamers at their moorings. (Federal Information Department, Southern Rhodesia)

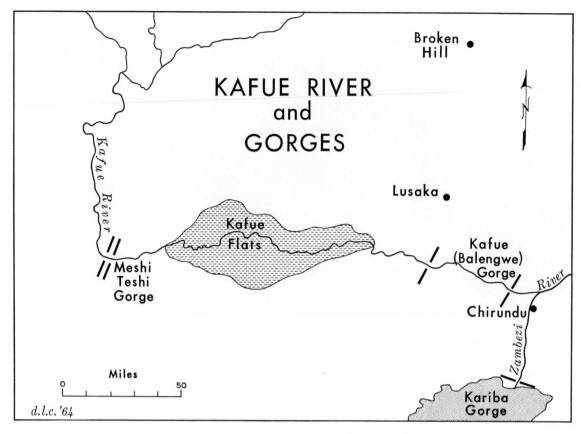

Map 38

banization in Nyasaland are insignificant. Although there are scattered deposits of such minerals as kyanite and graphite, the only mining activity is the quarrying of granite for road building and of limestone for cement manufacture. Aside from the apparent absence of good deposits, transportation costs and power supply would create insurmountable problems for any bulk product that would have to compete on the world market. Industrial development in the country consists of about two dozen establishments. This, consequently, is the least urbanized part of British-influenced Central Africa, although the total population is approximately the same as that of Southern Rhodesia. The only town of significance is Blantyre-Limbe, which has about 90,000 inhabitants and where the auction floors for Nyasaland's tobacco are located. The capital, Zomba, has less than 10,000 people. There is no railroad directly connecting Nyasaland with the other parts of the former federation, although the south since 1935 has been linked to Beira, its natural outlet, by rail.

Federation from the economic point of view, therefore, appears amply justified. Northern Rhodesia, with its overdependence upon copper, and Nyasaland, with its lack of mining and industry, were linked with a colony which not only possesses a diversified economy, but provides a market for products from regions north of the Zambezi and outlets for Nyasaland's excess labor. The federation could boast of a better-balanced economy than any single territory: Northern Rhodesia's mines, Nyasaland's agriculture, and Southern Rhodesia's industries formed part of one political entity, with the merger benefiting all three of its components. Indeed, whatever the political objections to the federal plan, there was unquestionable economic justification for the arrangement, even though it has not survived in the form in which it was created in 1953.

The Zambezi as a Unifying Agent: Kariba

Subsaharan Africa is notoriously poor in its mineral fuel resources. South Africa's coal production amounts to about 80 per cent of the total for the entire subcontinent, and although there have been oil strikes in Nigeria (which have proved of significance and may lead to self-sufficiency) and Angola, the continental geology indicates that the general situation is not likely to improve greatly. Africa does, however, possess the world's greatest potential for hydroelectric development. The Niger, Congo, Nile, and Zambezi all provide good sites for dam construction, and many lesser streams such as the Volta, Shire, and Kafue also possess favorable qualities. The problem in Africa has been the market for the power thus generated; industrial development has been small enough that high capital investment in dam construction appeared unjustified. In those countries where a certain amount of industry did develop, South Africa and the Rhodesias, there was sufficient coal to generate power by thermal plants. In addition, the limited transmission distances prevented the utilization of remote but physically ideal sites. Furthermore, thermal plants require less capital investment than hydroelectric schemes, and cheap labor helped keep the price of coal at a low level.

The Rhodesias and Nyasaland are especially well endowed with sites for hydroelectric projects. The middle, "gorge" course of the Zambezi River, separating the two Rhodesias, possesses several such locations, and both the Kafue and Shire rivers, in Northern Rhodesia and Nyasaland, respectively, also present magnificent opportunities. The Kafue site lies rather close to the Copperbelt but somewhat farther from the Southern Rhodesian industrialized areas, and the Shire lies in Nyasaland's southern proruption into Moçambique, prohibitively far from the markets for the power to be produced. Since the Second World War, technological advances have greatly increased the distances over which power may be transmitted, and in the 1950's both the Kafue and the Zambezi possessed dam sites which could serve the Copperbelt and the Great Dyke. The growth of mining in Northern Rhodesia and the rapid development of industry in Southern Rhodesia led to an unprecedented demand for electricity at a time when the Southern Rhodesia Railroads were already employing 34 per cent of all rolling stock for the transportation of coal to the thermal plants. These three factors, the suitability of several sites, the increased transmission distances, and the overloading of the railroads with coal traffic, led to the decision in Rhodesia to build a great hydroelectric plant which would relieve the current pressures and provide scope for almost unlimited future development.

The initial problem was one of site selection. In Northern Rhodesia, the Kafue River presents two locations where hydroelectric projects might be developed. Immediately after elbowing eastward, the river flows through the Meshi Teshi Gorge and then enters the Kafue Flats. This latter area, subject to frequent flooding, contains some potentially excellent farmlands, and the regulation of the Kafue in its flow through this area is most desirable.[4] After leaving the flats and before joining the Zambezi River, the Kafue flows through the Kafue (Balengwe) Gorge, where the fall is over 1,700 feet.[5] A large dam in the Kafue Gorge would permanently flood a large section of the Kafue Flats, however. Two dams, one in the Meshi Teshi Gorge and one in the Kafue Gorge, would regulate the flow in the flats and control the level in the Kafue Gorge.[6]

The regimen of the Kafue is not well known. At the time when the site of the project was being determined, several years of

---

[4] E. E. Foster, "Potential Utilization of the Kafue Flats of Northern Rhodesia," Geographical Review, XLIII, No. 3 (July, 1953), 366.

[5] Wellington, Southern Africa, I, 406.

[6] W. Halcrow, et al., Report on the Kafue Hydroelectric Project (London: Her Majesty's Stationery Office, 1953), pp. 2 ff.

observation were still required to determine the flow at Meshi Teshi and to estimate the evaporation on the flats and the inflow in the intermediate catchment area. The Kafue had been gauged only since 1946, and little was known about its silt content, which is of vital importance in the life of any dam.

Within 50 miles of the Kafue Gorge, the Zambezi River flows through a region known as the Gwembe Trough, part of which is known as the Kariba Gorge. This gorge is one of several steep-sided valleys through which the river passes after plunging over the Victoria Falls, and it is one of the most inhospitable regions of the Rhodesias. There, the river flows over hard basement rocks, and the damming of the Kariba Gorge would create a long, narrow, and deep lake, the most desirable shape in terms of evaporation, silt accumulation, and volume. The Zambezi had been gauged accurately since 1924 at Livingstone and since 1937 at Chirundu, just above the Kafue confluence. Its silt content was known to be only 1 in 1,600 by volume, and the life of a dam built in the Kariba Gorge was estimated at 1,000 years. Since the Kariba and Kafue gorges are situated close to one another, the factor of location did not materially affect the decision. On the basis of short-term observations, it was thought that Kafue might possess advantages over Kariba, but because the Zambezi's regimen was better known, the choice fell upon the latter. This did not imply abandonment of plans to develop the Kafue site, but the delay would provide time for gathering additional data.

The decision to proceed with Kariba was not well received in Northern Rhodesia, especially by those who had visualized in Kafue a prime advantage for Northern Rhodesia over the wealthy south in the new federation. There were general doubts concerning the ability of the federation to carry the financial burden of a scheme which involved certain risks, but when the federal parliament was confronted with a resolution to proceed with dam construction, it approved the move by 25 votes to 7.

Northern and Southern Rhodesia were not the only territories to be directly involved in a hydroelectric scheme on the Zambezi River. The Zambezi by treaty is an international river, and no impediments to its flow may be created without international consultation.[7] This problem was solved in 1950 at a conference held by representatives of the Portuguese and Rhodesian governments.

The second problem involved the financing of the huge Kariba undertaking. Those who advocated the building of additional thermal plants feared the high costs of the Kariba Dam, and there were doubts that the Rhodesias could raise the required loans.[8] The predicted cost of the Kariba project was $317 million, while the capital required for the construction of thermal plants of equivalent capacity was $283 million.[9] Of course, the capacity of Kariba was far in excess of immediate requirements, so that the thermal stations then needed would have been smaller and would have cost less than the figure quoted. However, thermal stations, once built, continue to require coal deliveries (the major problem Kariba solved), and the efficiency of such plants is far less than that of hydroelectric projects. In other words, the thermal station, due to rising fuel costs or obsolescence and reduced efficiency, may become uneconomical, while the hydroelectric plant, although requiring a high initial investment, is likely to continue operating at maximum efficiency and produces electricity which can be sold at constantly decreasing cost. Indeed, the federal power board was able to show that the first decade (1960–70) of operation would actually save the federation $89 million if thermal power were the alternative.

These figures are very high for a group of countries whose combined import and export totals amounted to $213 million and $176 million, respectively, in a year shortly

---

[7] E. Hertslet, *The Map of Africa by Treaty* (3rd ed.; London: Harrison & Co., 1909), III, 1022.

[8] See, for instance, A. J. Bruwer, "Industrial Development," in A. Welsh (ed.), *Africa South of the Sahara* (Oxford: Oxford University Press, 1951), p. 183.

[9] H. J. de Blij, "Some Aspects of the Kariba Hydroelectric Project in the Central African Federation," *Journal of Geography*, LVI, No. 9 (December, 1957), 413.

The Kariba Hydroelectric Project. This photograph, taken in 1960, soon after the Kariba project was formally opened, shows the great dam wall in the Kariba Gorge, the lake slowly filling in the left distance, and the roadway across the dam under construction. An idea of the scale can be gained by observing the vehicles on the dam wall and the two-lane suspension bridge below at the right (United Nations)

before the loans were required, 1949.[10] It was a measure of the optimism with which the future of the Rhodesias and Nyasaland was viewed in the early 1950's that the loans were soon obtained: in 1955, the federal prime minister was able to announce that the International Bank for Reconstruction and Development had agreed to back the Kariba project. Loans were also obtained from Copperbelt mining companies, the British South Africa Company, local banks, and from as far afield as the Katanga. Thus, a substantial part of the total capital investment required came from local sources.

The third set of problems involved the preparations for dam construction and the actual building of the dam wall itself. Once again, the remoteness and hostility of the Zambezi Valley made themselves felt. Densely bushed and disease-infested, the hot Gwembe Trough possessed no roads, and even survey mapping remained to be done. The building of access roads was the first in a series of steps preceding the first stages of dam wall construction. Plans were laid for the evacuation of the 50,000 BaTonka people occupying this isolated part of Rhodesia, now to be inundated by Lake Kariba, and their resettlement elsewhere. Pylons for no less than 935 miles of transmission lines were constructed; 3,600 were required, and most were placed in dense bush country through which a swath had to be cut.[11] Bush was also cleared from

---

[10] L. D. Stamp, *Africa*, p. 540. But ten years later the figures were $420 million and $520 million, respectively, with a record favorable trade balance and evidence that optimism was justified.

[11] "Preparation for Kariba Transmission Lines," *Newsletter* (Salisbury: Federal Information Department, February, 1957).

159

the dam sides to 60 feet below the expected water level. Then began the construction of a temporary town of Kariba and the transportation of required materials to the dam site.

These operations alone placed a considerable strain upon the federal economy. All transportation facilities were overloaded as never before by Kariba-bound goods. Cement was required in quantity, and industries as far afield as Nyasaland benefited from this demand, but the building industry suffered. All efforts, however, were directed toward the dam construction, and temporary difficulties elsewhere were accepted as the price for success at Kariba. Actual construction began during the low-water season of 1955, and the first turbine was set in motion early in 1961. Lake Kariba, which will be over 140 miles in length, a maximum of 20 miles wide, and 390 feet deep near the dam wall, was well over half filled by the beginning of 1962. Facing unprecedented flood conditions in the wet season of 1958, the Italian contracting company had nevertheless managed to complete the project ahead of schedule. The result is a dam wall nearly 2,000 feet in length and over 400 feet in height, creating the world's largest artificial lake. Long the dividing line between the Rhodesias, the Zambezi now has become a vital part of progress upon which north and south alike depend.

The Assets of Kariba

What advantages have accrued as a result of the construction of a large dam in one of the most remote areas of Southern Africa? The fortunes of Kariba are being scrutinized by several other countries in Africa which possess sites suitable for similar projects. A major question is whether the availability of cheap electric power would draw consumers to the region. In other words, would cheap electricity at Inga on the Congo induce bauxite-refining companies (using bauxite from West Africa) to locate plants in the Leopoldville area? Would the construction of a dam on the Shire River bring enough development

to the Shire Highlands and surrounding areas to warrant the investment?

Kariba was built, first, because its market was guaranteed. There was a need for electricity on the Copperbelt as well as in Southern Rhodesia, and rather than being an object of national prestige, the dam was an economic necessity. As time goes on and the various loans are repaid, the price of electricity in the Rhodesias will be constantly reduced, as Table III shows.

The most important asset of Kariba, of course, is its ability to cope with the increasing needs of mining and industry, providing enough power for unlimited development. In countries where mineral fuels are scarce or where coal transportation to thermal stations presents problems, the growth of manufacturing may be inhibited because of the attendant uncertainty concerning power supply and consequently increased risks. Kariba has eliminated this, at least for over a decade, and already, the project on the Kafue River is designed to supplement Kariba power in the 1970's.

From the point of view of communications and transportation in the Rhodesias, the contributions of Kariba are several. By relieving the pressure on the Rhodesia Rail-

TABLE III

ESTIMATED COST OF KARIBA POWER, 1961–72

Year	Price in Cents per Unit
1961	1.014
1962	.686
1963	.597
1964	.569
1965	.557
1966	.541
1967	.484
1968	.425
1969	.399
1970	.375
1971	.352
1972	.330

Source: D. L. Anderson, "Kariba Hydroelectric Power for Central African Development," *Optima*, VI, No. 2, (June , 1956), 37–43.

ways, much rolling stock has been released for use elsewhere. This had become a matter of urgency by 1953, and the reduction in coal traffic came none too early. Furthermore, the dam wall itself creates a physical connection between Northern and Southern Rhodesia, thus becoming the third such link in the entire region. On top of the dam wall, there is space for a four-lane highway, and the dam lies close to the straight-line connection between the capitals of Salisbury and Lusaka.[12] Hence, when modern roads have been built to link these places, the Kariba bridge will doubtless become the most commonly used Zambezi crossing.

Lake Kariba itself is expected to contribute to communications in the federation. A network of shipping services is planned, and Binga, located about halfway along the lake, is to become the most important harbor and an administrative center. The lake surface will be very unlike the raging Zambezi, and connections between the opposite shores should be easily maintained. It has been suggested that the lake will affect the orientation of communications in the area, which has been north-south in the past, while the new lake trends east-west.[13] Unless some significant development takes place in the north of Southern Rhodesia or in the south of Northern Rhodesia, however, such a development seems unlikely.

In addition to enhancing the prospects for mining and manufacturing in the Rhodesias, the Kariba project also has stimulated other industries. Lake Kariba is being stocked with fish, and the fishing industry is expected to make an important contribution to protein consumption in the region. Although there do not appear to be opportunities for irrigation along the shores of the lake, studies downstream from the dam, from near Chirundu to the border with Moçambique, indicate that the regulated river may provide such possibilities there. Flood control and regulation of

the Zambezi are major assets of the Kariba dam, the benefits of which are felt as far away as Moçambique. There, an area known as the Pungwe Flats, subject to periodic flooding and consequent swamp conditions, may become suitable for rice cultivation. Navigation on the lower Zambezi River also will cease to be seasonal due to periods of low volume: regulation will eliminate the great contrasts which have marked the Zambezi regime. Eventual control of the Kafue and Shire tributaries will lead to even greater predictability of the lower Zambezi's volume.

As in many other African countries, the tourist industry is of importance to the former federation. Kariba has become a major attraction and is visited by thousands of tourists each year. Nearly 150,000 visitors entered the federation in each of several recent years, every year producing a new record. About half of this influx comes from the Republic of South Africa.

In spite of its magnitude, Kariba will only temporarily be capable of supplying Rhodesia's power needs. Even before the last turbine is installed at Kariba, work will begin on Kafue. However, Kariba has demonstrated the feasibility of great projects of this kind in Subsaharan Africa, and the lessons learned in its execution will be applied throughout the subcontinent. There are many additional sites which will be developed in the future, and some will present even greater advantages than Kariba. Within the Rhodesias, the harnessing of the Zambezi and its utilization for common progress is one of the accomplishments that kept the federal state economically viable. For the rest of Africa, Kariba is an example of what may be achieved with the continent's great remaining potential for hydroelectric power production.

Progress, Problems, and Trends

The comparative prosperity of the Central African Plateau is evident from the material progress that has been made in this region. Salisbury and Bulawayo are large,

[12] J. P. Jansen, "Recent Developments and Trends in Africa: The Kariba Gorge Hydroelectric Scheme," *Journal for Geography*, I, No. 3 (September, 1958), 49.

[13] *Ibid.*, p. 53.

modern, industrialized cities. The annual increase in rate of gross output as late as the early 1960's was 5 per cent. Modernization, on a scale applying to all of Subsaharan Africa, has gone far. Currently, however, the rate of economic growth is declining, and the decline appears to be more than the leveling-off to be expected after the phenomenal expansion of the 1950's.

The reduced rate of economic growth is in part the result of the imposition of the federal arrangement itself. Initially, the economic stimulation of federation produced great impetus for development, but eventually the political overtones began to dominate the scene. In 1953, political objections to federation were denied in favor of economic expediency. By early 1963, the federation had all but failed, as the secession of both Nyasaland and Northern Rhodesia seemed only a matter of months away. Formal dissolution of the federal state came on December 31 of that year. From the very beginning, it was clear that one of the tests for the federal program of partnership would be the amount of benefit received by the poorer partners north of the Zambezi, where two-thirds of the people involved live (Northern Rhodesia, 2,700,000 Africans, 80,000 whites; Nyasaland, 3,000,000 Africans, 9,000 whites).

Ten years after the beginning of federation, it was clear that African objections on political grounds had not been removed by spectacular economic benefits. In the north, there simply has not been the kind of economic upswing that might have had the desired effect. On the contrary, little has changed in Nyasaland since federation, and, apart from the region in the vicinity of the railroad line and the Copperbelt, little has changed in Northern Rhodesia. It was, of course, too much to expect immediate and far-reaching improvements, but such events as the choice of Kariba over Kafue and Shire, the omnipresent employment problem in Nyasaland (in which little improvement was felt), and the lack of tangible progress in, for instance, communications all helped to keep African distrust in the federal scheme alive. Eventually, these and other circumstances led to serious disturbances, especially in Nyasaland, where a state of emergency was declared in

1959. Thus, the federation had reaped a harvest not only of economic progress in certain regions, but also of the major impediment to the continuation of such progress, political instability.

Political instability, also induced by a series of efforts by the government to restrict African participation in elections, began seriously to affect the economy in the late 1950's. As in South Africa, the inflow of capital investment was reduced, and serious signs of retardation appeared as confidence in the federation's future decreased. African leaders in Nyasaland threatened secession, and similar sentiments were expressed in Northern Rhodesia. In the south, there was agitation against the Land Apportionment Act and against other forms of discrimination in the urban centers, where serious riots took place. The federal government's efforts to retain control of the situation included what Africans to the north of the Zambezi had feared when the federal plan was first proposed: the use of the federal military, normally confined to the southern colony, in the north. The sort of problems which had not faced Nyasaland in the past arose: African leaders were jailed in large numbers, and a racial bitterness developed which has always been foreign to British protectorates.

The British government has taken a hand in the situation, not so much to preserve the federation as to prevent the federal government from taking undue steps to preserve it. Indeed, the secession of Nyasaland and Northern Rhodesia has now occurred, and Africans have a majority in the local government. In recognition of the need for agricultural reforms, the Nyasaland government is undertaking the sort of vigorous reorganization of farm practices which only Africans can impose upon Africans. In reality, it is an effort to combine the farmer's desire for an individual piece of land with a communal effort in soil conservation, and if it were now imposed by whites, it would be as unpopular as the Land Husbandry Act is in Southern Rhodesia. Nyasaland is poor, however, and secession may mean that some important outlets for its labor may be closed. Thus, there is urgent need for greater self-sufficiency, and since the economy must be based on agriculture, it is agriculture which must be improved.

The stresses to which the federation has succumbed result partly from proximity to black Africa and the wind of change. As the core of the buffer zone, and comprising territories whose historical differences have been intensified rather than ameliorated by time, the federation experienced internal strains and external pressures which combined to cloud the economically bright horizon. This was a white man's federation in what will be the black man's Africa, but whoever governs the Rhodesias will have to acknowledge the economic soundness of the federal idea. African leaders have suggested that their present desire to dissolve the federation may in the future be replaced by a desire to reconstitute it when each of the component parts is under majority rule. While this sentiment prevails among the Africans, who are gaining in political strength, business cannot be expected to display a great deal of confidence and interest in the country, for such dismemberment and reassembly of the federation will almost certainly affect the economy negatively. In spite of Kariba and all other justifications, therefore, the price of federation in terms of political stability in the Rhodesias has been high, and this is now having its impact on the economy of the entire region.

8

THE BUFFER ZONE: ANGOLA AND MOÇAMBIQUE, CONTRASTS IN THE VULNERABLE FRINGE

FLANKING THE RHODESIAS and Nyasaland are two territories whose history involving Europeans, unlike that of the plateau interior, goes back several centuries. Parts of Angola and Moçambique were in Portuguese possession before the end of the first quarter of the sixteenth century. Conquest of the interior and delimitation of the boundaries between the Portuguese and British, Belgian and German interests did not, however, take place until the second half of the nineteenth century.[1] In the many decades between the first Portuguese settlement and the consolidation of Portuguese colonies in Subsaharan Africa, progress in Angola and Moçambique was virtually nonexistent. After that, it was slow until after the end of the Second World War, when the pace increased somewhat. But Moçambique and Angola in the 1960's remained colonial possessions whose internal conditions resembled those of another century.

Both Angola (481,000 square miles) and Moçambique (298,000 square miles) are large territories whose characteristics of size and shape are of politico-geographic importance. Angola, inhabited by over 5 million people, is a compact entity occupying what Wellington has called the South Equatorial

Divide and surrounding regions.[2] Technically, however, Angola is fragmented, for beyond the mouth of the Congo River is an exclave, Cabinda, which forms a part of the Portuguese province.[3] Angola's capital, Luanda, is located in a peripheral position along the northern coast. Although considerably smaller than Angola, Moçambique has a larger population numbering about 6 million. Moçambique's attenuation is emphasized by the fact that its northern extremity, Cape Delgado, is over 1,200 airline miles from the capital, Lourenço Marques, also peripherally located. This is farther than Johannesburg, South Africa, is from Elisabethville, Congo. Furthermore, Nyasaland forms a lengthy proruption into northern Moçambique, while the latter extends up the Zambezi River as far as Zumbo, likewise forming a proruption. Moçambique tapers southward; the northern border with Tanganyika, along the Rovuma River, is some 400 miles in length, while the southern border with Natal is less than 50 miles long.

In the political geography of Moçambique and Angola, shape, size, and relative location are all significant factors. The internal politico-territorial organization of the areas has always been the responsibility of the non-African minority, numbering about

---

[1] Delimination did not occur without friction among the interested powers. For a detailed analysis of some of the major points of conflict, see P. R. Warhurst, *Anglo-Portuguese Relations in South-Central Africa, 1890–1900*, Royal Commonwealth Society Imperial Studies No. XXIII, 1962.

[2] *Southern Africa*, I, 5.

[3] Angola and Moçambique were accorded provincial status mainly to prevent the United Nations from considering them as "dependencies."

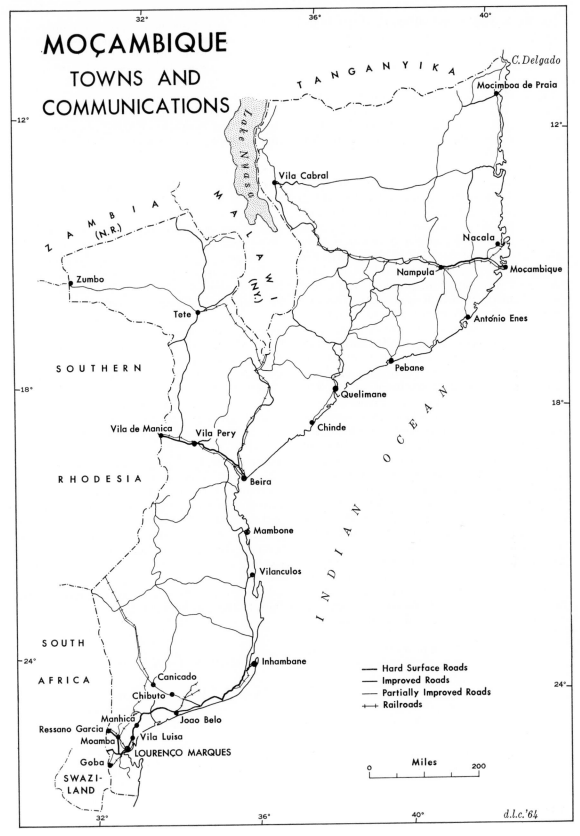

MOÇAMBIQUE
TOWNS AND
COMMUNICATIONS

C. Delgado

Mocimboa de Praia

TANGANYIKA

Lake Nyasa

Vila Cabral

ZAMBIA (N.R.)

MALAWI (NY.)

Nacala

Nampula

Moçambique

Zumbo

Tete

António Enes

SOUTHERN

Pebane

Quelimane

Vila de Manica   Vila Pery

Chinde

RHODESIA

Beira

INDIAN OCEAN

Mambone

Vilanculos

SOUTH

AFRICA

Inhambane

Canicado

Chibuto

Manhica

Ressano Garcia

Moamba   Vila Luisa

Goba   LOURENÇO MARQUES

SWAZI-
LAND

Joao Belo

—— Hard Surface Roads
—— Improved Roads
—— Partially Improved Roads
+—+ Railroads

Miles
0   200

d.l.c.'64

Map 39

200,000 in Angola and 90,000 in Moçambique. In Moçambique, the focus of most spheres of activity has long been in the south, where the important cities lie and where most of the non-African ruling class lives. The railroads linking Moçambique with the interior all pass through the southern section of the country, and control over the population has been more complete there than in the north. The dividing line, once again, is the Zambezi River, and as is noted below, the river divides Moçambique into two parts which are alike in some respects, but significantly different in others. In the political geography of present-day Africa, it is northern Moçambique that adjoins newly independent Africa and faces the full impact of the wind of change. But the independent countries bordering it have achieved sovereignty in peaceful ways, and were formerly British dependencies. This factor has helped to retard violent change in northern Moçambique. In addition, the border with Tanganyika is physiographic rather than geometric, is clearly demarcated by nature, and does not run through regions of dense forests as does that of northern Angola. The boundaries marking the two proruptions of Nyasaland and Moçambique may come to present the most serious control problems for the Portuguese. The political emancipation of Nyasaland and Northern Rhodesia has lagged behind that of Tanganyika, however, so the full impact of black Africa upon northern Moçambique had not yet been felt in 1963.

From a theoretical point of view, the shape of Moçambique is an inescapable liability for the territorial administration based in Lourenço Marques and the Portuguese government in Lisbon. Several observers have already noted the possibility of fragmentation, which would tend to duplicate the events of Central Africa on either side of the Zambezi River.[4]

Angola, being compact, would perhaps present fewer problems of control were it not so large. It has a border with the turbulent Congo, extending over more than a thousand miles, which is partly physiographic in type, but also partly geometric and super-

imposed. It is possible to speak of a superimposed boundary here, since the lower Congo region had some aspects of political unity before its invasion by Europe, and the boundary certainly cuts through ethnic units, primarily the BaKongo people. In other parts of Africa, irredentism has been a strong force in the relations between adjoining countries, and independence in the Congo (and therefore for Congolese BaKongo, but not for Angolan BaKongo) helped precipitate serious hostilities on the Angola-Congo border. Furthermore, the terrain has been most helpful to insurgents, so that effective control by the Portuguese in northern Angola has not existed since 1961.

Angola's vulnerability as a flank of the buffer zone is partly the result of her location. Not only does it extend northward deep into the basin of the Congo, it penetrates the Kalahari Desert in the southeast, bordering the teeming African reserves of northern South West Africa and the land of the Barotse in Zambia (Northern Rhodesia). Thus, while southern Moçambique, at least, is firmly anchored in white Africa, Angola, with the dissolution of the Rhodesian federation, has become an island of European control. The Congro is independent, Zambia's sovereignty is assured, and northern South West Africa is Bantu territory, although under South African control. While South Africa and Southern Rhodesia need southern Moçambique for reasons of economic geography, Angola's hinterland included the Katanga and Copperbelt, now both part of black independent Africa. Without doubt, South Africa has interests in assisting Portugal to retain control in Angola, and will support the Portuguese, but the republic's major concern is with Moçambique south of the Zambezi River.

Economic Geography

Neither Angola nor Moçambique has yielded minerals to the same extent as have Rhodesia and South Africa. There is no Witwatersrand or Copperbelt in Portuguese Africa, although Angola has diamonds and some iron ore among her major exports. But both

[4] J. Duffy, *Portugal in Africa* (Harmondsworth: Penguin Books, 1962), p. 206.

166

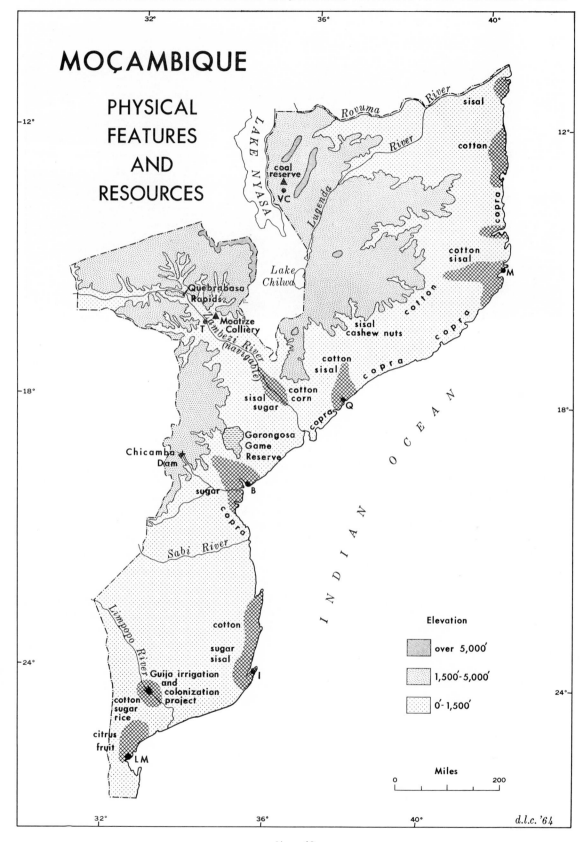

MOÇAMBIQUE

PHYSICAL
FEATURES
AND
RESOURCES

LAKE NYASA

Rovuma River

sisal

Lugenda River

cotton

coal
reserve
▲
● VC

copra

cotton
sisal

*Lake
Chilwa*

● M

Quebrabasa
Rapids

cotton

Moatize
▲ Colliery
T

Zambezi River (navigable)

sisal
cashew nuts

copra

cotton
sisal

cotton
corn

copra

● Q

sisal
sugar

INDIAN OCEAN

Gorongosa
Game
Reserve

Chicamba
Dam ✦

copra

sugar

● B

copra

Sabi River

cotton

Limpopo River

sugar
sisal

Guija irrigation
and
colonization ✦
project

● I

cotton
sugar
rice

citrus
fruit

● LM

Elevation

▨	over 5,000'
▨	1,500'-5,000'
▨	0'-1,500'

Miles

0   200

d.l.c. '64

Map 40

The Port of Lourenço Marques, Moçambique. The photograph shows the mouth of the Tembe River, the Bay of Lourenço Marques (Delagoa Bay), and the downtown area of the capital of Portuguese East Africa. Three ships are lying at anchor awaiting a berth. A good idea can be gained of the extent to which the harbor is protected from the open sea. The central business district is at the left, the railroad emplacement at the right.

Angola and Moçambique have benefited from the riches of the interior, for much of the volume of imports and exports of the developing plateau has passed through Portuguese ports. The handling of this trade has become a major source of revenue, especially for Moçambique. Lourenço Marques serves the Witwatersrand and is connected by rail also to Rhodesia, while Beira is the major outlet for Southern Rhodesia and Nyasaland.[5]

Angola and Moçambique have not attracted a white population as large as that of South Africa or even Rhodesia. In recent years, the rate of immigration has increased sharply, encouraged by promises and grants made by the Portuguese government. Economic opportunity has always been very limited, due partly to the relative poverty of the provinces and partly to stultifying policies of the administration. The recent change is a result of the recognition of the strategic value of a large white settler population. Even today, however, the number of whites in Angola and Moçambique together (290,000) is of the same order as that of Southern Rhodesia alone, and less than one-twelfth that of South Africa.

Agriculture employs the great majority of the people of both provinces. Most of the Africans practice various forms of subsistence agriculture, but there are regions in both territories which permit the cultivation of cash crops. Africans have been forced by government decree to grow such crops as cotton and rice in Moçambique, but the income from agriculture there has not, as was hoped, become the mainstay of the economy.[6] Opportunities exist in Moçambique for the growing of sugar, cashew nuts, copra, sisal,

---

[5] W. A. Hance and I. S. van Dongen, "Lourenço Marques in Delagoa Bay," *Economic Geography,* XXXIII, No. 3 (July, 1957), 238.

[6] This practice officially came to an end in 1961 in the case of cotton. See A. Moreira, *Portugal's Stand in Africa* (New York: University Publishers, 1962), p. 195.

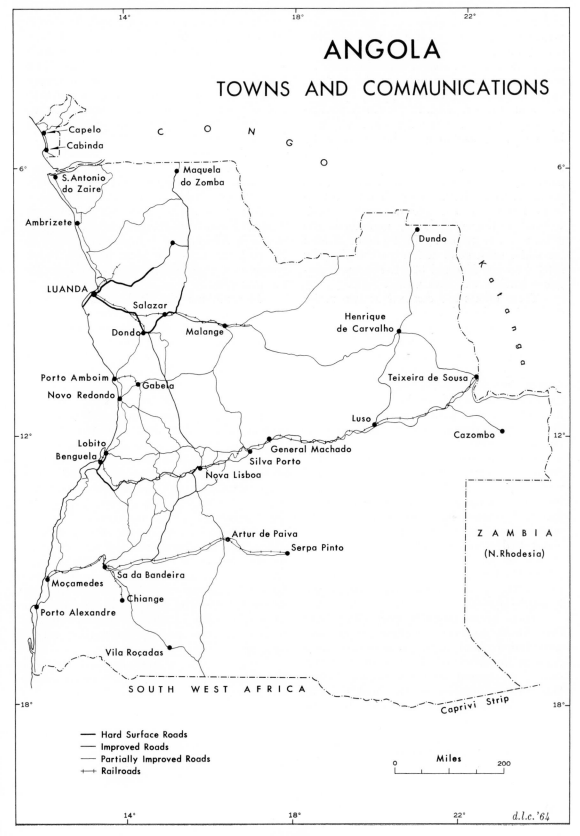

ANGOLA
TOWNS AND COMMUNICATIONS

Capelo
Cabinda

C O N G O

S. Antonio
do Zaire

Maquela
do Zomba

Ambrizete

Dundo

LUANDA

Salazar

Dondo   Malange

Henrique
de Carvalho

K a t a n g a

Porto Amboim
Novo Redondo

Gabela

Teixeira de Sousa

Luso

Cazombo

Lobito
Benguela

General Machado
Silva Porto

Nova Lisboa

Z A M B I A
(N. Rhodesia)

Artur de Paiva

Serpa Pinto

Moçamedes

Sa da Bandeira

Chiange

Porto Alexandre

Vila Roçadas

S O U T H   W E S T   A F R I C A

Caprivi Strip

— Hard Surface Roads
— Improved Roads
— Partially Improved Roads
+++ Railroads

Miles
0   200

d.l.c. '64

Map 41

and tea, which in addition to cotton are the principal export crops of the province. Recently, the Portuguese government, recognizing the need for a stronger agricultural sector in Moçambique's economy, has shown more vigor in promoting cash cropping by black and white farmers alike. In the Limpopo Valley, a quarter of a million acres of land are to be put under irrigation, to be occupied by 10,000 families. Referred to as the Lower Limpopo Valley Scheme, this project is the most extensive ever to be undertaken in the province. In the hinterland of Beira, the Chimoio District is the site of another agricultural settlement scheme, and there the government is preparing 75,000 acres of land for white settlement. It is expected that, by 1964, between 200 and 300 European Portuguese families will have settled there.

These efforts are directed at two major goals. Moçambique's exports are almost without exception agricultural, and each year the country has a large trade deficit. This is made up by income from other sources, and there is always the possibility that they might fail. Angola, for example, has long benefited from the income derived from the Lobito-Katanga railroad. The new political situation has suddenly reduced that income drastically. A similar development in Moçambique would be disastrous, and thus the administration is supporting agriculture by means of irrigation and settlement projects. The second goal, in addition to the reduction of the trade deficit, is that of European immigration. In 1930, the white population of Moçambique was only about 16,000, and in the next decade it increased by only about 10,000. But in the decade of the 1940's it grew by over 20,000, and the 1950's saw an increase from about 48,000 to nearly 90,000.

These figures might be misleading, however, for by no means all these people have settled on the land. In fact, most of them have come to the cities, which grew spectacularly during the period after the Second World War.[7] Moçambique more than makes up its trade deficit through income derived from the

wealth of the South African and Rhodesian interior, as reflected by increased trade and transportation through Portuguese territory and ports, and an increased demand for Portuguese African laborers. Both Lourenço Marques and Beira have been modernized and expanded recently to accommodate the increasing flow of goods, amounting to over 6 million tons (Lourenço Marques) and 3¾ million tons (Beira) in 1960. Especially lucrative has been the use of Moçambique laborers in South African mines. For each laborer crossing the border to work in South Africa, the Portuguese receive about $5.50. Taxes are then withheld from the laborer's wages paid in South Africa. The system was abused in the past and has since been modified, but it continues to provide substantial income for the province.[8]

Moçambique also is benefiting from a rapidly growing tourist industry, likewise a reflection of the increasing prosperity of the interior. The Portuguese, however, have come to recognize that the territory's dependence upon external sources of revenue is excessive, and that a reversal of trends in the interior could be ruinous for the province. The inescapable fact is that Moçambique is not economically viable under present internal conditions, that it is vulnerable to the effects of any reduction in trade passing through its ports, and that it has too long delayed such preparations as might cushion the blow. In fields other than transportation, the lag is more serious even than in agriculture. In the upper Zambezi Valley region (the vicinity of Tete) there may be mineral deposits of consequence, but in the 1960's the major accomplishments remained the mining of a few hundred thousand tons of coal and a fruitless search for oil. The Portuguese government's long-term policy of discouraging private enterprise is now having unfortunate consequences.

Angola, physiographically more favored than Moçambique, has been the major object of Lisbon's efforts to increase the pace of de-

[7] H. J. de Blij, "The Functional Structure and Central Business District of Lourenço Marques, Moçambique," p. 57.

[8] Among the first writers to expose the undesirable elements of the labor situation in Moçambique was M. Harris, *Portugal's African Wards* (New York: American Committee on Africa, 1958).

Lourenço Marques, Moçambique. The capital, largest city, and major port of Moçambique, Lourenço Marques is located in the extreme south of the province, opposite the Witwatersrand of South Africa. Shown here is the central business district with its many modern buildings and wide avenues. In the distance the cranes of the well-appointed harbor can be seen.

Modern Buildings in Lourenço Marques. The Portuguese have reclaimed land immediately to the east of the central business district, and presently the city is expanding into this area just as Cape Town is occupying its reclaimed "foreshore." Shown here is part of this reclaimed area, with the Bay of Lourenço Marques (known also as Delagoa Bay) in the background. Modern multistory structures built in the late 1950's and early 1960's rise above older, poor buildings forming part of the original "middle zone" of the city (right). Much space remains for further development.

velopment toward viability and security.
Providing more opportunity than low-lying,
pedologically poor Moçambique, Angola's
growth during the 1950's can only be described as spectacular. Indeed, the amount of
progress made during one decade reveals the
extent to which neglect had caused stagnation in previous years. Duffy has summarized
the philosophy which formed the basis for
these changes:

*Thus an agrarian society was to be
achieved through the settlement of Portuguese peasants in government colonization
projects, in some of which the African was to
participate, and through the establishment of
African agricultural colonies which would
create conditions favorable to the native's
economic and spiritual assimilation. What the
policy really envisaged was the creation of a
semi-literate population of Africans and Portuguese holding rural Portuguese values, in-
dustrious, dedicated to the land, and politically
conservative. Presumably such a society
would absorb or divert the energies of the
emergent African and at the same time not
be a threat to the large European estates, the
main economic props of both colonies.*[9]

Angola, unlike Moçambique, has a favorable balance of trade. The province receives
proportionally less revenue from its ports than
does Moçambique, its agricultural sector is in
better condition, and some minerals rank
among the major exports. At the end of the
railroad from the Copperbelt and Katanga is
the port of Lobito, which in 1959 handled 1½
million tons of goods (about one-quarter of
the volume shipped that year from Lourenço
Marques). Lobito is the only port in Angola
handling significant amounts of foreign trade,
and the entire volume shipped in the same
year at Luanda (600,000 tons) represents domestic trade.

Much of Angola is plateau land of medium elevation, well grassed and reasonably
well watered, and cattle raising there is a far
less difficult enterprise than it is in disease-
ridden Moçambique.[10] In the northwest, the

Lobito, Terminal of the Benguela Railroad. Although
well-appointed, the Benguela railroad and its Lobito
terminal in 1960 were operating near carrying capacity. Mechanical loading equipment (above) is
transferring a recently arrived cargo of ore. Note the
rapid rise of the land toward the interior plateau in
the distance. Harbor sheds, buildings, and the railroad terminal are shown below. (Centro de Informaçao de Angola)

---

[9] *Op. cit.,* p. 169.

[10] For an early description of Angola, see D.
Whittlesey, "Geographic Provinces of Angola," *Geographical Review,* XIV, No. 1 (January, 1924), 113–
26.

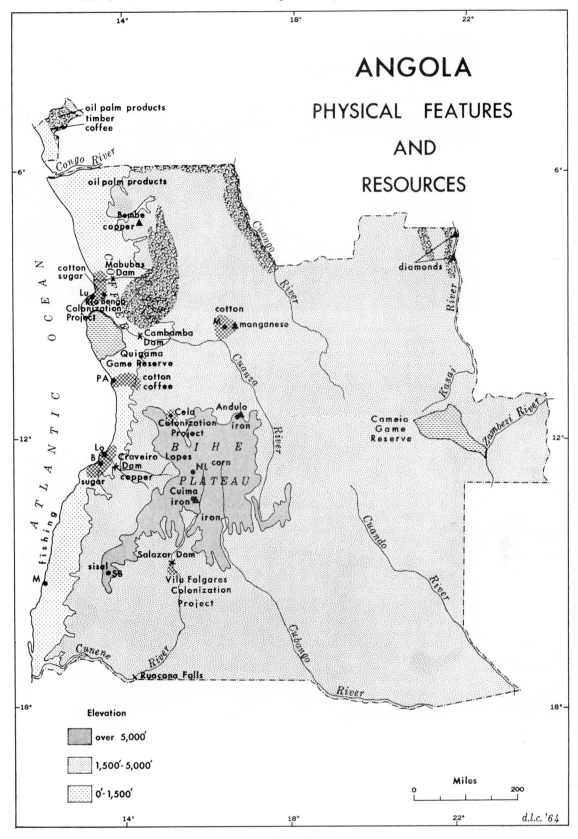

ANGOLA
PHYSICAL FEATURES
AND
RESOURCES

oil palm products
timber
coffee

Congo River

oil palm products

Bembe
copper

cotton
sugar

Mabubas
Dam

Lu
Rio Bengo
Colonization
Project

Cambamba
Dam

Quiçama
Game Reserve

PA

cotton
coffee

Cuango

River

diamonds

Kasai

River

cotton

manganese

Cuanza

River

Cela
Colonization
Project

Andulo
iron

B I H E

Lo
B

Craveiro
Dam

copper

Lopes

NL corn

PLATEAU

Cuima
iron

iron

Cameia
Game
Reserve

Zambezi River

Cuando

River

sugar

A T L A N T I C

O C E A N

fishing

M

Salazar Dam

sisal
SB

Vila Folgares
Colonization
Project

Cunene

River

Ruacana Falls

Cubango

River

Elevation

over 5,000'

1,500'- 5,000'

0'- 1,500'

Miles

0   200

d.l.c. '64

Map 42

Luanda, Capital of Angola. Luanda is the largest city in Portuguese Africa. Its port is situated on an artificially improved spit (above). A small fishing fleet is based in Luanda (below). Modern buildings of the business district can be seen in the background. (Centro de Informaçao de Angola).

hinterland of Luanda provides a combination of soils, relief, and climate that permits the cultivation of coffee. In some years, coffee from northern Angola has accounted for nearly half of the total annual export revenue. The country also lends itself to the cultivation of sisal, and exports corn, cotton, and sugar. It is capable of a far greater variety of crops, and the Portuguese peasant settlers on the colonization projects are growing fruits and vegetables, rice, tobacco, and wheat, among a host of other crops.

Thus, the scope for the settlement of whites is considerable, and several such projects are under way. The immigrants are given a long-term loan, a house, livestock, the necessary seed, and an amount of land varying around 100 acres. Among the examples to be copied is the project at Cela, where dairying is carried on. Indeed, Angola's livestock industries have made major strides during the decade of the 1950's.

Economically, therefore, Angola would appear to be anything but vulnerable. Compared to Moçambique, and many other African territories as well, the economy is well diversified, the second ranking export being a mineral (diamonds), the variety of crops being large, the livestock and forestry industries growing, and the fishing industry regaining importance. The possibilities for increased mineral exploitation are real, and iron ore, first exported in 1957, now ranks among the first six exports by value. Manganese and copper exist in payable quantities, and although the exploration for oil has led to disappointingly small yields, it has not been fruitless.

These conditions are all reflected by the rapid growth of the urban centers and the influx of European population. Luanda doubled its population in one decade (1950–60), and, as in Lourenço Marques, the whole townscape was changed by a building boom producing modern avenues, skyscrapers, theaters, schools, and hospitals. Development plans brought hydroelectric plants to the major rivers, which are now supplying Luanda and Lobito, among other places, with most of their power. Industries were established, an indication of the confidence and growing self-sufficiency of the province. The

white population grew even more rapidly than that of Moçambique, from 44,000 in 1940 and 78,000 in 1950 to 200,000 in 1960.[11]

Each of the two territories under consideration has proved itself capable of producing an annual profit. In Moçambique, the trade deficit is more than made up by incomes from other sources. In Angola, a favorable balance of trade was recorded for several successive years during the 1950's, a recession during the latter part of the decade causing a slight setback. Certainly, a bleaker economic picture would emerge if some other African territories were scrutinized. What, then, renders these Portuguese provinces vulnerable in the politico-geographic sense?

Portugal Overseas

Most political geography textbooks begin with the premise that any politico-territorial entity, in order to survive as a whole (in the form of a state or otherwise), must possess, in addition to a certain areal extent, a body of people bound by some extralegal ties, and organization in a variety of forms. In other words, there must be some ties among the population, however loose they may be, other than those of law and government. And the people must be involved in the many internal organizations of the country—educational, religious, health, political, and so forth. Naturally, not everyone can participate in every form of organization, but some will be compulsory (for instance, education and health), while participation in others is voluntary. As time goes on, the participation in such country-wide organizations may help to produce those subtle ties needed to create what might be called national cohesion. A national consciousness develops, and the state consolidates. This is happening in Africa today, and it has happened in Europe. Some European countries have assisted African territories in the development of their own various organi-

[11] A. de Figueiredo, *Portugal and its Empire: the Truth* (London: Gollancz, 1961), p. 127. Between 1955 and 1960 alone, the increase was from 90,000 to 200,000.

Loading Ore, Angola. Modern equipment is shown at work in Lobito, loading iron from the Bihé Plateau and copper from the Katanga (above). In Luanda, laborers are filling buckets by spade and by hand (below). The ore loaded here is manganese from near Malange in the Angola interior. (Centro de Informaçao de Angola)

zations, but others have tried to channel the Africans toward the European state, in a process of assimilation. France abandoned that effort some years ago. Portugal is currently making its major attempt to create a permanent Portuguese presence amid the pressures of African nationalism.

Portuguese Africa's vulnerability lies not so much in its economic framework as in the prevailing social order. Today, Portugal rules between 11 and 12 million black Africans, few of whom have had the opportunity to escape the subsistence mode of farming. Except where the land has been alienated for use by European settlers or is occupied by white-owned plantations, these Bantu Africans remain scattered throughout both provinces, often far from any communication lines and hardly touched by the progress Africa has made during the past twenty years. The growth in economic strength refers, of course, to the European interests in Portuguese Africa, and the African has shared only to a very small extent in its rewards. The developing urban centers are European cities, the hydroelectric power plants serve white men's homes and factories, the new communication lines benefit the European investor. One noticeable consequence for the African has been the spiraling cost of living, but in the interior, remote and devoid of contact with the hub of progress, life has gone on almost unchanged, not just during the past two decades, but during the past centuries.

In looking at the accomplishments of Portugal in Africa, it is easy to forget the degree to which these are islands in a sea of stagnation. A glance at the map reveals a number of towns, Portuguese not only in name but also in character, a road network, international railroads, power plants, irrigation projects, and plantations, but fails to convey to what extent the intervening areas have been isolated from all this. Schools, hospitals, and other amenities are available to people in the urban areas (mainly the Europeans, therefore), but most of Portugal's black African subjects have never seen a doctor, much less an infirmary. In terms of education, the situation is little better. In 1955, the African population was 98 per cent illiterate, and today the figure is probably about 90. With

reference to the cooperative philosophy in organized agriculture, "by generous estimate . . . cooperatives (in Moçambique) have had a direct influence on about one-twentieth of one per cent of the native population."[12]

In other words, the indigenous population of Angola and Moçambique, with a few exceptions, has not participated in the beneficial forms of organization the Portuguese state might have brought to its African domain. The contrast with the former Federation of Rhodesia and Nyasaland is striking. Whatever sphere one chooses for the purpose of a comparative study—education, health provision, politics—a far greater number of Africans have been affected by progress in these fields in Rhodesia than in Portuguese Africa.

The situation is explicable in part in terms of conditions in European Portugal. The country is among the poorest on the continent, with a per capita annual income under $250, or about one-sixth of that of Sweden. More than a third of all European Portuguese remain illiterate, and many more are semiliterate. Infant mortality rates are among the highest, not only in Europe, but in the world. Industrialization is in its cradle, by modern standards, and Salazar's government has been conservative at home as well as in the overseas provinces in the fields of industrial expansion and modernization. About 20,000 new jobs are created each year, but the labor force expands by at least 50,000 annually.[13] The majority of Portugal's inhabitants make a living in agricultural pursuits, and such products as cereals, wine, and potatoes produce most of the export revenue. Fishing also contributes to the meager national income, which would be severely reduced if two of Portugal's major trading partners, Angola and Moçambique, were lost.

Such a reduction would be inevitable, and not only because Portugal would have to seek new markets for over one-quarter of her exports and new sources for almost 15 per

---

[12] Duffy, *op. cit.*, p. 170.

[13] J. Gottmann, *A Geography of Europe* (New York: Holt, Rinehart & Winston, 1962), p. 551.

cent of her imports. The Lisbon government retains strong control over the provincial economies, and keeps prices paid for raw materials well below world levels. In addition, imports into Angola and Moçambique are subject to protective duties, benefiting the European Portuguese manufacturer. Thus, Portugal, claiming political unity by referring to Angola and Moçambique as provinces, erects economic barriers to the progress of provincial industries, thereby favoring the metropolitan entity. This, of course, has given rise to discontent among the provincial manufacturers, but the situation is favorable to European Portugal, and European Portugal makes the decisions. Clearly, then, the loss of Angola and Moçambique would be a disastrous blow to the Portuguese economy, for the import and export figures do not adequately reflect the degree to which the provincial manufacturers of raw materials are underpaid and the Portuguese producer is protected against competition. Portugal could buy far less on the world market with the money she spends in Angola and Moçambique. This is what European Portuguese mean when they refer to the provinces as profitable, thanks to Salazar's economic policies.

There is more to the matter than Portugal's economic condition alone, however. Political and social conditions in European Portugal have also played their part in bringing about the present state of affairs in Angola and Moçambique. Reference has been made to the fact that illiteracy rates are high in Portugal, and that a "surplus population" continues to expand each year. There is little chance for progress, and masses of people in the rural areas are the poorest of peasants barely eking out a living. It is not surprising that large numbers could be found to emigrate to the provinces, there to be given land and loans; for decades, Portuguese have been leaving Portugal for Brazil and other Latin American countries with far less inducement than that. Thus, the government saw three major assets in the rapid emigration projects of the 1950's: population pressures in European Portugal would be reduced, the provincial economy would be bolstered, and the strategic situation there would be improved.

But most of the Portuguese peasants who come to the provinces have lived in Portugal in ways not very different from the African peasant. If the rural African in Moçambique and Angola has not received many benefits from living under the Portuguese state, neither have many Portuguese in Europe, and many are not much more aware of the modern world than are their African counterparts. While the state religion has permeated Portugal to a greater degree than the African provinces, many white Portuguese never see a school—most never see a high school—or a hospital, just like Portugal's African subjects. Furthermore, Salazar's dictatorship has deprived virtually all Portuguese of their opportunity to voice responsible political opposition to the course of events affecting the republic, and those who have tried to change the system are in exile, in jail, or underground.

"In a country where four of the greatest landlords between them own 235,000 acres of land, the same acreage as is owned by 50,400 small farmers, the pattern of socio-economic development is patently circumstantial and unbalanced."[14] Yet backward, poverty-stricken Portugal is attempting to assimilate a population larger than its own on a continent thousands of miles removed. Portuguese have been educated less, can take part in politics less effectively, earn less, have less scope, and eat less well than Briton, Belgians, Italians, and Frenchmen. These latter countries have been able to make contributions to Africa and can survive without former colonial realms. Portugal has not even achieved in Europe what she would like to impose on her African domain.

The Vulnerable Fringe

Portuguese Africa's vulnerability, then, is Portugal's vulnerability. The weaknesses of Portugal are repeated in Africa, but whereas stability has been maintained in European Portugal through authoritarian control and immense expenditures on the military, Portu-

---

[14] De Figueiredo, op. cit., p. 53.

gal in Africa faces the onslaught of African nationalism from outside the provinces as well as within, and there is some discontent among the white inhabitants as well. The failure of effective control in northern Angola had immediate consequences upon the coffee harvests. The final incorporation of Katanga into the Congo drastically reduced the volume of trade carried by the Benguela Railroad. The cost of maintaining active armies in Angola and Portuguese Guinea—and a waiting one in Moçambique—has required even greater expenditures on the armed forces than before 1960, to the further detriment of fields such as education and health.

In order to comprehend how such remarkable progress as is reflected by modern Lourenço Marques could have left nearby areas virtually unaffected and more remote areas completely untouched, it is necessary to view the internal political geography of the two provinces and the manner in which the administrative framework was set up to accomplish a number of things. In the first place, the Portuguese required a certain number of laborers to work in the towns and on various public works. An excessive influx of Africans into the urban areas was to be avoided, however. Secondly, the African labor force remaining in the rural areas, engaging in subsistence agriculture, was to be encouraged to work in adjacent countries if international labor conventions so stipulated and such labor was required by South African, Rhodesian, and other concerns. Thirdly, the population still in the rural areas must make a contribution to the Portuguese economy.

The map of Moçambique shows European settlement to have taken place in three main areas. Along the coast, cities such as Lourenço Marques (130,000) and Beira (50,000) and towns including Quelimane and Moçambique have arisen. Settlements have also sprung up along the railroads into the plateau interior and connecting parts of Moçambique to the coast. The most important local railroad is that linking the new port of Nacala (just north of the town of Moçambique) with Vila Cabral, for it serves all of northern Moçambique from Lake Nyasa to the Indian Ocean. Finally, important settlements have developed along the major rivers, including

agricultural colonies along the Limpopo and Zambezi and towns such as Tete and Sena. There are roads leading from Lourenço Marques to South Africa and from Beira to Rhodesia, but the connection between Lourenço Marques and Beira along the coast remains difficult. Including the poorest tracks, only in the triangle between Quelimane, the town of Moçambique, and Vila Cabral has a road network developed. Much of the remainder of the province is without communication lines that can be used all year around. The rest of Moçambique is hot, densely bushed, inadequately watered savanna land, and there live the majority of the province's 6 million people.

Angola, too, has a number of important coastal cities and towns, including Luanda (200,000), Lobito at the head of the Benguela Railroad, and Moçamedes. Both Luanda and Moçamedes are connected by rail to local hinterlands, of which that served by Luanda is by far the most important. But east beyond Malange and Serpa Pinto, and away from the central railroad, interior Angola is as isolated as interior Moçambique. In fact, a line drawn longitudinally through General Machado separates "developed" Angola, where the vast majority of the towns, plantations, farms, and roads lie, from "empty" Angola, which is among the most remote areas of all Subsaharan Africa.

The Portuguese system of administration, aimed to reach the three major goals set out previously, can be best understood when studied in the province where it was best developed, Moçambique. Salazar determined that the reservoir of African population should be put to good use by the state, that these people should be drawn into the economic framework of the republic and the province, and that the remote parts of Overseas Portugal should be made to contribute financially to the well-being of the empire.

It is in the political geography of Moçambique that the contrasts between those regions to the north of the Zambezi and those to the south come strongly to the fore. Southern Moçambique adjoins the developing plateau of South Africa and Rhodesia, and there are no insurmountable problems to the establishment of effective communication lines

179

with these areas. Northern Moçambique, on the other hand, adjoins densely populated, agricultural Nyasaland and the subsistence agricultural regions of Northern Rhodesia. Whereas labor from Southern Moçambique could be used in South Africa's and Rhodesia's mines and cities, the Copperbelt drew labor from Northern Rhodesia and Nyasaland, and labor from northern Moçambique was not required. Contact between Northern Rhodesia and northern Moçambique has always been very limited, as reflected by the fact that only one second-class road leads from the Moçambique proruption into the former protectorate.

Since Moçambique's important ports, dam sites, railroads and roads, and major settlements all lie south of the Zambezi River, it is natural that the Portuguese government established an organization there that was designed to make the best use of one major resource, the labor force. The system whereby Moçambique has been administered is that of the circumscription, an idea that originated with Antonio Enes in the 1890's and was modified by Eduardo da Costa in the early 1900's. At that time the foundations of the present-day administration of Portuguese Africa were laid (the system is in effect also in Angola), although the economic possibilities have been most fully exploited by Salazar's *Estado Novo*.

The circumscription is perhaps best defined as a geographical area inhabited by a dominantly rural African population, controlled by a single administrator assisted by one or more "chiefs-of-post." In 1958, the median population under the control of a single administrator in Moçambique was 63,000, and 15 of the more than 80 such districts had populations numbering over 100,-000.[15] The circumscriptions were arbitrarily defined, incorporating a certain number of villages and surrounding lands. Boundaries were almost never demarcated, but the African headmen and chiefs were informed under whose jurisdiction they fell. Each circumscription has a central station, which is the headquarters of the administrator, and to which African headmen are occasionally summoned for orders.

Because of the degree of urbanization of southern Moçambique and the labor traveling to South Africa's mines, the African population of this part of Portuguese Africa has been more mobile than in any other part of the provinces. Naturally, the urban areas form an attraction to those trying to make a living off the difficult African soil. In order to channel the movements of the labor force into organized patterns, and to restrict the influx to the cities, the administrators of the circumscriptions were given extraordinary powers. No African may leave or enter a circumscription without the chief-of-post's permission. The order is easily enforced through the placing of responsibility upon the shoulders of African headmen.

For the majority of Africans in Portuguese Africa, therefore, the circumscription is the enforced place of residence for life. Especially is this true for the women. According to labor laws long in operation, the men must be in gainful employ or, between the ages of 18 and 55, must serve the state six months every year (if they are not in military service). Thus, the men are liable for conscription to work, for very low wages and under severe conditions, and do leave the circumscription repeatedly for labor on roads, railroads, dams, harbors, or other projects. Such labor is also available for farm work. Since southern Moçambique has more need for workers than the north, more men are away from the land there than elsewhere. But as soon as the period of labor is over, the workers are returned to their circumscription, where they resume their village life under the administrator's scrutiny.

The activities of the African inhabitants within the circumscription are closely controlled by the administrator's staff. He has jurisdiction over the amount of land to be placed under crops, the types of crops to be grown, and all transactions involving cattle must carry his approval. Hence, the individual has virtually no chance to progress. Small wonder that many adult males volunteer for work in the South African mines. Estimates of the total Portuguese African male population temporarily or permanently, legally or illegally absent from the provinces have run as high as 2 million, out of a total of less than 12.

---

[15] Harris, *op. cit.*, p. 9.

What of those circumscriptions which lie far from the hubs of the provinces, where labor for the state is required in smaller quantities? There, the enforced contribution until very recently was the growing of a prescribed acreage of crops (cotton in northern Moçambique) and the sale of the annual harvest at specified prices (well below world averages) to the government. In a sense, the people under the forced-crop system were worse off even than those working for the state on public projects, for the system reduced the acreage upon which subsistence crops could be grown, and at times had disastrous effects on the food situation. The system was in the process of being abolished during the early 1960's, but not before decades of ill effects had accumulated on the population.

A number of consequences are of significance to the political geography of the provinces. First, the circumscription arrangement has divided even further an already tribally heterogeneous population. This internal fragmentation has isolated the people, not only from the islands of progress, but also from each other. There is no better example of the "divide and rule" philosophy. Second, the hopelessness of life in the circumscription and the recurring prospect of low-wage work for the state have driven many men from the territories. This has resulted in disruption of family life and has shifted a burden onto the women who remain behind that is even more heavy than the traditional one. Third, the system has practically prevented, especially in interior Moçambique, the mental association of the people with their whole homeland, the whole province. Not only has it prevented circulation, it has also eliminated communication, to an extent not repeated anywhere else in Subsaharan Africa. It is probably true, as the Portuguese have claimed, that African nationalism had not reared its head in parts of the provinces even by 1963. This attests to the effectiveness of the administrative system. Fourth, the black populations of Moçambique and Angola are probably farther removed from nationhood than any others in Subsaharan Africa. Administrative fragmentation has been superimposed upon tribal divisions, and the African's various cultures have been negated and rendered dormant. The uneducated masses are swept along in a maelstrom created and perpetuated by a few political leaders, but unlike Rhodesia, most have not even seen democracy in action among the whites. The Portuguese rule by force today, and whoever rules tomorrow will have little alternative but to use the same means. This is the price of the neglect of centuries.

Thus, Moçambique and Angola are vulnerable because in a rapidly changing Africa they have little that will not be destroyed by the inevitable changes. In a country where the vast majority of the population has never participated in any sort of political decision-making, change will come by violent revolution. When people have little or nothing to lose, they will be prepared to disturb the order of things. The consequences for the fragile economies are obvious. Of the two provinces, Angola may survive as a political entity; the complete disruption of Moçambique, as the Central African Federation was disrupted, is a real possibility.

Part 3

EQUATORIAL AFRICA

9

LOWLAND AFRICA: PROBLEMS OF DEVELOPMENT IN THE CONGO REPUBLIC

EQUATORIAL AFRICA between latitudes 5° north and 10° south consists of two contrasting physiographic regions. In the west lies what may be called lowland Africa, the vast basin of the Congo River and its tributaries. The densely forested, hot and humid heart of the Congo probably comes closest to the "jungle" image that has so long been the popular view of tropical Africa. In the east lies a very different region, perhaps best referred to as highland equatorial Africa, dominated by the plateau backbone of the continent. The physical barrier between these two regions lies approximately along the series of lakes in the Western Rift Valley: Albert, Edward, Kivu, and Tanganyika.

The major part of lowland equatorial Africa is occupied by the Congo Republic, although other countries share parts of the Congo Basin.[1] Highland Africa in the east is divided among Kenya, Uganda, Tanganyika, Rwanda, and Burundi. The Congo Republic, covering well over 900,000 square miles, is the second largest state in Subsaharan Africa as defined in this book, with only the Sudan Republic being larger. It is larger than all five of the highland states

combined. Unification was imposed upon this huge area by Belgian colonialism, but it has never been marked by ethnic, linguistic, or cultural unity.

The Congo is a land of great distances, difficult communications, and severe environmental obstacles to progress. Only in the south, east, and northeast does the land rise out of the central lowland, where elevations are less than 1,500 feet. The entire northwestern quarter of the country (Equator Province) lies in the heart of the basin, the Ubangi River, one of the major Congo tributaries, forming the boundary there. This area once was one of the great interior lakes of Africa and was filled by sedimentary rocks; Lake Leopold and the many swamplands of the northwest form remnants of this feature. The familiar crystalline rocks of the African plateau make their appearance along the rim of the basin, which is almost completely surrounded by highlands: the Crystal Mountains cutting it off from the Atlantic Ocean in the west, the South Equatorial Divide in Angola, the Eastern Plateau around the rifts in the east, and the North Equatorial Divide in the north.

Much of the Congo's productive capacity is concentrated in these crystalline rocks and therefore lies in the distant interior. The shape of the country is such that it has only a narrow proruption leading from the compact interior along the lower Congo River to the Atlantic coast; Angola and Congo (Brazzaville) share most of the western uplands.

---

[1] Among the countries sharing the Congo Basin physiographic unit is the "other" Congo, west of the Congo Republic. To distinguish the two Congos, they are commonly referred to as the Congo (Leopoldville) and the Congo (Brazzaville), after their capital cities. In this chapter, only the Congo (Brazzaville) will be so identified, since the former Belgian Congo is the subject of discussion.

The Congo River at Stanleyville, Oriental Province. The river is a major transport route in the Congo, and steam vessels, barges, and dugout canoes ply its length. (United Nations)

Thus, if the Congo is to export its own produce, all of it must pass through that narrow zone leading from the capital, Leopoldville, to the port of Matadi. This means that all of it must pass through lowland interior, for it must go through Leopoldville, center of communications there in the west, which lies at the edge of the basin proper.

Although the hot and forested Congo Basin is obviously a liability to the country from several points of view, its flatness and intense drainage pattern do combine to produce an asset few parts of Africa possess: rivers that are navigable over lengthy stretches. The Congo, for instance, is navigable from Leopoldville to Stanleyville and for several stretches upstream. The Ubangi can be used by ships as far as Bangui, and the Kasai to a point beyond Port Francqui. The streams converge upon Leopoldville, but there everything must be transferred to trains for the

journey to the ocean port of Matadi. Between Leopoldville and its mouth, the Congo plunges over a series of rapids as it traverses the Crystal Mountains.

Whatever the Congo's interior produces, therefore, must be priced sufficiently highly to permit several transshipments. The nonnavigable sections of the Congo have been circumvented by railroads, but each break of bulk increases the cost of the product. Henry Morton Stanley, the first white man to know the Congo well, said that without railroads the country is not worth a penny, but even with railroads linking the navigable stretches of the major rivers, the value of the goods produced is considerably lowered during their laborious journey to the sea.

Transportation is but one of the economic problems facing the Congo. The country's vastness and the huge costs of building communications between the various areas of

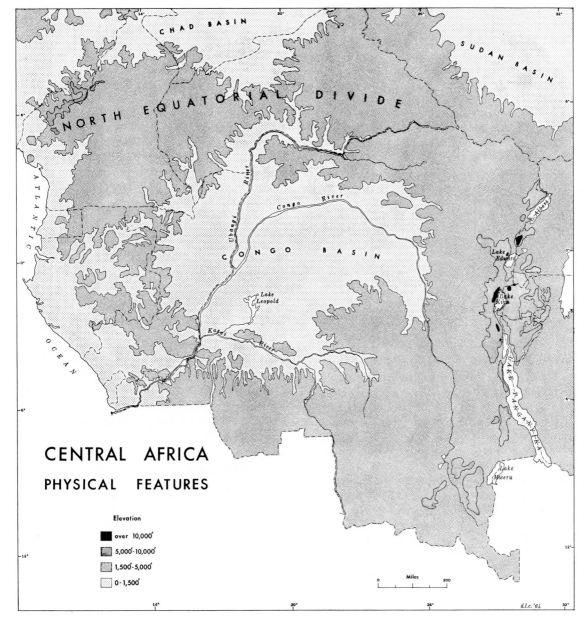

Map 43

population concentration scattered around the "empty heart" have perpetuated a high degree of internal fragmentation and have delayed the evolution of a Congolese people that might be referred to as a nation. When communication lines were built, the motive was usually economic, and the object was to facilitate the exporting of profitable products. Many parts of the country remained isolated from modern transportation, in spite of the fact that the Belgian administration built over 90,000 miles of roads. Road transport in the Congo is severely limited by the climate, and during the rainy season roads may be

187

impassable for weeks. A very small mileage, mostly near the urban centers, is asphalted and usable throughout the year.

Yet the Congo has been called the most promising country in Africa[2]—all of it—and certainly the country would have developed more had it not been bedevilled, almost throughout its recent history, by a series of setbacks arising from the nature of its government. Three distinct phases can be recognized during the period from the early 1880's to the present, and each produced obstacles to progress above and beyond those of physiography and environment. During each phase, the country had a different name. From 1885, it was the Congo Free State; from 1908, the Belgian Congo; from 1960, the Congo Republic.[3]

Congo Free State

The explorer whose name became closely connected with the Congo was Henry M. Stanley, a British-born, American journalist. Having succeeded in his earlier search for Livingstone (whom he had found at Ujiji on November 10, 1871), Stanley for the first time penetrated the Congo Basin. After his initial contact with the unknown interior, he went to Europe, trying first to interest the British in establishing their influence in this part of Africa. The "scramble for Africa" began to gain momentum, and Stanley's work became known to King Leopold II of Belgium. Leopold, who had visions of an empire for Belgium, saw his country without colonies at a time when Britain, France, Portugal, and the Netherlands already possessed vast overseas realms. In 1876, the king convened the Brussels Geographic Conference, with the purpose of supporting exploration and research in equatorial Africa. In 1878, Leopold and Stan-

---

[2] Most recently by G. H. T. Kimble, author of *Tropical Africa*, in *U. S. News and World Report*, February 11, 1963, p. 76.

[3] Previous to this period, the Portuguese had made contact with the rulers of the African empire of Kongo, situated around the mouth of the Congo River. See Chapter 3.

ley met and established an association which aided Stanley on a number of subsequent journeys through the Congo. In effect, the explorer was now working for the Belgian king, founding settlements (including the capital, Leopoldville) and signing treaties on behalf of Leopold with Congolese chiefs.

Thus Belgium entered the colonial scene in Africa and became involved in the disputes which marked that period of expansion. In 1884, Bismarck called the Berlin Conference where an attempt was to be made to settle these colonial conflicts by agreement on arbitrarily defined boundaries. Belgium, relative latecomer in Africa, found herself backed by Germany in her claims to rights in the Congo region, because Germany wished to impede the expansionist efforts of her chief rivals, Britain and France. Hence, the International Congo Association, an outgrowth of the original committee supporting Stanley's explorations, achieved recognition in Berlin, and a Congo Treaty was signed. The sovereign state thus created was named the Congo Free State, and later in 1885 the Belgian Parliament authorized King Leopold II to become king of this country also. In this manner, the Congo Free State initially became the personal possession of King Leopold rather than a Belgian colony.

INITIAL SETBACKS

The Congo Treaty gave Leopold the tasks of suppressing the slave trade in this area, creating effective control over the country, and improving living conditions for the Africans who had become his wards. The Belgian Parliament was willing to grant the king total control over the Free State because it feared the cost of administration and the fulfillment of the obligations embodied in the treaty. Leopold was very wealthy, but he visualized the Congo experiment as a moneymaking venture, and he expected quick returns for his initial investments. Immediately after assuming control, he took possession of all unoccupied land and sent a large number of agents into the Congo whose duty it was to gather specified quantities of ivory and rubber. While the agents forced the local population into collecting these products, the empty lands were parcelled out to concession-aires who paid levies on their profits.

During this early phase, therefore, the products of the Congo came from the low-lying basin rather than the rim of the north-ern, eastern, and southern periphery. Barges were floated on the rivers, and produce-col-lecting stations were established at various points along their courses. Wild rubber was by far the most important product (today it ranks far down on the list), and since labor costs were low and the demand great, profits were considerable.

The Congo itself, however, benefited but little from this arrangement. In fact, the change in the producing areas was largely detrimental: the king's agents used barbaric methods to enforce the gathering of quotas, and African opposition was met with devas-tating force. Entire villages were burned and their inhabitants decimated. It has been esti-mated that the African population during Leopold's reign was reduced by between 3 million to 8 million. As Legum has put it, the African's fear of the slaver had been re-placed by a fear of the white man. Mean-while, Leopold long failed to adhere to one of the major conditions of his assumption of control over the Congo Free State: slavery remained rampant in the east until near the turn of the century, and the long-awaited campaign against it came only after the most powerful of the slavers began to pose an economic threat to the king.

During the years the Congo Free State existed, other colonial powers elsewhere in Africa were engaged in wars of pacification. In few places, perhaps none, were the local losses so serious and the gains so negligible. Social disorder was complete. The effect of Leopold's acquisition of unoccupied land was that in a region where shifting, "patch" agri-culture, hunting, and gathering are necessary adjustments to environmental conditions, the tribal peoples were confined to lands which, at the moment he acquired them, were only temporarily occupied, and which were too small and unfit for permanent habitation. Thus, the local economies, such as they were, were totally disrupted. Forced labor destroyed tribal organization and broke up families. Local famines resulted.

A country's development involves more than the extraction and sale of minerals and the gathering and exporting of forest prod-ucts. It involves, also, the betterment of the people through the improvement of farming methods; the provision of social amenities, education, and health facilities; research on the eradication of local diseases; the introduc-tion of better types of crops; and so forth. During its Free State period, the Congo pro-duced a revenue that dwarfed the profits made in many other African territories. But the improvement of local conditions—one of the prime requirements stated in Berlin in 1885—was minimal, except where the export-oriented communication system was con-cerned. For instance, from 1898 to 1903, the value of exports was $46 million, while im-ports totalled a mere $20 million.[4]

The major contributions of Leopold and Stanley were the expansion of the area of the Congo, especially in the southeast, and the organization of a transport system that could efficiently handle the products of the interior. Leopold realized that the plateau surrounding the Congo Basin proper might contain valuable resources, and he managed to appropriate the area today known as Ka-tanga at a time when the African chiefs there were planning to request protection from the British. When, in 1892, he acquired the Ka-tanga, there was little to indicate the eco-nomic wealth it contained. The boundaries there and elsewhere were defined in a series of treaties with the other colonial powers active in equatorial Africa, and by the end of Leopold's rule, the Congo had practically taken its modern shape, only slight adjust-ments of boundaries remaining to be made.[5]

Considerable headway was also made in linking the rubber- and ivory-producing in-terior to Matadi. A railroad connecting Ma-

---

[4] H. A. Gibbons, *The New Map of Africa* (New York, The Century Company, 1916), p. 154.

[5] One exchange of land that was yet to take place involved a narrow strip of land near Matadi, required by the Belgians for the rebuilding of the Matadi-Leopoldville railroad (1927). The Portuguese yielded the area of over one square mile in exchange for 480 square miles in the southwest (the "Dilolo Boot").

tadi and Leopoldville was begun in 1890 and completed in 1898. Construction of the line between Stanleyville and Ponthierville did not commence until 1903, however, and was completed as late as 1906. Thus, the Stanley Falls had been bypassed, but another rail link was needed to connect Kindu and Kongolo. It was built immediately afterward, so that the Katanga was linked to Matadi. But no less than five transshipments were necessary. When the railroad through Northern Rhodesia reached the Katanga, therefore, the effect was to develop a large traffic southward rather than along the Congo River route.

The Katanga, however, did not assume real significance in the economic picture until after the end of the Congo Free State. By 1904, the international outcry regarding the "Congo atrocities" had forced Leopold to appoint an official commission of inquiry. Although the commission shed a favorable light upon the signs of "advancing civilization" when dealing with the developing communications, it reported fully upon the prevalent abuses, the Conscript Law in the name of which forced labor was practiced, the hate and fear of Europeans, and the disorganization of the interior. Leopold was forced to abandon his Free State, and in 1908 the Belgian Parliament assumed responsibility for the territory.

Belgian Congo

From 1908 until 1960, Belgium administered the Congo as a colony, and it was early in this period that the first real steps were taken in development toward the modern state. This does not mean that the Belgian government was immediately able to throw off the legacy of liabilities left by Leopold, but for the first time the whole of the Congo —profitable as well as subsistence areas—became effectively administered, and some internal consolidation began to take place.

Among the legacies of Leopold was a number of concession companies, to which the king had granted long-term rights prior to the termination of the Free State. As early as 1891, such concessions had been granted

to the Comité Spécial du Katanga, and in 1906 to the Union Minière du Haut Katanga. The Belgian government continued to recognize these concessions, and as a result these big companies exerted considerable influence over Belgian decisions concerning the colony. Shortly before 1960, the Union Minière stock stood at just under $2 billion, when it was contributing almost half of the Congo's annual tax revenue.

Great changes came to the economy of the Congo between 1910 and 1920. In 1913, the export of rubber, long the major product, fell by 50 per cent. The full impact of the mineral wealth of Katanga began to be felt, and whereas the economic heart of the Congo had long been in the forests, the minerals of Katanga now came to form the country's backbone.

Meanwhile, other mineralized areas were discovered. In the southern Congo, west of Katanga, industrial diamonds occur in quantities unequalled anywhere else, and the Congo became the world's first exporter of this commodity. Gem stones also occur in this region (specifically, the valley of the Kasai River), and in the Kilo-Moto region, northwest of Lake Albert, gold was located. Coal deposits of significance were found to lie near Albertville. The concession companies grew into major financial empires with a great and growing influence in Belgian government and Congo administration, and these empires made tremendous profits out of the new-found wealth of the Congo. Although some of this money was applied to social development in the colony, the bulk of it formed a buttress for the Belgian economy.[6]

The politico-territorial aspect of the Congo is that of a vast, compact state with two proruptions, both of which are of immense importance. The western proruption lies along the lower Congo River, and it not only forms the country's one outlet to the sea, but also its administrative headquarters. Here lie the major military installations, the most important single stretch of railroad, and a great potential site for the development of hydroelectric power. The capital, Leopold-

[6] P. R. Gould, "Congo Crisis," *University College of Syracuse University Paper No. 25*, p. 14.

View over Leopoldville, Congo. The capital of the Congo Republic and major river port on the Congo-Ubangi-Kasai river system is also the largest city in lowland equatorial Africa. Shown here are the port facilities, the central business district, and some of the sprawling suburbs beyond. (Courtesy William J. Knight)

ville (400,000), has developed into one of Africa's largest cities. In the southwest, Katanga's narrow stretch of upland contains the economic mainstay of the Congo, its business and industrial capital, Elisabethville (200,000), and the best-developed areas of the entire country. A large labor force from distant areas (including Rwanda and Burundi) works in the mines of the mineral-rich Katanga, which lies about as far from the Atlantic coast as it does from the Indian Ocean.

As the Belgian Congo developed, the peripheral location of the administrative and economic core areas, and the relative inaccessibility of the latter, became factors of ever increasing significance. The endless and impenetrable heart of the Congo, parts of which are almost devoid of human inhabitants, ceased to make any important contribution to the economy. The inability of its latosols to carry successive crops, the prevalence of diseases, and the absence of pasture form a strong contrast to the higher, cooler, and pedologically more favored margins.

In general terms, development in the formerly important lowland is confined to two ribbons (in addition to the Kasai diamond areas, which may, however, be said to lie on the southern margin of the basin). One of these ribbons lies along the Congo River, where transportation and administration are the main activities, and break-in-bulk places like Kongolo and Kindu as well as administrative centers such as Stanleyville and Coquilhatville have developed. This was the first intra-Congo exit route, largely completed and in operation before the end of the Congo Free State period. The second ribbon has been the result of the construction of a more efficient route. A railroad was built from Bukama to Port Francqui, via Luluabourg. This reduced transshipments from Katanga to two over a distance of 1,725 miles and captured much of the trade that had been going via Indian Ocean ports.

Away from these transport routes, the basin has seen little progress. Once, the gathering of wild rubber and the wholesale slaughter of elephants rendered this hot basin

191

The Port Facilities of Leopoldville. The Congo River port of Leopoldville is shown in the foreground, with a "train" of river barges being piloted away. The sheds and railroad terminal are along the shore, the downtown area in the background. (Belgo-American Development Corporation)

Commercial Center, Leopoldville, Congo. The postwar development of Leopoldville was spectacular, with many multistory buildings arising in the heart of the city. This general view over the central business district shows the vertical development, with some construction still going on, around the Boulevard Albert. (Courtesy William J. Knight)

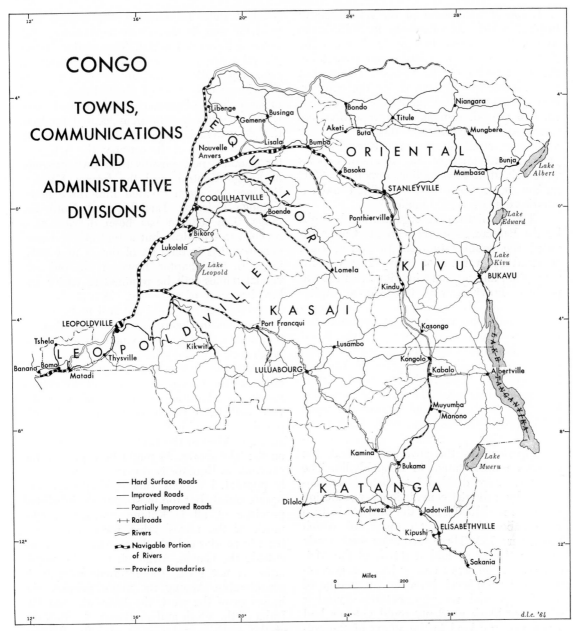

CONGO

TOWNS,
COMMUNICATIONS
AND
ADMINISTRATIVE
DIVISIONS

Hard Surface Roads
Improved Roads
Partially Improved Roads
Railroads
Rivers
Navigable Portion
of Rivers
Province Boundaries

Miles
0   200

d.l.c. '64

Map 44

economically the most important part of the Congo, but, today, only palm kernels, palm oil, and a little rubber produce some revenues, dwarfed by those from copper, diamonds, cobalt, cotton, and coffee. The focus of activity during the colonial period was increasingly on the Katanga's mining areas and along the fertile slopes of the east and north, where a wide variety of crops was grown.

From the days of Leopold until the end of the colonial period, the white population increased, to reach a maximum of over 125,000 Europeans. The heaviest concentration of whites was in the Katanga, which as early as 1930 was the second largest concentration

193

of European settlement in the inner belt of tropical Africa. As elsewhere in Subsaharan Africa, these people brought with them the skills and capital to initiate and perpetuate the exploitation of the Congo's riches, but the benefits which accrued for the country, even during the comparatively benevolent colonial period, remained disproportionately small. As recently as 1959, the last full year of Belgian administration, the trade balance gives an indication of the situation: exports were valued at $489 million, imports at $308 million, but revenue at $270 million and expenditure at over $350 million.[7]

The administrative organization brought by the Belgian government to the Congo divided the country into six provinces, each centered upon a major town. The western proruption and adjacent interior became Leopoldville Province, with the colonial capital as its focus. The southeast, centered upon Elisabethville, became Katanga Province. Between these two units, in the south, was Kasai Province, focusing upon Luluabourg. Coquilhatville was made the capital of Equator Province, and Stanleyville the headquarters of Oriental Province. The smallest province, Kivu, lies in the east and is centered upon Bukavu, formerly Costermansville. Each province was ruled by a governor, whose immediate superior was the governor general, the Crown's representative in Leopoldville. The provinces were divided into districts administered by a district commissioner, numbering 23 in the mid-1950's, and the districts in turn were subdivided into territories, of which there were 132. These territories were made up of native areas, and at this level the African population was more or less self-governing. At the top level, however, the people of the Congo had no representation: neither white nor black residents could vote or had a voice of any kind in the affairs of the colony. Decisions were made in Brussels and conveyed through the Crown to the governor general, who in turn issued orders to the lower levels of the administration.

In 1963, the six provinces of the former colony were fragmented into 21 units, each of which became a province in the newly independent state. In addition, the city of Leopoldville and its immediate surroundings became a Federal District. Two major factors played a role in this experiment: pronounced ethno-regionalist sentiments in some parts of the Congo (like that of the BaKongo people in Leopoldville Province), and dissatisfaction with the *status quo* in areas located far from the old provincial capitals.[8] In the new political organization of the country, the BaKongo, for instance, now possess their own province of Kongo Central, and the former Katanga Province has been divided into three units: Katanga Oriental, Lualaba, and Nord Katanga. The scheme has been decried as a reversal to tribalism, but actual ethnic homogeneity exists in only six of the 21 new provinces. In this chapter, however, the old provincial names will be retained as easier and broader zones of reference, since at the time of writing several areas are still to be put to referendum to determine their final disposition, and a number of boundaries are yet to be defined and delimited.

Although it is a large country, the population of the Congo is only about 15 million today, and densities are not great. Leopoldville and Kivu provinces are most densely peopled, Leopoldville in the lower Congo area and Kivu in the northeast and southeast, on the lake shores. As might be expected, the province of Equator is among the least densely populated regions (about 12 persons per square mile), but the most sparsely inhabited province of all is Katanga, which is why much of the mines' labor force long came from territories outside the province and even outside the Congo. Although the total population is not great, the internal diversity is considerable. Among the major peoples, the BaKongo of the west, the BaLunda and BaLuba of the south and southeast, the BaKuba of the south-central Congo, and the Warega of the east are the most numerous. Tribal identities were retained in the circulation-stifling system of colonial administration. "Under Belgian administration very little was done to draw the various regions and peoples

---

[7] G. H. T. Kimble, *Tropical Africa* (New York: Twentieth Century Fund, 1960), II, 482.

[8] M. Crawford Young, "The Congo's Six Provinces Become 21," *Africa Report*, VIII, No. 9 (October, 1963), 12.

Copper Mine at Kolwezi, Katanga. Open pit mining of copper ores is possible in the Katanga. One of the Union Minière's huge mines is shown here. (United Nations)

together under the flag of a single and unified state."[9]

In order to comprehend the factors underlying the course of development in the Congo during the Belgian colonial period, it is necessary to refer briefly to the forces involved in this process. The Belgian government, having annexed the colony in 1908, naturally was the major force. The Roman Catholic Church made its influence felt in two ways: many of the government members (like 90 per cent of the Belgian people) were Catholic and supported Catholic institutions in the colony, and in the field of education provided by mission schools the Church made a great impact. Finally, the influence of big business always was strong, the Belgian state owning large shares in the major companies operating in the Congo. Out of this triumvirate arose the mutual-interest policy of paternalism, to the detriment of the Congolese Africans' chances for progress and unity.

If the profits of big business did not benefit the Congo to the extent they might

had the Congo possessed self-determination, the Belgian government did show itself interested in accelerating the pace of development, especially after the Second World War. In 1950, a Ten-Year Plan was initiated, aimed at the general improvement of economic and social conditions. Through the stimulation of economic development, it was thought, living standards in the colony would be raised. This stimulation was to be derived from the development of power and communications in the Congo, providing a base for industry and stabilizing the economy. As the decade progressed, it became clear that the costs of the Ten-Year Plan had been greatly underestimated, but Belgium rose to the challenge and made the expenditures required to achieve the goals of the plan. The port of Matadi was improved, railroad links constructed, airfields expanded, and hydroelectric projects built. The largest part of the money was spent on projects of this kind, although funds also were made available for housing, educational, and other facilities.

The problem is that the over-all effects of such a plan are slow in coming, and the

[9] A. P. Merriam, *Congo* (Evanston, Ill.: Northwestern University Press, 1961), p. 28.

195

Miners' Housing, Kolwezi, Katanga Province. The large companies mining the Katanga's ores have created conditions for their labor forces which are among the best in Africa. Good housing and medical facilities have been provided. Largest of the companies is Union Minière, which produces about three-quarters of the total mining exports from the Congo. A workers' village with rows of neat cottages, built by the Union Minière, is illustrated here. (United Nations)

Congo did not survive sufficiently long as a colony for them to be felt. Had political stability marked the decade of the Ten-Year Plan and additional years beyond, the Congo might have reaped greater benefits from it. As it was, Belgium found time running out when the reforms were only half-completed, as a political revolution took place which was another setback to Congo development. This revolution was itself partly the result of the tightness of the control Belgium had exercised through its paternalist colonial policy, the lateness of the major effort to speed up internal development, the nature of the politico-territorial organization imposed upon the Congo, and the distribution of the country's revenues.

A Congolese nation never developed, largely because of the country's geography. The degree of internal fragmentation imposed by the provincial–district–territory–native area system was equalled only in Portuguese colonial areas. This is not to suggest that nation states have arisen out of formerly British and French African territories, but the Belgians failed totally to give the Congolese a sense of belonging to their own country. At best, the provincial capital was regarded as the center of administration, more frequently it was the district headquarters or the chief in the native area. Never having participated, in the Western sense, in the political decision-making affecting the Congo as a political entity, the Congo's peoples were not ready to accept a Western type of state when the political revolution came. They had not only been deprived of the chance to negotiate with the white leadership, but, eventually more importantly, they had done little negotiating with each other. In short, the old ethnic

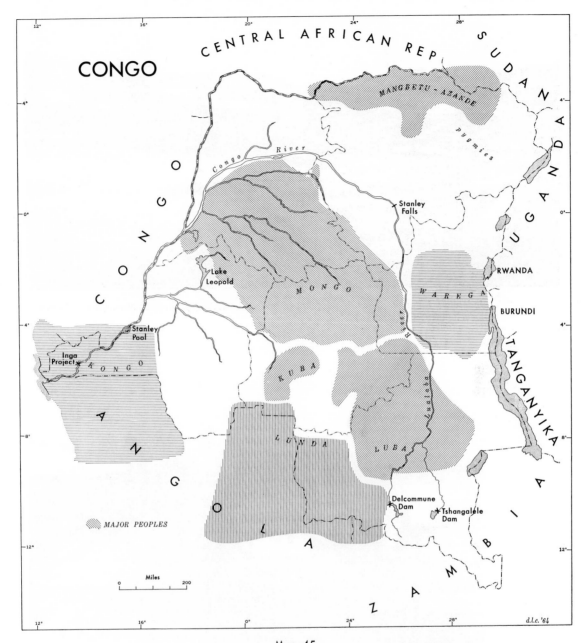

Map 45

realities of the BaKongo Empire or the Lunda Empire—tribal grouping, in fact—were every bit as strong, and probably stronger, than any real Congolese nationalism. The Belgians had thrown a girdle around an area and ruled it as a colony, admirably from several points of view, but only the whites were in a position, generally, to see the whole and plan for its future. The political revolution reflected the internal fragmentation in a variety of ways. Political parties really did not have a united Congo as their major goal, and centered upon peoples and regions. Of the few leaders who were able to see beyond tribal limits, several also saw that Belgian administrative fragmentation of the Congo provided

197

Jadotville, Katanga. Shown is the plant of one of the Katanga's largest mines. (Belgo-American Development Corporation)

The Port of Port Francqui, Congo. The meeting place of the navigable Kasai waterway and the railroad to Katanga, Port Francqui is the Congo's most important internal break-in-bulk station after Leopoldville. Some of the river boats, cranes, sheds, and the Kasai River are shown here. (Belgo-American Development Corporation)

opportunities for the secession of areas in which they dominated. As the colonial period ended, the Congo teetered on the brink of feudalism, the provinces of Oriental, Kasai, and Katanga each attempting to go its own way, independent of any central government in Leopoldville.

The Congo Republic

The third phase of the Congo's modern existence began in the middle of 1960, when the independent state of Congo was created. The pivotal region of the country was where most development had taken place, the Katanga. Although it may be true that the Congo state could survive as an economically viable entity without the Katanga, such a statement is based upon the potential of other parts of the country (which is considerable) but not upon the realities of the situation in the 1960's. The whole history of the Congo during the colonial period was one of increasing economic dependence upon the wealth of Katanga; transportation routes were built to serve it, investments were made to accelerate development there, internal communications, hydroelectric projects, housing for the labor force, schools, and many other public works and facilities were constructed. Taxes collected from the products of other provinces were used to improve conditions in Katanga. During the colonial years, the Congo's investment in the Katanga was considerable, and the returns less than desired. Naturally, the sovereign Congo of 1960 wished to begin collecting a larger share of the wealth of that part of the country.

Although the province is located in the central part of Africa, no less than six transport routes converge upon the Katanga (and its neighbor, the Copperbelt). It is important to note how these routes serve or have served the region, for the development of the Katanga itself was closely bound up with the provision of transport facilities to the coasts. Mention has been made of the Congo Route via Stanleyville and Kongolo, requiring five transshipments. This route was in operation by 1911, and soon afterward the Germans

completed a railroad in Tanganyika connecting Dar es Salaam to the lake port of Kigoma, while the Belgians connected Kabalo to the western shore of the lake. This second route, involving river, lake, and railroad transport, required four transshipments and initially captured some of the Katanga's copper traffic, but soon the lower costs of easier exit routes eliminated it.

One easier route was southward, and by 1909 the Rhodesian railroad had reached Sakania on the Katanga-Copperbelt boundary. The Belgians immediately began the construction of a link to Bukama, but after reaching Elisabethville the construction was interrupted by the First World War and was not completed until 1918. During the prewar period, while the Rhodesian connection was still under construction, Dar es Salaam handled some Katanga trade, but after 1918 much of the traffic went southward via Victoria Falls to Beira, itself still a lengthy and expensive journey.

Between 1923 and 1928, the route was built which has since carried a large share of Katanga's produce, linking Bukama to Port Francqui. Requiring only two transshipments, this route carried about 48 per cent of the Union Minière's copper shipments (35–40 per cent of the Katanga's) before the upheaval of independence. The first section, the rail link between Elisabethville and Port Francqui, is 984 miles in length, freight taking about 9 days to cover the distance. The second section is the 513-mile-long stretch of water transport on the Kasai and Congo rivers to Leopoldville, involving 12 days, including rail-to-ship and ship-to-rail transfers in Port Francqui and Leopoldville, respectively. The third and last stretch is the 4-day rail journey (for freight) from the capital to Matadi, a distance of about 227 miles.

Very soon after the completion of the Port Francqui route (now known as the "National Route"), the shortest link to the coast was constructed, namely, the Benguela Railroad through Angola, directly westward over a distance of 1,312 miles (as against 1,724 miles to Matadi). Completed in 1931, the Benguela Railroad was built partly with Belgian capital, and of course no transshipments were required. Its terminal is the ocean port

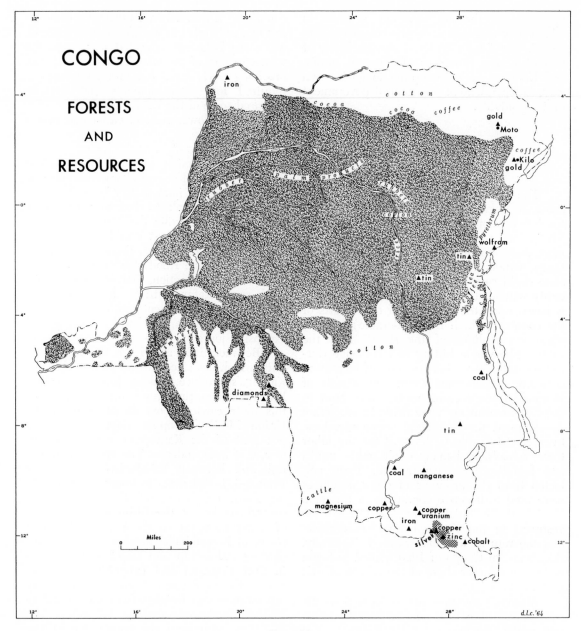

CONGO

FORESTS

AND

RESOURCES

Map 46

of Lobito. Its initial effect was the almost complete diversion of the Katanga's copper traffic from the east coast (Beira) route. Later, however, development within Angola and rising production in the Katanga put strain upon the west coast routes, and Beira, 1,624 miles from Elisabethville by rail, again began to handle Katanga exports.

The last railroad to be constructed to handle Katanga and Copperbelt products was that linking Lourenço Marques to the Rhodesian system, but it has not been of major importance to the former. During the late 1950's, 48 per cent of Union Minière's copper production traveled via Matadi, 30 per cent went through Beira, and 22 per cent via Lo-

Delcommune Dam, Katanga Province. Electricity supply is one of the problems of the Katanga's developing complex. In addition to shipping coal from the vicinity of Albertville and buying Kariba power from Rhodesia, the large companies operating in Katanga have built dams to furnish power locally. One of the Union Minière's dams is shown here. (United Nations)

bito. In addition to the six routes—two to Matadi, and one each to Lobito, Beira, Dar es Salaam, and Lourenço Marques—the Katanga is connected to the South African system, although South Africa's ports lie very far from the region and the location of the Southern Rhodesia–South Africa line through Bechuanaland virtually precludes the use of Durban.

What the Katanga produced, therefore, was sufficiently valuable to overcome the region's inaccessibility. This very factor led to some industrial development near the major cities such as Elisabethville and Jadotville: to reduce the bulk of the export product, smelting furnaces were built to transform the copper ores to crude copper. Although the copper ores of the Katanga are the richest in

Bridge across the Lualaba River, Congo. The Congo's major domestic export route is the "National Route" via Port Francqui. River transport goes on unhindered by this impressive structure, a major link in the Elisabethville-Matadi route. (Belgo-American Development Corporation)

First-Class Road, near Elisabethville, Katanga. Much of the development in the Congo has been in Katanga, where communications are better than in any other Congo province. By constructing narrow asphalted roads such as this, the mileage has been extended. (Belgo-American Development Corporation)

the world, they average less than 6 per cent purity. An early problem, also, was the provision of coal, required in large quantities by the mines. The Wankie fields of Southern Rhodesia supplied this commodity at first, but later Congo coal found near Albertville came into use. The power problem also led to the construction of several hydroelectric projects in Katanga, and to Belgian investment in Rhodesia's Kariba Dam in return for a guaranteed share of the power produced.

From all this it would appear that one part of the Congo, at least, experienced rather few "problems of development." The region at one time ranked as the world's fourth copper producer, and at another provided nearly two-thirds of the Western world's uranium supply. It has produced between one-half and three-quarters of the world's cobalt in certain years. Tin, zinc, and other associated minerals occur in mineable quantities. But it is imperative not to lose sight of the region's relationship to the remainder of the Congo. True, the other provinces do contribute to the economy: coffee is grown successfully in Kivu, cocoa along other parts of the eastern slopes. Tea, sisal, sugar, cotton, and citrus are grown along the peripheral

of one of the early routes to the interior, the Ogowe River.

French exploration continued between 1880 and 1890, when the upper reaches of the Ubangi River were penetrated and treaties signed. The object of France's push into this interior region was the establishment of an axis across Africa as far as the borders of what was then Abyssinia, and French flags were eventually planted that far east. But, eventually, British power forced the French to withdraw from the entire Nile Basin. German influence, meanwhile, was established in Cameroun, and the British had also taken most of present-day Nigeria, while the Congo Free State had been created to the south. French penetration was thus confined to a northerly path, and hence Chad became a part of the corridor of France's realm in equatorial Africa.

After the period of exploration and consolidation came the first attempts at administration. The Berlin Conference had adopted a resolution which affected the Belgian as well as the French sphere of influence in the Congo Basin: a free-trade zone was to be recognized there. Thus, it was felt that direct French government efforts to administer the region might lead to international protests, and, moreover, the system of permitting private companies to exploit the Congo Free State was deemed successful. A similar solution was used in the French areas, and thus the period of exploration was followed by a phase during which concession companies, which possessed a monopoly of trade and a measure of sovereignty, literally ruled the region. The consequences resembled those that led to the outcry over the "Congo atrocities":

In establishing a balance sheet for this period . . . the debit . . . was crushing. Ivory had virtually disappeared from the conceded areas, and the rubber vines had been depleted owing to the companies' failure to replant; trade was stagnant and the population was decimated. Disillusionment regarding the Congo was almost total on the part of the French Government and the French public alike. Not only was the colony considered a dismal economic failure, but, on humanitarian grounds, the exposure of brutalities there had dealt a shocking blow to French prestige in the world.[1]

The situation altered but little during the interwar period, and it was not until 1940 that a radical change began to take place. The French rulers of French Equatorial Africa, except Gabon, decided to re-enter the war in spite of the Franco-German armistice, and soon the colony was the hub of activity. Raw materials were needed, rubber-gathering was revived, cotton cultivation expanded, gold mining again encouraged. Communications were improved, and with the interruption of overseas connections, local raw materials began to be used in local factories. Local businesses thrived as officials and troops arrived in large numbers. Although the newfound prosperity was temporary, conditions in French Equatorial Africa never again returned to their prewar state.

French Colonial Administration: Control and Culture

French colonial policy until after the end of the Second World War was aimed at the imposition of French civilization and culture upon the peoples of *France d'Outre Mer*. In these respects, France's administration of her overseas possessions was basically different from that of Britain and Belgium, but not unlike that of Portugal. Education took place in French, and the elite which arose was politically and culturally French; it is this elite which has produced the leaders of the now-independent states in the French Community and the upper class of the new republics.

Until 1934, each of the units of French Equatorial Africa had its own lieutenant-governor, its own budget, and a good deal of local autonomy. This was in part the result of an almost perpetual shortage of state officials to serve in Equatorial Africa on behalf of France, and the sole unifying factor prior to

---

[1] V. Thompson and R. Adloff, *The Emerging States of French Equatorial Africa* (Stanford, Cal.: Stanford University Press, 1960), p. 16.

205

1934 was the office of the governor general himself. In that year, French Equatorial Africa was made into a single colony, and the component parts were known as *régions*. In 1937, the system was revised somewhat, and they became known as *territoires*. Brazzaville became the capital of the entire colony, and individual governors remained in Libreville (Gabon), Bangui (Ubangi-Shari), and Fort Lamy (Chad).

A major change came in 1946, when a constitution was enacted in Paris whereby all French Overseas Territories came to form an integral part of the French Union, some being allotted a higher and others a lower status in the political hierarchy. For instance, whereas Reunion became an Overseas Department, French Equatorial Africa became an Overseas Territory. All legislation continued to emanate from Paris, where each part of France's overseas realm had representation. This high degree of centralization proved a serious obstacle when pressure arose in favor of independence, but many African politicians did have the opportunity to serve a political apprenticeship.

Cameroun in 1946 became a United Nations Trust Territory and remained, as it had since 1922, outside the politico-territorial organization of Equatorial Africa.[2] French policies of land ownership and concessions during the term of the mandate had aroused criticism, but in general terms Cameroun's economic condition remained better than that of Equatorial Africa proper.

In 1958, De Gaulle in his famed speech at Brazzaville offered the territories of French Equatorial Africa and West Africa the choice of independence without France or self-government as sovereign republics within the French Community. A referendum took place in each of the countries later that year, and they chose independence within the Community. In 1960, Gabon, the Congo (Brazzaville), the Central African Republic (Ubangi-Shari), and Cameroun became sovereign states, as did other French territories elsewhere in Africa. Ties with France, and control by France, continued to exist. Economically poor countries, the young republics' degree of dependence upon French aid and investment is considerable. Whatever the political attitude and connections of the French Community states, however, the imprint of French culture, as reflected by the character of the elite, the common use of the French language, political philosophies, education systems, and such other features as urban landscape, appears permanent.

France and the Economic Geography of Equatorial Africa[3]

Equatorial Africa forms a vast corridor extending from a relatively short coast line onto the North Equatorial divide, as far west as the Sudan and as far north as the margins of the Sahara Desert. In the south, the region is dominated by the Congo Basin, and there almost impenetrable forests separate the populated areas. For instance, it is very difficult to reach Gabon from Congo by overland routes, yet they are neighbors in the south of the region. Northward, Cameroun, with its brief coast line, occupies the bulk of the highlands separating it from Nigeria and reaches to Lake Chad. The country rises toward the interior divide and bounds the Central African Republic (formerly Ubangi-Shari), the country lying across this broad upland. The Shari River, the only important stream entering Lake Chad, rises in the Central African Republic, and in the south lie the Ubangi and its tributaries.

---

[2] Kamerun, prior to the German annexation of French territory, consisted of about 196,000 square miles. The League of Nations established a French Class B Mandate over 166,000 square miles, while giving responsibility for the remaining 30,000 square miles (adjacent to Nigeria) to Britain. The southern part of the British region has since voted to rejoin the independent state of Cameroun.

---

[3] Cameroun is included in this general discussion. In this chapter, only the Congo (Leopoldville) will be specifically identified. "Congo" here refers to the former French territory.

Rapids of the Congo River. Between Brazzaville and its mouth, the Congo River traverses a series of rapids, rendering navigation impossible. A small section of these rapids is shown here (French Embassy Press and Information Division)

In the whole region, only the Central African Republic and Congo form anything resembling an interconnected whole; the other parts of equatorial Africa are quite isolated due to the difficulties in establishing transportation links there. The unity of the two is due in large measure to the natural communication links of the major river system of the northern Congo Basin: the Ubangi River is navigable as far as the capital of the former, Bangui. Together with the railroad between Brazzaville and Pointe Noire, this rail-river link was referred to as the Federal Artery. The entire problem of communications in equatorial Africa is related, of course, to the wealth of the area; there is no Katanga or Witwatersrand in the interior, and so no web of railroads leading to a rich hinterland has developed. The region possesses all the liabilities and few of the assets of its large southern neighbor, and has always lagged behind it in development.

Initially, it was thought that boundless wealth lay in this part of Africa, but after the early rush of exploitation of wild rubber and ivory by the concession companies, the reality of the situation began to penetrate. This part of Africa was, and still is, hot, humid, and disease-ridden. The tsetse fly eliminates the use of oxen or horses for transportation of goods overland, road-building materials are scarce, the forest dense, the population sparse,

207

The Brazzaville–Pointe Noire Railroad, Congo. Running through dense rainforests and over deep valleys, the railroad is the first link in the Federal Artery. Seen here is a train going through a rainstorm as it crosses one of several bridges along the route. (French Embassy Press and Information Division)

and the labor supply limited at best. Thus, human portage, with its tremendous cost, along tedious and narrow pathways was the only way of carrying supplies to the interior settlements and exports to the coast. This was true until as late as the mid-1930's, when finally the railway between Brazzaville and Pointe Noire, begun in 1922, was completed.

Just as Stanley had emphasized the need for railroads in the Congo (Leopoldville), so De Brazza had envisaged a railroad system for French Equatorial Africa, of which the priority project should be the building of the Pointe Noire–Brazzaville line. But De Brazza wanted the line to lie entirely in French territory, not, as Leopold suggested, partly in Belgian and partly in French territory as a joint enterprise. Thus, the Matadi-Leopoldville line was built by the Belgians alone, and

materials too heavy for human portage sometimes reached the interior of French Equatorial Africa via that connection. However, French Africa benefited but little from the Belgian link: the port of Matadi was congested, and the railroad operated near saturation point, so that there was little space for French freight. It is a reflection of the contrasting conditions in French Equatorial and Belgian Africa that the French railroad was completed more than thirty years after the Belgian one.

The location of the French line with reference to the French territories is very differ-

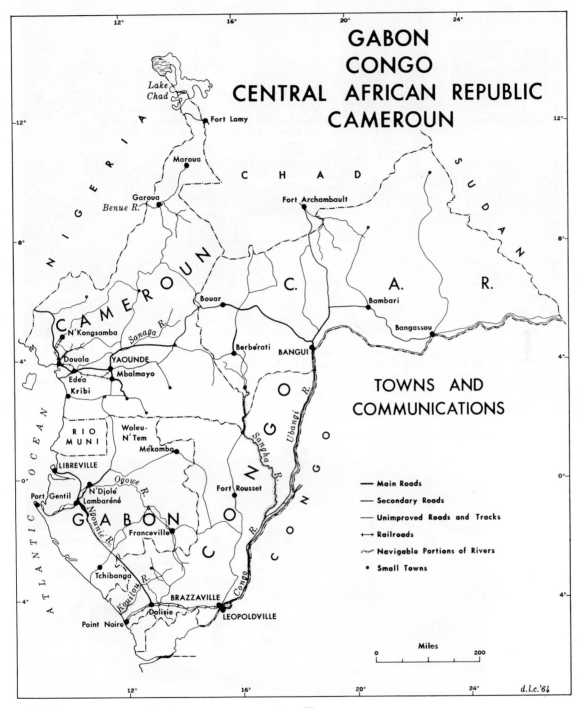

GABON
CONGO
CENTRAL AFRICAN REPUBLIC
CAMEROUN

TOWNS AND
COMMUNICATIONS

Main Roads
Secondary Roads
Unimproved Roads and Tracks
Railroads
Navigable Portions of Rivers
Small Towns

Miles
0   200

d.l.c.'64

Map 47

The Forest, Gabon. Extracting wood from the rainforest is not merely a matter of cutting down trees and floating them downstream. The desired trees must be found among the dense growth shown here, and much clearing is required before cutting and sawing can be done. (French Embassy Press and Information Division)

Logs on the Ogowe River, Gabon. The wood is floated down to the coast for export, and for this, skilled rowers are required. Here, the logs are being tied together in preparation for their long journey. (French Embassy Press and Information Division)

ent from that of the Belgian line with reference to the Congo (Leopoldville), however. The latter forms a focus for the whole country, as the Kasai and its tributaries, the Congo, and the Ubangi (also serving the northern Congo) all lead to the railhead at Leopoldville. But the French line, though creating a link between Bangui and Pointe Noire, really extended an artery (the navigable Ubangi River) serving only the extreme south of the country. Even the Sangha, a major northern tributary of the Ubangi, is navigable to a point only just beyond the southern boundary of the Central African Republic. The areas on the North Equatorial divide and the interior of Gabon and Cameroun, as well as Chad, remained as isolated from an effective outlet as ever.

Where are the potential and actual outlets for the other countries? Gabon's major navigable river is the Lower Ogowe, which lies in a basin much of which is densely forested. Along with its navigable tributary, the N'Gounié River, this was virtually the sole communication link until after the Second World War. The Ogowe River, navigable for 155 miles upstream to N'Djolé, has permitted the exploitation of the country's timber resources. But Gabon in 1964 still had no railroads, and the capital, Libreville, still was not effectively connected to all parts of the relatively small and compact state.

In Cameroun, on the other hand, the navigable stretches of rivers (such as the Sanaga) are short and confined to the narrow coastal belt, because the country rises rapidly toward the plateau interior. There, railroads have been built to the port of Douala, but goods from the interior often travel to the Benue River port of Garoua. From there, they go down the Benue and Niger rivers and via Port Harcourt.

When, after the end of the Second World War, France found herself confronted with a need for stimulating development in this grossly underdeveloped part of her colonial realm, she faced several major obstacles, not the least of which was the detrimental effect of decades of neglect. Distances are great—as great, indeed, as those in the Congo (Leopoldville). The known mineral resources were few, agricultural diversification had barely

begun, communications were rudimentary. As in the case of Belgium, France initiated a Ten-Year Plan with an emphasis upon transportation, both external and internal. Begun in 1946, the program bogged down in several areas simply because local conditions were not sufficiently well known or understood. Ultimately, however, its effect was at least to create a structure upon which further development could be based when the year of independence came to French Equatorial Africa.

Gabon: Forests and the Future

Gabon, the smallest and least populous of the new states of equatorial Africa's former French sphere, is a land of forests. The initial impression of the country is that of a small (and by some reports declining) population numbering barely over a half-million, scattered through a vast, unhealthy tropical rainforest covering the bulk of the area of about 100,000 square miles. The compact country, dominated by the valley of the Ogowe River, has extensive mangrove swamps along its coasts, from where the land rises gradually toward an interior in places exceeding 3,000 feet in elevation. The climate is moist and hot, and in combination these features do not seem to form a favorable economic geography.

If equatorial Africa has one resource in abundance, it is the forest, but timber industries there have suffered from a series of conditions detrimental to their growth. In the first place, industries based on the exploitation of certain tree varieties must cope with the fact that a multitude of trees make up the rainforest, and any specific type is likely to be widely dispersed. Thus, trees may have to be moved over considerable distances, even to the waterways along which they can be floated down to the coast, and this presents its own problems. Then, the labor supply is limited, and, of course, the internal consumption of wood is small, so that most of it must be exported overseas. Loading facilities at the small coastal ports are not adequate, and wood is a bulky, heavy, and expensive prod-

211

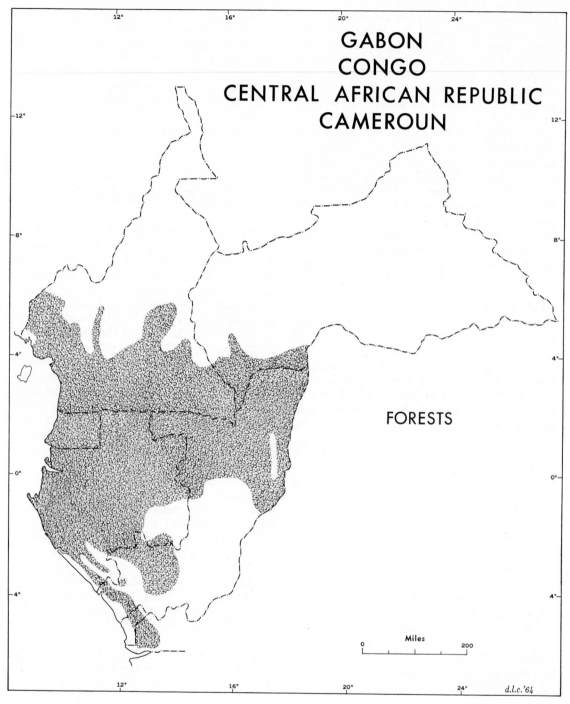

GABON
CONGO
CENTRAL AFRICAN REPUBLIC
CAMEROUN

FORESTS

Miles
0   200

d.l.c.'64

Map 48

uct to ship over long distances. Thus, only the most valuable woods, commanding a high enough price on the world market to withstand the cost of production and transportation, can form the basis for a successful timber industry.

Gabon is fortunate in that its forests contain some of the most valuable woods produced anywhere. Indeed, the development of this country has not taken place in spite of the forest, but because of it, and because of the fact that a system of navigable waterways, focusing upon the Ogowe River, traverses it. What has limited the timber industry (in addition, of course, to fluctuations in the world prices) has been the perennial shortage of lumberers and skilled rowers more than the scarcity or wide dispersion of tree types. Gabon, along with Congo and Rio Muni, has the world monopoly on the production of okoumé, a light wood used in the manufacture of plywood. The forest also yields ebony and mahogany, and in recent years these woods have produced between 80 and 90 per cent of the country's export revenue.

Inevitably, some of the mismanagement characteristic of the rubber- and ivory-exploiting concession companies also has marked the timber industry. The coastal belt has been practically worked out, and reafforestation and other conservation practices have become imperative. Fortunately, such programs are being developed, and there are reasons to view the future of the industry with optimism.

Although fortunate in being able to exploit its forests, Gabon's excessive dependence upon returns from this single industry have long been a matter for concern in this country. The recent past includes years of widely fluctuating prices and real financial problems, so that the diversification of economic activity is a matter of urgency. Here again, Gabon's maritime location is a great advantage, for no part of the country is farther than about 450 miles from the major port, Port Gentil at the mouth of the Ogowe River, and many areas are near permanently navigable streams. In Gabon, whose major export since 1902 has been wood, a coming mineral phase is confidently predicted. In 1956, petroleum was discovered near Port Gentil,

and by 1960, the annual production had already risen to 5 million barrels, exported as crude petroleum and valued at some $12 million. In the Upper Ogowe Valley near Franceville, an extensive manganese deposit is about to be exploited by a corporation in which United States Steel has a 49 per cent capital contribution. Transport facilities, so direly needed in this country, are under construction: a 47-mile cable railway and 180 miles of railroad will link the deposit with the Brazzaville–Pointe Noire railroad, where the new and modern loading facilities will be employed. In addition, an iron ore deposit has been discovered near Mékambo in the northeast, which may be of sufficient quality to merit exploitation. Reserves are estimated at some 250 million tons, and the iron content is about 60 per cent. This, however, is a most difficult part of the country to be connected to the coast by rail, and for this reason exploitation is likely to be years away. The Tchibanga iron deposits, though of inferior quality, lie much nearer to the shipping facilities and may be exploited first.

While Gabon's future, from the economic point of view, may be a relatively bright one, the country cannot escape the effects of its physiographic and demographic situation upon the agricultural industry. In the first place, the problem of marketing is all-pervasive, and the example of rice, produced around Tchibanga in the south, is symptomatic. Because of the lack of roads, the production, which is inferior in quality to that imported from other parts of the world, must be transported by airplane, with obvious consequences to the price paid by the consumer. Furthermore, the availability of wages in the lumber and mining areas draws the men to the urban centers and interior settlements, and lands are left unattended. The effects of the forest cover upon sedentary agriculture are obvious. The agricultural areas, such as they are, therefore lie along the slopes surrounding the central Ogowe Basin, and the most successful region is that around the Woleu and N'Tem valleys in the extreme north, where cocoa cultivation is beginning to support a sedentary peasantry. Still, it is necessary to record the small scale on which the industry is carried on: in the early 1960's pro-

Port Gentil, Gabon. A number of vessels are awaiting lighterage in the growing port. Mostly wood and petroleum are handled here, and some improvement has been made to increase the port's efficiency. (French Embassy Press and Information Division)

The Port of Pointe Noire, Congo. Part of the modern facilities at the western terminal of the Brazzaville railroad are shown here. (French Embassy Press and Information Division)

Urban Center of Pointe Noire, Congo. The familiar radial road pattern of French-influenced cities is evident here, in the central section of the important port city of equatorial Africa. (French Embassy Press and Information Division)

Site for the Kouilou Hydroelectric Project, Congo. The Kouilou River, in its lower course, flows through a series of deep gorges. Here, a large hydroelectric project will be built which will supply Pointe Noire and its vicinity with ample power, and areas such as southern Gabon as well. (French Embassy Press and Information Division)

duction varied around a mere 3,000 tons annually. The first measurable coffee exports were harvested in 1949 from fields in the southern upper river valleys, but production has not yet reached 1,000 tons.

Despite its small area and population, its dense forests, and its difficult topography, Gabon's economic geography is among the most favorable in French Africa. Much of the development is potential rather than actual, but Gabon's location on the Atlantic coast and the variety of its proven resources suggest a relatively bright future in a region of poor countries.

Congo (Brazzaville):
the Assets of Location

The Congo's major asset lies in its geographical location. The elongated state stretches from the narrow Atlantic coast line

(at 5° south latitude) along the Congo and Ubangi rivers to nearly 4° North, but its area of just under 140,000 square miles contains very limited known resources. The north, lying within the Congo Basin, is densely forested and subsistence country, but the south is more open territory, lending itself to other forms of human occupation. The Congo has been the gateway to the interior ever since the French began their administration of equatorial Africa: northward in Gabon the Ogowe route bogs down in the forests, and southward was Belgian territory. But in the east of the southern Congo is the end of the Ubangi waterway, and in the west a site for port development. This east-west route became the means of survival for the territory and endowed it with major assets amid lowland Africa's poverty: former French Equatorial Africa's only railroad, its largest urban center (Brazzaville, 150,000) and its biggest and best port, Pointe Noire.

Thus, the transit of goods to and from

215

The Port Facilities of Brazzaville, Congo. Part of the repair facilities and harbor sheds, as well as the sprawling city, are shown. In the distance, the edge of the higher interior can be seen. (French Embassy Press and Information Division)

The Congo River Between Brazzaville and Leopoldville. The former Belgian and former French capital lie opposite one another, and both have river port facilities and railroad terminals. In the distance, the skyline of Leopoldville can be seen. Note the water hyacinth, terminals. In the distance, the skyline of Leopoldville can be seen. Note the water hyacinth, it spread through the interior waterways.

the interior has been the major source of revenue for Congo, and it further benefited from the location of the French administration's federal headquarters in Brazzaville. This asset disappeared in 1960, when the combined territories in French Equatorial Africa broke apart and went their individual ways politically, and it may cost Brazzaville its eminence among the urban centers in the region. But the dependence of the interior upon the Federal Artery remains. Furthermore, there are plans for the development of a hydroelectric power plant on the Kouilou River, which would supply electricity to a wide region, including countries beyond Congo's borders. If this materializes, the dependence of other states on Congo will be further intensified. In addition, it is anticipated that Pointe Noire will become the center of an important industrial complex, something which has been conspicuously lacking in equatorial Africa.

The Congo's great liability is the paucity of its resources. The country has much variety in its mineral and agricultural production, but very little quantity. As in the case of Gabon, there is a great degree of dependence upon wood and other forest products, but there is nothing like Gabon's bright prospect of future diversification. The high degree of urbanization (for equatorial Africa) has had its negative as well as its positive features: the country may have impressive cities and towns, but it also has a large unemployed urban population. The well under 1 million people, moving away from the land at too rapid a rate, are not growing even the staple foods, so that these must be imported. Yet the long list of crops actually harvested might give the impression that this is an area with great possibilities: bananas, rice, citrus fruits, tobacco, coffee, cocoa, peanuts, and sugar are but a partial selection. Indeed, this may be a country with real potential, but at present the rural population is simply too small and poor to produce any of these crops in quantity. What can be done was indicated after the Second World War, when a group of Frenchmen settled in the Niari Valley and began to cultivate, among other crops, rice, peanuts, and tobacco. The scheme has been an example for other, similar ones, but these developments, being recent and still experimental, are making only a small contribution to the export total. A small group of individual farmers producing certain locally cultivable crops is one thing, but the development of a stable, growing peasantry is quite another. Thus, palm products continue to be the main agricultural export of the country, ranking second to woods. Among the many other crops grown, tobacco and banana exports combined failed to exceed 2,000 tons in 1960, and all other crops ranked far less than that in volume and value.

Added to the problem of the small and scattered rural population, agriculture in the Congo faces the normal difficulties of lowland tropical Africa: the forest cover extending over most of the north and central parts of the country; poor, sandy soils over nearly half the total area and latosols elsewhere, reducing cultivable land to pockets scattered across the southern half of the region; and the omnipresent heat and humidity, eliminating all but a few of the western, higher parts from practically all forms of animal husbandry.

In the area of mineral exploitation, also, the Congo can boast wide variety but little quantity. Copper, lead, gold, zinc, and diamonds have been produced, but only lead has ranked regularly among the exports, largely because of the deposits' proximity to the Brazzaville–Pointe Noire railroad. Thus, there appears little chance for diversification there. Equally bleak is the industrial situation, which is of course related to the smallness of the local market and its poverty. Once again, the list of establishments is impressive (shoe, cigarette, textile, and soap factories, mills handling agricultural produce), but the total volume of production is insignificant. With the realization of the Kouilou Project, the western part of the country may be transformed, but that is likely to require decades.

The meagerness of the total assets of the Congo lends emphasis to its good fortune from the point of view of location. The northern forests have long produced the bulk of the export revenue, but were it not for the country's transit and administrative functions, the economic picture might have been as dismal as any in equatorial Africa. Now, the development of the more heavily populated

Views in Brazzaville, Congo. As in other French-influenced African cities, streets converge radially upon a central traffic circle (above, left), which forms the heart of the city with modern buildings and the highest class stores. Major avenues, such as that along which the United States Information Center is located, are wide and well-planned (below, left). Some four-lane highways were built (above, right), and some remarkable architectural experiments made, such as that of the cathedral (below, right).

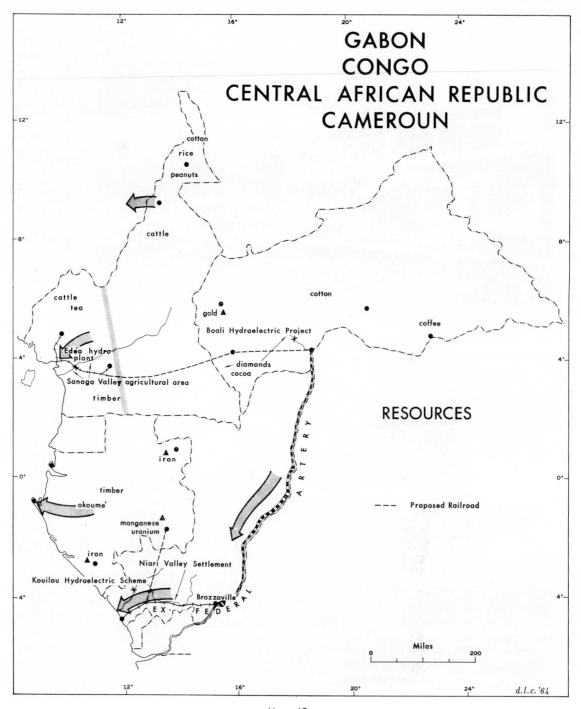

GABON
CONGO
CENTRAL AFRICAN REPUBLIC
CAMEROUN

cotton

rice

peanuts

cattle

cattle
tea

gold ▲

cotton

Boali Hydroelectric Project

coffee

Edea hydro
plant

diamonds
cocoa

Sanaga Valley agricultural area

timber

RESOURCES

iron

timber

okoume'

manganese
uranium

--- Proposed Railroad

iron

Niari Valley Settlement

Kouilou Hydroelectric Scheme

Brazzaville

EX FEDERAL

ARTERY

Miles

0   200

d.l.c. '64

Map 49

Bangui, Capital of the Central African Republic. The Ubangi River, whose lengthy navigable stretch is interrupted just above Bangui, can be seen in the background. Bangui lies at the northern end of the Federal Artery and is the largest town in the republic. Note the typical radial pattern of the roads, converging upon a traffic circle in the center of the city; the pattern is repeated throughout French-influenced African cities. (French Embassy Press and Information Division)

and urbanized southwest is a matter of urgency, for unless the Kouilou Project succeeds and Congo can maintain a hand in developments beyond its borders, it may lose its geographic advantages in addition to those derived from its administrative functions. Other equatorial African countries may develop transport links with the coast, and what happened to Brazzaville may happen to Pointe Noire. Brazzaville, shining administrative center, was always a city without a hinterland; it performed a break-in-bulk function between the coastal railroad and the Ubangi River, but the region surrounding it was little developed. Its *raison d'être* was its governmental headquarters, and with independence it was faced with stagnation and decay. Pointe Noire retains the monopoly over the external trade of a large part of interior equatorial Africa. That monopoly may not be permanent, and when it ends, the internal development of the Congo must be capable of withstanding the impact.

Central African Republic: the Products of the Past

Ubangi-Shari, as the Central African Republic was formerly known, lies landlocked more than 400 straight-line miles from the nearest coast. Its 240,000 square miles are stretched east-west along the central part of the North Equatorial divide, and, like Chad, the region has been a crossroads throughout much of its history. The ethnic variety among its population of only 1½ million attests to the migrations that passed there, and boundary adjustments in modern times have involved the Belgians, Germans, and British.

The Central African Republic lies across an upland that forms the transition zone between the forested Congo Basin and the steppe-and-desert basin of Chad, and it occupies part of the Sudan-Chad divide as well. Thus, it partakes of several climatic and vegetation belts. The southwest is covered by the dense forests of the Congo, but northward an increasingly dry savanna replaces this growth. Since the country lies higher than either Gabon or the Congo, the climate is somewhat cooler in the central parts, and perhaps the best evidence for this amelioration is the cattle population of nearly a half-million (against a mere 15,000 in Congo). The most important consequence of the republic's location with reference to the major physiographic features of equatorial Africa, however, is that a certain variety is brought to the economic picture. While there is not the exchange of goods which takes place in West Africa between the peoples of the dry north and the forested south, the resource base is more diversified, for instance, than that of Gabon. Its volume, in addition, is greater than that of its southern neighbor, Congo.

While favorable in some respects, the location of the republic also has some disadvantages. Its capital and major river port, Bangui, is more than 900 miles from the sea. Toward the east and northeast, the country gets very dry, and there is a rainfall deficiency over much of the nonforest zone. Soil erosion is rampant in some parts of the country due to careless cutting for plantation development. As elsewhere in equatorial Africa, there are labor problems, and the country shares with Gabon and Congo an excessive movement of the rural people to the towns, especially to Bangui (100,000).

To a large extent, the human problems of the Central African Republic are the result of the abuses of the recent past. There, the rule by the concession companies led to the worst conditions in all of French Equatorial Africa, and the Africans' opposition was bitter and desperate. When the period of exploitation came to an end, there remained an enmity between black and white which continues to delay progress today. The past hangs heavily over the Central African Republic for in a sense the forced labor on the land, imposed by the companies, alienated the African from the soil and led to the exodus to the cities after the Second World War. The government's major effort to stimulate the cotton industry—the country's major source of revenue—has been impeded by these factors, even though a number of areas in the central and southern part of the country are suitable for the cultivation of this crop.

Involved also has been the fact that some two-thirds of the acreage under coffee, the republic's second export, was in European hands. Coffee does well along the edge of the forests in the Upper Sangha Valley and the Upper Ubangi Valley, and it is an easier crop to grow than cotton. Africans accused Europeans of attempting to divert African coffee growers' efforts toward cotton, leaving the easier, more profitable crop to the Europeans. Such difficulties have beset the country throughout the period of contact with Europe, and they are continuing after independence. Nevertheless, time may solve the human problem, while the economic opportunities remain. In addition to cotton and coffee, such crops as sisal, tobacco, cocoa, and rice can be cultivated. In general, the areas offering the best opportunities lie in the southwest, in the region of the Upper Sangha, and in the southeast, along the northern slopes of the Upper Ubangi, broadly in the vicinity of Bangassou.

The availability of road materials and the presence of an intensive river system have produced a network of communications which, for equatorial Africa, is good, although it does not much reduce the high cost of the lengthy journey of all exports to the sea and their overseas markets. Although the mineral exports, diamonds and some gold, are not bulky, the heavy freight charges on the agricultural exports have led to a search for alternative ways to the sea. Under consideration at present is the construction of a railroad from Bangui via Berberati (through the region of the Upper Sangha) to the railhead at Yaounde in Cameroun, the republic's west-

Cotton Harvesting, Central African Republic. A major effort is being made in this country to increase the production of cotton. Africans are seen here picking cotton on a large estate. (French Embassy Press and Information Division)

ern neighbor. The port of Douala is not only nearer to the Central African Republic, but the journey would be much faster than the river-rail route to Pointe Noire and would require no transshipment. Such a link would greatly stimulate development in the western half of the country, but would, of course, be detrimental to the interests of Congo.

Meanwhile, sight must not be lost of the real degree of development in this as well as other parts of equatorial Africa in the French cultural sphere. Industrial development can barely be said to have begun, when a few tanneries, a textile mill, a brewery, a shoe factory, a small soap industry, and some sawmills, located near the terminal of the Federal Artery at Bangui, practically represent the whole. A major asset is the Boali Hydroelectric Project, about fifty miles from Bangui, providing power for these enterprises; indeed, the major problem is not power supply, nor is it marketing, as is the case in Gabon. Rather, it is the fluctuating production of raw materials, to be traced back to the unfortunate legacy of maladministration.

Federal Republic of Cameroun: Progress and Participation

The wedge-shaped state of Cameroun, extending from Lake Chad in the north and the Sangha River in the east to a narrow but important coast line in the west, never was formally a part of French Equatorial Africa. Influenced in turn by the British (until 1884), the Germans (until the First World War), and the French (who held a Mandate over the bulk of the territory from 1922 to 1946 and a Trusteeship until 1960), Cameroun forged ahead of the remainder of equatorial Africa at an early stage and has remained in the lead ever since. Reunited with part of the British sector of the original Mandates, this is the most populous country in former French-administered equatorial Africa (5 million people), though it is by no means the largest (184,000 square miles).

Cameroun's internal physiographic va-

The Port of Douala, Cameroun. With Pointe Noire, this is the only well-equipped port along the equatorial African coasts of the French-influenced countries. Short but important railroads lead into the interior. (French Embassy Press and Information Division)

The Dam on the Sanaga River, Edéa, Cameroun. Edéa is a growing industrial center in western Cameroun, located favorably between the port of Douala and the administrative center, Yaoundé, and connected by road and rail to both. (French Embassy Press and Information Division)

riety is considerable, and as a result a wide range of crops can be cultivated. Its north-south extent is no less than 10 degrees of latitude, so that in the south and along the rather narrow coastal belt, conditions are those of the tropical rainforest, whereas in the north, dry savanna and steppe lands occur. Topographically, the country rises in a series of escarpments toward an interior plateau covering the bulk of its area, but a number of prominent features mark the landscape: Mount Cameroun (13,354 feet) in the extreme west, and the Adamawa Highlands farther north rise from the coastal belt and the interior plateau, respectively. In the extreme north, Cameroun partakes of the central part of the Chad Basin, Lake Chad, and the land also drops in the extreme southeast, where the rivers are tributaries of the Congo.

Most of the development has taken place to the west of a line drawn north-south, slightly east of Yaounde. Included in this western region are the important highlands of the former British section of Cameroun, which are among the more densely populated parts of the country and the scene of early settlement by Europeans, as well as most of the major towns and communications. There also lie the major port, Douala, with a capacity of the same order as that of Pointe Noire, the agricultural region of the Sanaga Valley, the capital, Yaoundé, and the growing industrial center of Edéa, near a major hydroelectric project on the Sanaga River. Two railroad arteries lead to Douala: one connects the port to N'Kongsamba, the railhead for the highlands, and the other leads to Yaounde, serving the Sanaga Valley and Edéa.

Cameroun's potential for development is by no means limited to this western area, however. The initial extraction of the usual products from the coastal and southern rainforest, the proximity to the coast and a good harbor, and the western location of the highlands, where much of the early development took place, have led to the early and continuing pre-eminence of the west in terms of economic geography. But in the absence of major mineral deposits (except possibly bauxite, of which local deposits may replace the imported variety smelted at Edéa's plant),

the country's major asset lies in the variety of crops that can be grown, a variety that is as large as it is because of the internal environmental diversification of the republic.

Apart from the usual unfortunate consequences of military conquest, the peoples of Cameroun were more fortunate than many others in Africa as far as the nature of their colonial administration was concerned, and this has much to do with the present potential for progress. The German administration at a very early stage embarked upon a program of crop research and drew up an economic blueprint calling for an embryo transportation system, limitations to land alienation, the perpetuation of certain facets of African traditional authority, and the participation of Africans in the agricultural development of the country. Despite the brevity of their period of tenure, the Germans had made some notable progress by the time the French took over the responsibility for Cameroun. Although certain aspects of French administration in the Mandate were not designed to reap the maximum possible harvest from the base that had been laid, Cameroun was and remained ahead of French Equatorial Africa proper. Development was accelerated after the end of the Second World War, and today the annual export revenue far exceeds the combined total for all four of former French Equatorial Africa's territories, while the per capita income is perhaps twice as high.

TABLE IV

APPROXIMATE PERCENTAGE OF NATIVE PRODUCTION IN CAMEROUN EXPORTS OF 1938

Cotton	100
Peanuts	100
Corn	100
Cocoa	99
Palm Oil, Kernels	92
Rubber	43
Coffee	40
Bananas	19

Source: *French Equatorial Africa*, "Geographical Handbook Series" (London, Naval Intelligence Division, British Admiralty, 1942), p. 409.

Former British Cameroons: Banana Packing. The southern part of the territory of Kamerun, long administered by Britain, elected to rejoin former French Cameroun when independence came. Although largely subsistence country as far as the African inhabitants are concerned, bananas are exported in some quantity from this area. Shown here is a group of workers wrapping banana bunches in cellophane. (United Nations)

Coffee Drying in Cameroun. Coffee is one of Cameroun's leading exports. The beans are seen drying prior to packing and export to France and the United States. (French Embassy Press and Information Division)

Especially important has been the early introduction of cash crops and the encouragement given to African farmers at an early time. Thus, cocoa made its appearance among the country's exports before 1914, and by 1938, African producers were exporting significant quantities of several valuable agricultural commodities.

This early participation of African growers has greatly facilitated the introduction of other crops found suitable for the region. Tea is now grown along the highland slopes, and rice is cultivated in the far north in addition to cotton and peanuts. The Adamawa Highlands and the high areas in the former British Cameroon territory support a sizeable cattle population. Although soil erosion is a serious problem on the central plateau (beyond Yaoundé, especially), the introduction of improved farming methods and the treatment of livestock against diseases have met with a positive response.

The modest success in the development of Cameroun's essentially agrarian economy must be measured against the results of similar efforts in other parts of lowland equatorial Africa. Major problems still confront the country, whose political geography has always been a difficult one. The northern regions suffer from their remoteness from the country's capital and core area, and their natural outlet is still through Nigeria (with which there are also many social affinities). The long-term division of the country into British and French territories has presented problems upon the reunion of the southernmost British section with the French zone. Lying across the Bantu-Negro transition zone in the southwest, and penetrating the Moslem African world in the north, Cameroun's internal ethnic variety is as great as that of its physiography, and this has been an obstacle in the struggle for national unity. Political turmoil marked the republic, which has been drawn tightly into the French economic sphere, throughout the period before and after 1960, the year of independence. Inevitably, its effect upon the economy was detrimental. The return of stability should, nonetheless, bring a bright future. In a continent of agonizingly slow progress in agriculture, Cameroun is comparatively well endowed.

11

HIGHLAND AFRICA:
TANGANYIKA AND THE PROBLEM OF RESOURCES

THE CONTRASTS BETWEEN lowland equatorial Africa, as exemplified by the Congo region, and highland Africa in Tanganyika, Kenya, and Uganda are sharp and significant. East of the western chain of lakes (the Western Rift Valley), virtually all aspects of the equatorial physiography are conditioned by the rise in elevation out of the Congo Basin. Rift faulting, volcanism, peculiar drainage conditions, and climatic variety are but a few of the features of East Africa's physiography, which in terms of pedology and flora also differs vitally from lowland Africa to the west.

Highland East Africa is occupied by five political units,[1] three in the former British sphere (the former protectorate of Uganda, colony of Kenya, and United Nations Trust Territory of Tanganyika) and two in the former Belgian sphere (Rwanda and Burundi, until 1962 the United Nations Trust Territory of Ruanda-Urundi). Of the five, Tanganyika is by far the largest—larger, in fact, than all others combined. It is also the most populous, its 10 million people constituting several major and dozens of minor tribal groupings, and including also a permanently resident Asian minority. The vast majority of these people are peasants and nomadic or semi-sedentary pastoralists, and depend upon the land for their living; the nature of their adjustment to Tanganyika's various environ-ments varies widely. Much of Tanganyika, especially the central area, is dry, bush-covered plateau country, where crop cultivation and even pastoralism are very difficult. However, mineral production is limited and manufacturing in an initial stage, so that soil and water supply form Tanganyika's most important resources, and agriculture is the country's central concern.

The Water Resource

The major problems of water supply in savanna East Africa have been touched upon in Chapter 3, and in Tanganyika their impact is especially severe. Although it is a tropical country, rainfall totals are remarkably low, and variability high. A broad belt stretching from northeast to southwest across the heart of the country has less than 20 inches of annual rainfall, and only on the highest topographic prominences are totals over 70 inches recorded. Even where the annual rainfall is higher, it may come during a relatively short wet season, limiting cultivation and rendering pastoralism a very precarious business during the dry season. An associated feature of rainfall thus highly concentrated is its arrival in intense storms, leading to excessive runoff and erosion. The high temperatures and great amount of evaporation further limit the usefulness of the precipitation.

---

[1] Zanzibar is excluded from this discussion, to be considered in the Appendix.

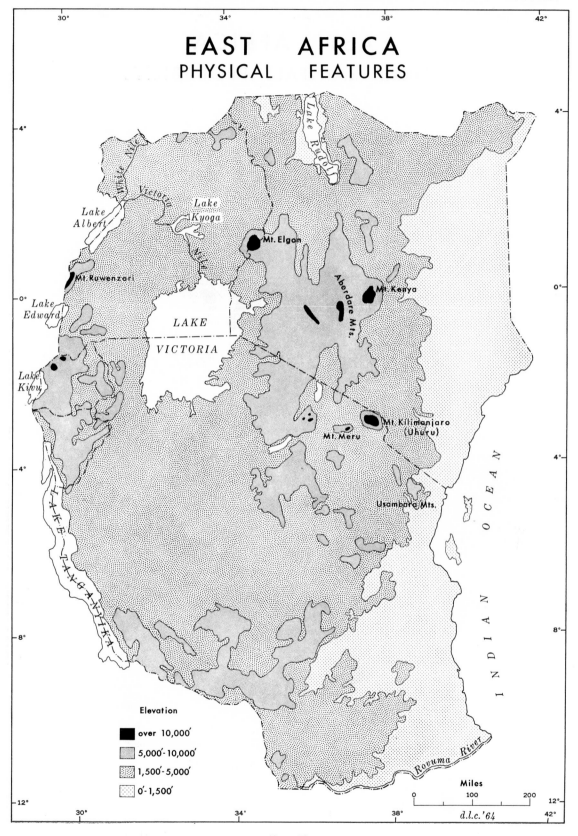

EAST AFRICA
PHYSICAL FEATURES

Lake Rudolf

White Nile

Victoria Nile

Lake Albert

Lake Kyoga

Mt. Elgon

Mt. Ruwenzori

Lake Edward

Mt. Kenya

Aberdare Mts.

LAKE VICTORIA

Lake Kivu

Mt. Meru

Mt. Kilimanjaro (Uhuru)

LAKE TANGANYIKA

Usambara Mts.

INDIAN OCEAN

Rovuma River

Elevation

- over 10,000′
- 5,000′- 10,000′
- 1,500′- 5,000′
- 0′- 1,500′

Miles

0   100   200

d.l.c. '64

Map 50

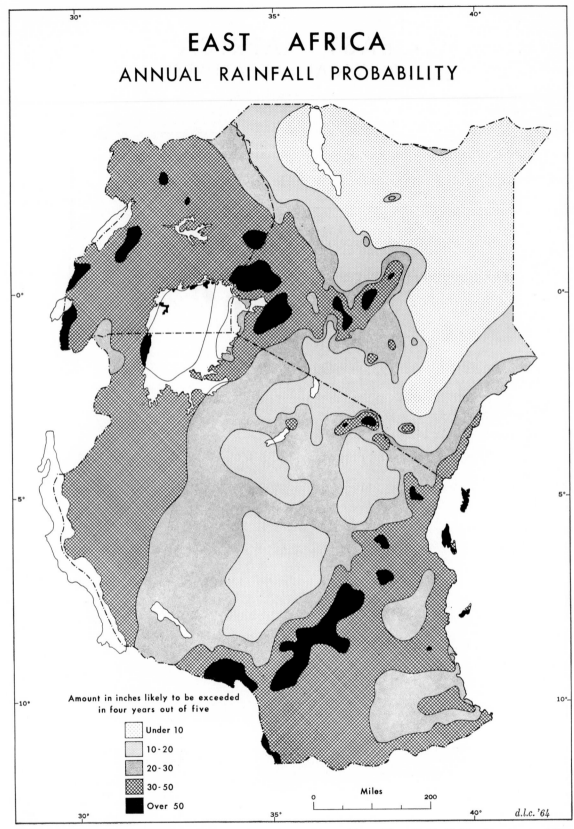

EAST AFRICA
ANNUAL RAINFALL PROBABILITY

Amount in inches likely to be exceeded
in four years out of five

Under 10
10 - 20
20 - 30
30 - 50
Over 50

Miles
0   200

d.l.c. '64

From a map in E. W. Russell, ed., *The Natural Resources of East Africa* (Nairobi: D. H. Hawkins in association with East Africa Literature Bureau, 1962).

Map 51

View of Dar es Salaam, Tanganyika. The capital of Tanganyika is also its largest city and first port. In the left distance is the central business district, in the foreground the new, modern port facilities capable of handling three ocean-going vessels at the same time. Lighterage still takes place in the bay, for space is limited along the quay. (Tanganyika Government)

The best-watered areas of Tanganyika lie spread about the dry heart of the country and include the coastal belt, the Kilimanjaro and Meru slopes and surroundings, the Lake Victoria region, the western section beyond Tabora, the Southern Highlands (around Lake Nyasa), and the belt extending from there northeast to Morogoro. In total, however, perhaps about one-third of the country may be described as adequately watered. Tanganyika, which forms part of the divide between three of Africa's greatest rivers (the Zambezi to the Indian Ocean in the south, the Nile to the Mediterranean Sea in the north, and the Congo to the Atlantic Ocean in the west), does not itself possess any such large watercourses. Indeed, the central part of the country has two major basins of internal drainage (Lake Rukwa in the south and the Rift Valley trough in the north), so that the local drainage systems are of but minor significance on a continental scale. The eastern part is drained largely by the Rufiji River and its tributaries, and, in the west, the Maragarasi River follows a brief course into Lake Tanganyika. Many streams are ephemeral or intermittent and are of no permanent value, so that the people during the dry season often have to undertake long treks to obtain water.

The Soil Resource

In addition to water, soil is Tanganyika's most important resource, yet much remains to be learned concerning the country's pedology. Soil analysis and mapping are slow and expensive, and, except in the important agricultural areas, the soils of Tanganyika are known only in general terms. It is clear, however, that the best soils lie in the volcanic regions that occur in the highlands of the north (Kilimanjaro, Meru) and the south and southwest (around the northern end of Lake Nyasa). Good soils, although variable in certain qualities, also are found in the alluvial valleys, where they await irrigation. The re-

TANGANYIKA

ADMINISTRATIVE DIVISIONS

UGANDA

Bukoba

RWANDA

WEST

LAKE

Mwanza

BURUNDI

KENYA

NORTHERN

Arusha

Tabora

WESTERN

CENTRAL

Dodoma

TANGA

Tanga

EASTERN

Morogoro

DAR ES SALAAM

CONGO

SOUTHERN
HIGHLANDS

Mbeya

EASTERN

ZAMBIA

MALAWI

SOUTHERN

Lindi

Miles
0   200

MOCAMBIQE

d.l.c. '64

Map 52

mainder of the country is largely covered by the familiar, deep-weathered, reddish soils that develop on the crystallines of the African plateau, with their limited carrying capacity. Under proper farming practices, including the application of fertilizers, these soils can produce annual yields in the moister areas.

Although Tanganyika does not possess the dense forests of lowland equatorial Africa, over two-thirds of the country lies under bush, parkland savanna, and patches of denser scrub. The natural vegetation has been affected by the activities of man, the original growth having been replaced over wide areas by a tree-poor grassland savanna. Well over half the country remains infested by the dreaded tsetse fly, which thrives under the prevalent conditions and limits human occupation; only small parts of the country are free from malaria.

Distribution and Distances

The zones of commercial agriculture in Tanganyika, therefore, lie scattered throughout the country's vast area, dependent as they are upon adequate water supply and reasonably good soils. Three such areas have developed along and near the coast. In the north, the port of Tanga is the focus for a hinterland extending from the immediate vicinity of the town to the important Usambara Mountains and beyond. The largest domestic market in the country, the capital (Dar es Salaam, 150,000), also lies in an agricultural production area, and in the south, the Mtwara-Nachingwea-Masasi triangle, scene of the Groundnut Scheme disaster, also continues to produce some cash crops. Each of these coastal places is the terminal for a railroad from the interior. Tanga's railroad leads as far as Arusha (a further extension is planned) and serves the important Kilimanjaro-Meru agricultural zones. The railroad to Dar es Salaam connects several important interior areas to the capital and major port: the Lake Victoria shore region and the farming areas around Morogoro, Tabora, and Kigoma. The railroad ending at Mtwara has

not been extended into the interior, although the recent independence of Zambia has revived talk of a Lusaka-Mtwara link. Meanwhile, the products of the other significant agricultural areas (around Iringa, and in the Southern Highlands) travel by road to the central railroad or all the way to the capital.

Thus Tanganyika's development, in a spatial sense, is peripheral, as many of the agricultural producing areas lie on or near the boundaries of the huge, compact state. Tanganyika is a country of great distances. The northwestern corner of the area lies not far short of a thousand miles from Mtwara, and Dar es Salaam itself is more than 600 miles from the shores of Lake Tanganyika. The dispersion of the areas of productive capacity, combined with the distances involved, present major problems to development and administration. The costs of transportation are high, even though this country does have several trunk railroads and some adequate major roads leading to the more densely populated and producing areas.

Development of Present-Day Tanganyika

The modern historical development of Tanganyika has taken place in several rather distinct phases. Prior to 1884, the region's main contact with the outside world was through the Arab trading and slave-raiding caravans entering from Bagamoyo, but except for the first efforts to build some coastal stations (including the settlement of Dar es Salaam), nothing was done by the Arabs to introduce any effective form of territorial organization.

The thirty years after 1884 mark the German period of occupation, and several of the tangible assets of Tanganyika were created during this time. Having initially used the settlement at Bagamoyo as the administrative headquarters, the Germans shifted the capital to Dar es Salaam and began to develop the site. Karl Peters, founder of the German Colonization Society and Governor of German East Africa, recognized the need for railway links with the interior,

German-Built Administrative Office, Dar es Salaam, Tanganyika. Dar es Salaam is a city of many influences; the Germans laid out the central city plan, the British developed it, and now the Africans are administering it. This German structure, built on the waterfront, served until the 1960's as a governmental office.

in the interests of both effective control over the rebellious African population and economic development. Thus, the railroad from Dar es Salaam to Kigoma was completed as early as 1914, having been begun in 1905. The line to Moshi, begun in 1893 (the first railroad to be laid in a German colony), was completed by 1911.[2]

Thus, the pattern of Tanganyika's spatial organization began to take shape. The first German settlements were on the coast, but the Tanga-Moshi railroad opened progressively distant areas for agriculture, and it was thought that the railroad to the great lakes would capture trade in that region. It was a miscalculation, the only sizeable volume of such trade coming during a brief period of early exploitation in Katanga. The *Mittelland Bahn*, after leaving the Morogoro area, traverses the dry heart of Tanganyika and then crosses the moister west, but it does

not, in these two regions, pass through any region comparable to the Southern Highlands or the Meru-Kilimanjaro-Usambara belt. Of course, it stimulated some development, and some towns sprang up along the route, but most of the volume of trade carried is brought to the line by feeder railroads and roads built at a later stage.

In addition to their work on the transportation system, the Germans, as in Kamerun, did much research in the field of agriculture. Unlike Kamerun, however, there was virtually no effort to stimulate African interest in cash cropping. The Germans established European-owned plantations and introduced, among other crops, sisal (which has become the country's leading export product), coffee, cotton, and tea. The plantations were situated on alienated land near the railroads in the hinterlands of Tanga and Dar es Salaam, but the period of expansion under German rule was too brief for the volume of exports to attain significance. The real contribution of the Germans was the successful introduction of several crops which in the future were to become mainstays of development.

---

[2] For an informative discussion of these developments, see M. F. Hill, *Permanent Way* (Nairobi: East African Railways and Harbours, 1958), II, 29–108.

What would have happened to German East Africa—and to other German colonies in Africa—had the First World War not terminated German rule remains a matter for conjecture. In any case, the territory in 1919 was placed under the Mandate System of the League of Nations and was divided between Britain, which became Mandate power over Tanganyika proper, and Belgium, which assumed responsibility over Ruanda-Urundi.[3] What Germany had begun was interrupted, and, in Tanganyika, development during the interwar period was intermittent. Nevertheless, some very important steps were taken. Not only was the war damage repaired and a governmental machinery established, but African participation in cash cropping was encouraged, despite objections from local white farmers. In the 1920's, for the first time, Africans really began to reap some of the harvests, in a literal sense, from the country's most important resource, the scattered areas of good, adequately watered soils. The first major step in this direction was taken when the Chagga people of the slopes of Mount Kilimanjaro began to respond to the administration's inducements, planting coffee as a cash crop where formerly only subsistence crops had grown. The Kilimanjaro Native Planters Association was formed, and crops were sold communally. As the production began to attain significance, the white planters, from whose estates the coffee trees had spread to the Chagga, expressed concern over the competition that would result and the dangers of inferior quality crops and inadequate protection against disease. It is to the credit of the British administration that it did not yield to the pressures of the whites in favor of reducing the Africans' land holdings, and that it prevented a proposed secession of the Kilimanjaro area to join Kenya. Eventually, the region was to become an outstanding example of interracial cooperation among farmers, occasional friction notwithstanding.

Meanwhile, other parts of Tanganyika were being brought into production, and the internal communication network was being improved. The Voi-Taveta-Moshi link with Mombasa had been constructed during the war years, so that the growing agricultural region of Kilimanjaro was now served by two competing ports. The extension line from Moshi reached Arusha, major center for the Meru coffee-producing area, in 1929. Development in the Lake Victoria region, including coffee cultivation in the vicinity of Bukoba and cotton-growing south of Mwanza, finally led to the construction of a feeder railroad from Tabora to the lake port of Mwanza. Today, the Lake Province has become the region with the highest population density, the greatest proportion of land under cultivation, and the largest livestock totals.

Much of what had been achieved was smashed in a matter of months toward the end of the decade. The year 1929 was one of disaster for the Mandate, and it opened with the most serious floods in the known history of the region. Largely as a result of these, there was an invasion of rats which did serious damage to the cotton crop. While the repair of the flood damage to communication lines was in progress, the Great Depression struck. Tanganyika had much to lose. Having developed the infrastructure of the economy, Britain was supporting a program of educational and medical services, and much of the projected financial support had to be withdrawn. For more than a decade, Africans had been encouraged to abandon subsistence agriculture in favor of various forms of cash cropping. For a sizeable number, the move had proved a success, and many African farmers depended almost entirely upon their cash sales. With the Great Depression came drastically reduced rewards, and dissatisfaction was rife. Tax returns declined greatly. There were many recriminations on the part of those who felt they had been lured into the practice of cash cropping at the cost of their security.

Three years later, Tanganyika again set out upon the path of recovery. There had been some mineral finds, including gold at Lupa, but the administration's main objective in the economic sphere remained the encouragement of cash cropping. The white population did not increase to any great ex-

---

[3] For details concerning the constitutional and political consequences, see B. T. G. Chidzero, *Tanganyika and International Trusteeship* (Oxford: Oxford University Press, 1961), especially pp. 115–74.

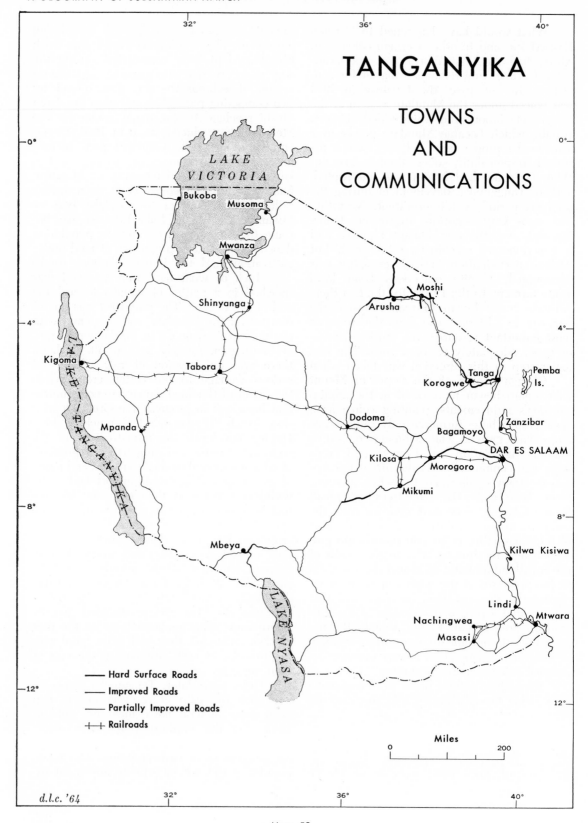

TANGANYIKA

TOWNS
AND
COMMUNICATIONS

LAKE VICTORIA

Bukoba
Musoma
Mwanza
Shinyanga
Kigoma
Tabora
Mpanda
Moshi
Arusha
Tanga
Korogwe
Pemba Is.
Dodoma
Zanzibar
Bagamoyo
DAR ES SALAAM
Kilosa
Morogoro
Mikumi
Mbeya
Kilwa Kisiwa
Lindi
Mtwara
Nachingwea
Masasi

LAKE TANGANYIKA

LAKE NYASA

—— Hard Surface Roads
— Improved Roads
— Partially Improved Roads
+++ Railroads

Miles
0   200

d.l.c. '64

Map 53

Mosque, Dar es Salaam, Tanganyika. Along the east coast of Africa, the influence of Islam has moved far to the south. Dar es Salaam, lying amost opposite the Arab trading town of Zanzibar, has several impressive mosques in addition to its Christian churches and shrines.

tent, largely because of the slowness of the deliberations between the Colonial Office and Governor Cameron. The latter felt that the immigration of many more whites from Britain, with their capital and skills, could transform barely populated sections of the territory into thriving farmland, stimulating Africans to follow the example, perhaps repeating the Kilimanjaro experience elsewhere, and bringing cash to the coffers of the Mandate. The risk of land alienation was recognized, and the possibility of racial friction considered, but this problem was thought to be less insurmountable than the absence of white settlers.

By 1933, however, a new factor had entered the scene, the fear that Tanganyika might again become German territory. As Germany increasingly came to occupy the center of the world stage during the decade, the possibility of large-scale immigration from Britain became increasingly remote. The positive aspect of this development was that a bitter racial struggle for land between the African majority and any sizeable white minority was avoided in Tanganyika.

AFTER THE SECOND WORLD WAR

Modern Tanganyika began to emerge after the end of the Second World War, but much of the progress recorded in the late 1940's was overshadowed by yet another economic disaster in the territory. The British government, in response to a shortage of margarine in Britain, decided to invest heavily in a vast peanut-producing scheme for East Africa, mainly in southern Tanganyika.

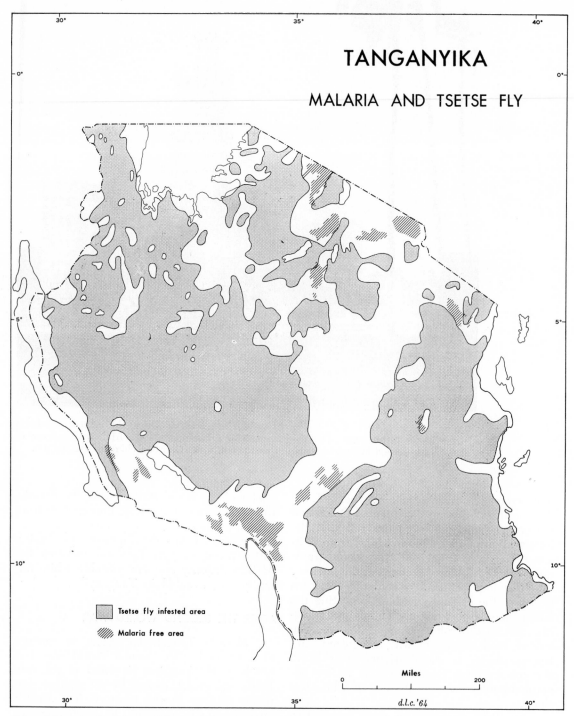

TANGANYIKA

MALARIA AND TSETSE FLY

Tsetse fly infested area

Malaria free area

Miles

0   200

d.l.c. '64

Atlas of Tanganyika (Dar es Salaam: Government Printer, 1962).

Map 54

Sisal in Transshipment. Sisal remains Tanganyika's most valuable single export product, and the fiber is seen here being transshipped after having been loaded at the port of Tanga. (United Nations)

With inadequate pilot testing, the project was initiated in 1947. Machinery rendered obsolete by the end of the war was sent to Tanganyika, where thousands of acres were cleared of their dense bush. The port of Mtwara, to be the major outlet for the producing region, was improved, and railroad construction was carried on. The plan was eventually to clear some 2½ million acres in Tanganyika alone, and nearly another million acres in Kenya and Northern Rhodesia. The expenditure was unlike anything ever experienced in East Africa previously (estimated at over $70 million), and the expectations were electrifying: the south of Tanganyika would be transformed into a thriving region in a matter of years.

The soils of southern Tanganyika, like tropical soils elsewhere (whether heavily leached or only moderately so), do not take well to the kind of disturbance perpetrated

there. The sun did its work, creating a hard layer of baked A-horizon overlain only by fine dust. Mechanical equipment broke down and could not be repaired. The first crop was minimal compared to what had been expected, and as early as 1949 it had become clear that the region was not suited to the type of agriculture being imposed upon it. The funds supporting the scheme were nearly exhausted, and the entire project had to be revised several times, until only a small fraction of the original plan remained.[4]

The failure of the scheme to grow peanuts did not amount to a total loss of all the effort and funds that had been poured into the country for the purpose.[5] The new har-

[4] J. P. Moffet, ed., *Handbook of Tanganyika* (Dar es Salaam: Government Printer, 1958), pp. 141–43.

[5] A. Wood, *The Groundnut Affair* (London: The Bodley Head, 1950). Also see *A Plan for the Mechanical Production of Groundnuts in East and Central Africa* (The "Wakefield Report") (London: His Majesty's Stationery Office, 1947).

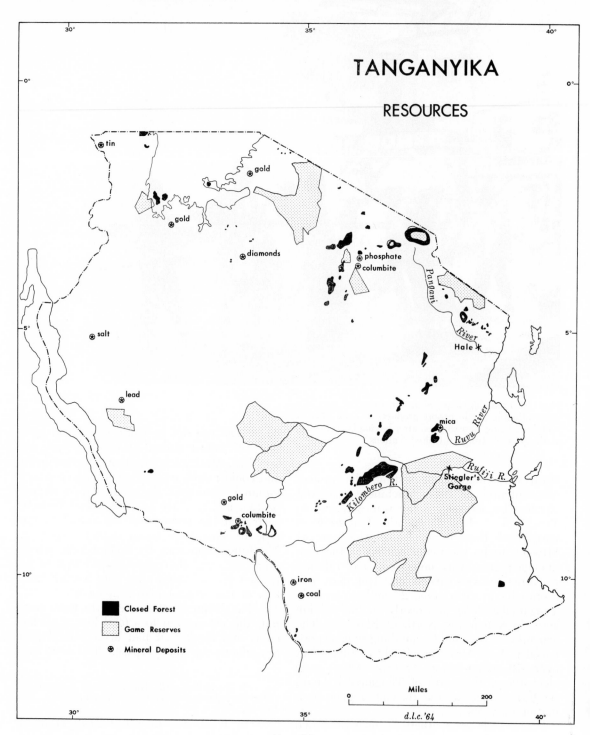

TANGANYIKA

RESOURCES

tin

gold

gold

diamonds

phosphate
columbite

salt

Hale

lead

mica

Stiegler's
Gorge

gold

columbite

iron

coal

Pangani River

Ruvu River

Rufiji R.

Kilombero R.

◼ Closed Forest

▨ Game Reserves

⊛ Mineral Deposits

Miles
0   200

d.l.c. '64

Map 55

240

bor at Mtwara, the railroad to Nachingwea, several training centers, a certain amount of permanently usable equipment, and a number of farms today are going concerns. In addition, the services and skills of many of the technicians who came to Tanganyika for work on the scheme were put to good use elsewhere, and some of them became permanent residents.

While the failure of the peanut scheme drew world-wide attention, Tanganyika was receiving the benefits of a less spectacular but eventually more important piece of planning. In 1945, Britain enacted a first Colonial Development and Welfare Act. Within its framework was a ten-year plan for the development of Tanganyika, which was put into operation in 1947. The plan, which was to cost over $50 million, proved a stimulus to the economy while also leading to a great improvement in social services. Since 1947, it has been revised and superseded by a number of more costly plans, the last of which was revealed in 1961 as a three-year plan to cost nearly $100 million. Of course, newly independent Tanganyika cannot receive any further colonial development funds, but the British government is now channeling aid into the country by other means.

The priorities listed in the 1961–64 plan are a significant indication of the country's economic direction. Tanganyika's most urgent objectives are considered to be the development of agriculture and livestock ranching, the improvement of the communications network, and the development of secondary and technical education. Since 1945, much improvement has already taken place in each of these spheres. The response has been favorable: in 1948, the value of the country's external trade was $100 million, and in 1960, it was nearly $270 million. During this period, several railroads were constructed, and additional lines were being built in 1964. From Kilosa a feeder line was built to Mikumi, which serves as the railhead for the Southern Highlands. From Kaliua a line was constructed to Mpanda, where lead was for some time mined. The most important link under construction in the 1960's was that between the Central Line and the Tanga Line. This link has the major advantage of permitting the transfer of rolling stock from one line to the other, the peak traffic flow on the two individual lines occurring at different times of the year.

The postwar period, including the years of independence (which came in 1961), has been a phase of accelerating development in which the African inhabitants have participated to an increasing degree. Sisal, coffee, and cotton, long the major export crops, continue to contribute about two-thirds of the export revenue, but some African-grown crops, such as cashew nuts and castor, are making increasing contributions. Although white-owned plantations produce almost all the country's sisal and tea, and most of the tobacco and pyrethrum, the African contribution in agriculture is such that today nearly two-thirds of all exported agricultural produce is grown by African peasants. In addition, contributions of increasing importance are made by the mining industry, and in the internal economy, fisheries, pastoral industries, and the tourist trade are of growing significance.

The Mineral Resources

Tanganyika's major problems remain the paucity of its resources, the great distances involved in their exploitation, and the insular nature of the areas of productive capacity. Tanganyika does not have an area where important mineral deposits lie juxtaposed with a region of agricultural importance, the whole supporting a core area of impressive urbanization. The country does not have a Witwatersrand, Copperbelt, or Katanga, nor does it have a Highveld or a highland core such as that of Kenya. Possibly one of the several agricultural regions will in time emerge, and such a core area will develop.

The mineral situation, in terms of its spatial pattern, is somewhat reminiscent of the insular developments in productive agriculture. The most important single deposit is of diamonds near Shinyanga in Lake Province. Although a very small output of diamonds had been recorded during the 1920's

241

and 1930's, it was not until 1940 that Dr. J. T. Williamson discovered a diamondiferous kimberlite pipe, similar to the type found at Kimberley in South Africa. The discovery was made at Mwadui, and since 1940, production has risen to some 540,000 carats (1960), producing about 60 per cent of the country's revenue from mineral exports, or about $12 million.[6]

Tanganyika's gold reserves have been its second most important mineral resource, and again several producing areas are scattered in various parts of the country. The major one is that on which the Kiabakari Mine is situated, east of Lake Victoria. South of the lake is the Geita Mine, and these two mines now produce four-fifths of the gold exports of the country. The center of the industry under the German administration was in the Singida District in the Central Province, where production is now small, several mines having been closed down. Subsequently, the Lupa District in southwestern Tanganyika became the center of gold mining, but the district was never connected to the main railroad, and as reserves were worked out the production dwindled. Further development appears possible in both the Singida and Lupa districts, but the grade of ore is low, and considerable investment would be required to support further exploration and to set up the equipment necessary to handle the ore in the large amounts necessary.

In 1942, lead deposits were discovered at Mpanda, and the estimated reserves were such that a large plant was built on the site and a railroad laid to connect the area with the Central Line. Production rose to a value of just under $3 million in 1958, the peak year, but it became clear that the original estimate of the reserves (which included some associated copper, silver, and gold) had been excessive. Further exploration yielded no encouraging results, and the mine was closed down in 1960.

In the Karagwe District in the extreme northwestern part of the country, a minor production of tin has been carried on for

several decades, but its significance is illustrated best by the peak year (1938), when a mere 400 tons were exported. A declining production of mica is extracted from the Uluguru Mountains near Morogoro, and some salt from the Western Province. But even in the small total of Tanganyika's mineral production, gold, tin, and all minerals other than diamonds produce insignificant revenues. The minerals that do occur are not found in close association along a mineralized belt, so that each distant deposit presents its own individual problems of exploration, mining, treatment, and transportation.

Tanganyika does possess some deposits, recently surveyed, which may support future mining. Near Lake Manyara, some 70 miles west-southwest of the railhead at Arusha, a major phosphate deposit has been located, capable of yielding 300,000 tons of treated product per year. The major problem is the cost of transportation (by road to the railhead and then by rail to Tanga and Mombasa would be prohibitive). But a subsequent discovery in the area of columbite in payable quantities has greatly enhanced the possibilities for mineral exploitation. This discovery was preceded by a similar one in the Southern Highlands near Mbeya, where a large deposit of pyrochlore was found in the mid-1950's. Coal has also been found, the main deposits lying in the valley of the Ruhuhu River, which flows into Lake Nyasa. But these coals lie in one of the remotest parts of the country, where, furthermore, there are several good sites for hydroelectric power development. In the absence of primary industries requiring large quantities of coal, internal use is unlikely in the near future. Export, requiring transport links and sufficiently high prices to withstand the long journey (and rather costly mining processes, since much of the coal lies beyond open-pit depths), is also an unlikely development. However, a little north of the coal deposits, a fairly large iron reserve has been discovered, and there is a possibility of producing pig iron.

The same problems facing the agricultural industry—isolation, limitations on areas with productive capacity, distances, and the like—confront the mining industry in Tan-

---

[6] In South Africa in the same year, production was about 3 million carats, a relatively small contribution to the revenue from mineral exports.

ganyika, and since the preceding summary covers the total known mineral assets of the country, it is not difficult to see that the agricultural and pastoral industries must remain the key to progress there.

Remaining Assets

Before returning to the agricultural development of Tanganyika, mention should be made of the resource aspects of the country's lake waters, forests, and game. The fisheries are mainly dependent upon the two great lakes, and although other inland fisheries based upon the rivers and dams have been growing rapidly in recent years, marine fishing is as yet unimportant.

The fishing industries of both Lake Tanganyika and Lake Victoria face several problems. Both lakes are highly productive and together yield some 50,000 tons of fish annually. Most of the catch is sundried and distributed in that form, but marketing (other than along the railroad lines leading from the centers, Kigoma and Mwanza) presents difficulties. Most of the catch, furthermore, is taken inshore, when there is real potential for deep-water fishing on both lakes. Here, the provision of equipment has been the limiting factor.

Inland, the stocking of lakes and dams with fish has had excellent results, the experiment at Kitangiri Dam, in the Central Province, which was stocked with fish and is now producing a sizeable monthly catch, being repeated elsewhere. Thus, one of the major shortcomings of the protein-deficient African diet can be counteracted.

Tanganyika's forest resources are not large, but they are nevertheless important. In 1960, some 46,000 square miles (over 13 per cent of the total area) was under forest reserves, of which only about 4,000 square miles, mainly in the higher altitude areas, are comparable to those of, for instance, the Knysna-Transkei area of South Africa. Most of the remainder of the reserves lie under more or less open woodland and some mangrove forests. Much of Tanganyika's woodland and bush, which in total probably cover

over half of the country, serves mainly the local population in supplying materials for the building of huts and other domestic uses. Some hardwood poles and floor materials are exported, mainly from the Northern and Tanga provinces.

In 1949, as part of the Colonial Development Corporation's program, wattle growing was begun in the Southern Highlands, and today some 50,000 acres have been planted, while further expansion is in progress, especially on African farmers' lands. The first tanning extract was produced in 1959. Other afforestation possibilities exist in the highland regions, where conifers promise to do well.

Another resource is the country's magnificent game reserves and scenic attractions. The Serengeti and Selous wildlife sanctuaries, Mounts Kilimanjaro and Meru, the Ngorongoro Crater (really a caldera), and the coastal regions of the lakes and Indian Ocean all rank among Africa's finest tourist attractions. The tourist trade is growing, but Tanganyika is not favorably located with reference to the main lines of communication. Nairobi is a far more frequented airport than Dar es Salaam, and internal communications, as well as hotels and other facilities, are better elsewhere in East Africa. Hence, Tanganyika has not reaped the maximum possible harvest from these assets, but the northern regions could become one of Africa's major tourist attractions when improvements have been made. From Kilimanjaro in the east to the lake shore (Victoria) in the west, lies a zone of incomparable scenery and wildlife variety.

Finally, one of Tanganyika's real assets lies in its river system, the hydroelectric power potential of which is more than sufficient to meet the country's needs. The focus lies in the valley of the Pangani River, which rises on the southern slopes of Kilimanjaro and reaches the ocean to the south of Tanga, thus traversing the entire developing northeast. A site has been developed at Pangani Falls, which serves the Tanga-Mombasa area, but Dar es Salaam has long been served by a thermal plant, which was expanded as the city's demands grew. Utilization of the lower Pangani course would permit the transmission of electricity to the capital and surrounding

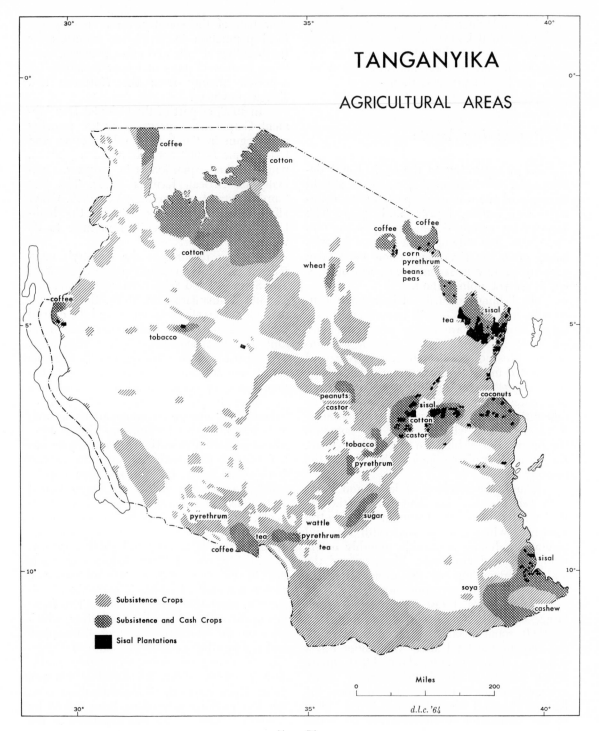

TANGANYIKA

AGRICULTURAL AREAS

coffee

cotton

coffee

coffee

corn
pyrethrum
beans
peas

cotton

wheat

tea

sisal

coffee

tobacco

peanuts
castor

coconuts

sisal
cotton
castor

tobacco

pyrethrum

pyrethrum

sugar

wattle
pyrethrum
tea

tea

coffee

sisal

soya

cashew

Subsistence Crops

Subsistence and Cash Crops

Sisal Plantations

Miles

0   200

d.l.c. '64

Map 56

244

The Slopes of Kilimanjaro, Tanganyika. The country of the Chagga around Moshi is one of Tanganyika's most important cash-crop-producing regions. Kibo, the snow-capped peak, can be seen on the left, with banana trees (the staple food here) on both sides of the road. Coffee is the major cash crop grown along with the bananas. (United Nations)

areas, and for this purpose the Hale Project was begun in the early 1960's. In the Rufiji Basin, a very favorable site for the development of a hydroelectric plant is at Stiegler's Gorge, 110 miles from Dar es Salaam.

Agriculture and Growth

Agricultural development in Tanganyika has taken place in three general ways. In areas which lie near the coast or on the major transport routes, estate agriculture has flourished to the extent of over 2 million acres. This is only 1 per cent of Tanganyika's total area, but the contribution of these sisal, tea, coffee, and other plantations has amounted to almost half the agricultural exports by value. The major area lies in the Dar es Salaam–Tanga–Kilimanjaro section, where sisal dominates and tea, coffee, pyrethrum, beans, and peas are also cultivated. In the immediate hinterland of both Dar es Salaam and Mtwara, plantations growing soya beans and cashew nuts as well as sisal have also been established.

From these estates, cash crops have often spread to African lands, where their cultivation has been successful.[7] The initial example of the spread of coffee into the subsistence areas of the Chagga around Kilimanjaro has been followed in many other parts of the country. Thus, much of agriculturally productive Tanganyika (a far larger area than that lying under estates) consists of peasant holdings on which both subsistence crops, such as bananas in the case of the Chagga, are grown along with cash crops. In the Mbulu District, Northern Province, wheat has spread to the peasants' lands from the estates nearby. Cotton, on the other hand, is grown by African peasant farmers exclusively, mainly around

---

[7] With independence, the government took over some of the formerly exclusively European-owned estates, when the white owners no longer saw a future in their efforts. However, many Europeans remained, and the administration is aware of the importance to the country's economy of the highly organized plantation form of agriculture.

In the Vicinity of Mount Meru, Tanganyika. The surroundings of Mount Meru, centering upon the town of Arusha, form an important agricultural region. Communications are better here than in many other parts of the country, as evidenced by the asphalted road. The bus is picking up people going to Arusha, where some will sell what they can carry on the market. (United Nations)

Lake Victoria. There, also, is the major concentration of livestock, resulting in overcrowding on the land, overgrazing, and soil deterioration. New lands southward from the shores of the lake have been opened up, but, as in the other cash crop-subsistence areas, the improvement of farming practices has been a slow process. In these areas, the problems of African agriculture—poor farming methods, resistance to change, continuing influence of customary modes of land tenure, lack of adequate equipment and capital, as well as managerial ability, and the limited positive effects of economic incentives—come to the fore. Tanganyika's soil resources are not sufficient to permit neglect of conservation policies, and the Lake Province is a good example of the dangers of such neglect. There are limits to the expansion of planted acreage that can take place, and when these limits have been reached, the continued prosperity of the region depends upon proper farming methods.

The subsistence crops grown along with the cash crops also make a major contribution to the country's development, as they enter the internal exchange economy in large and increasing quantities and variety. Bananas, often grown in association with coffee; corn, which grows in the Moshi-Arusha area, among other sections; coconuts, which grow in the eastern parts of the country; and cassava, millet, and oranges are among the many products.

Finally, there are the extensive areas of dominantly subsistence agriculture, often still of the shifting variety, and pastoralism such as that of the Masai. With negligible use of fertilizers, even when stock manure is available, there is soil exhaustion, more or less severe erosion, and declining yields.

Among the recent developments aimed at the improvement of agriculture and the further diversification of agricultural production are irrigation schemes and community development projects. Among the latter, the project at Rungwa, involving the introduction of crops, farming implements, fertilizers, modern transport, and so on, is dramatically bringing the area into the twentieth century. The possibilities for irrigation in Tanganyika are limited, and it has been estimated that

246

about 4 million acres, or about 2 per cent of the area of the country, can be opened up for crop production.[8] This is equal, however, to some 20 per cent of the total area of the country cultivated by African peasants.

The greatest potential for irrigation, part of which is today being developed, lies in the basin of the Rufiji River. This basin is characterized by a large plain in its interior (western) reaches, the wide Kilombero Valley in the central part, and the rather narrow Lower Rufiji Valley in the east. Of major interest is the Kilombero Valley, where over a half-million acres could be cultivated under irrigation, and a start has been made with the production of sugar. The railroad meeting the Central Line at Kilosa is being extended into the valley. There as well as in the valley of the Lower Rufiji River, flood control is a prime requirement before large-scale developments can be begun. In the Lower Rufiji Valley, nearly 300,000 acres could be placed under irrigation, and in addition there is the hydroelectric potential of Stiegler's Gorge, all within a little over a hundred miles from Dar es Salaam. Smaller irrigation possibilities exist in the Ruvu and Rovuma basins, while the Pangani Basin could perhaps support 200,000 acres, although engineering and pedologic conditions there are not favorable.

All these projects lie in the eastern part of the country, and the potential in the west appears to be far less significant, for reasons of both physiography and remoteness. In viewing the spatial distribution of the actual productive capacity and potential development in Tanganyika, the peripheral character of the important areas is emphasized. Tanganyika might be referred to as a country without a core, although it could be argued that such a core is in the process of developing now in the Dar es Salaam–Tanga–Meru triangle. It is true that most of the electricity consumed is produced in this region, that the intensity of cash cropping is great there, that most of the railroads concentrate in these sections, and that, with the discovery of phosphate and columbite and the future development of irrigation and hydroelectric power in the Rufiji, Ruvu, and Pangani basins, this will be the most highly productive part of the country. In addition, Dar es Salaam and Tanga form the major urban concentrations, the largest domestic market, and the site of virtually all of the country's limited, agriculture-based industrial development. But a closer look at the prospective core area of Tanganyika reveals that it still consists of distinct islands of activity, separated by wide, empty, undeveloped swaths of dry, low-potential land, which change has barely touched. Furthermore, the scale of things in Tanganyika should be kept in mind; in 1960, Tanganyika, two-thirds as large as South Africa and with two-thirds of South Africa's population, had a net national income one-twentieth as large as that of the republic. Such is the problem of resources and development in this part of East Africa.

---

[8] *The Economic Development of Tanganyika,* Report published by a Mission of the International Bank for Reconstruction and Development (Baltimore: The Johns Hopkins Press, 1961), p. 18.

12

KENYA AND THE PROBLEM OF LAND

A GEOMETRIC BOUNDARY was drawn to separate German East Africa from a territory known until 1920 as the British East Africa Protectorate. It was delimited from Lake Victoria along the northern slopes of Mount Kilimanjaro, and on to the coast. Although the product of convenient agreement rather than a carefully considered adjustment to local conditions, as is true of so many other African boundaries, this line ran through dry, relatively empty lands. The main people to be somewhat affected were the nomadic Masai cattle herders of the region.

One consequence of the definition of the German-British boundary in East Africa was the channeling of British penetration toward the Lake (Victoria) Region. What remained of the British sphere of influence in East Africa included only one port, Mombasa. Like the Germans, the British recognized that effective communications with the hinterland were a prime requirement for effective government and economic progress, and railroad construction from Mombasa toward the densely populated Lake Region began in 1895. This was nearly a decade earlier than the Germans' first steps in connecting Dar es Salaam with the interior by rail.

Although the Germans and the British had agreed on the location of the border between their respective claims between Lake Victoria and the coast, the hinterland around and beyond Lake Victoria remained in dispute. In 1888, the British East Africa Company was created, which campaigned in Britain to rouse government and public interest in spreading British influence in this part of Africa. The officials of this company realized that the kingdom of the BaGanda people, along the northwestern shores of Lake Victoria, was likely to play a leading role in a developing East Africa. In 1893, largely due to the efforts of the company, Uganda—of which the BaGanda Kingdom forms a part—became a part of the British sphere of influence. For years, the claim made by Peters to this region for Germany had been disputed, and the abrupt termination of the role played by Emin Pasha against the spread of British influence led to German recognition of British hegemony in Buganda.

Having thus secured the entire northern Lake Region, the British, less troubled than the Germans by rebellions, began to exercise control. The railroad begun at Mombasa reached the first of several escarpments in 1900, and a number of railway workshops were built where the city of Nairobi stands today. The British East Africa Company, unlike the British South Africa Company and the Royal Niger Company, did not thrive as a result of mineral concessions and agricultural development. Burdened with administrative functions which London was reluctant to take over, and hampered by a lack of direction in policy, the company was in frequent financial difficulties. Eventually, Britain assumed the responsibilities of a protectorate over the entire territory first opened by the company, including also Zanzibar and Uganda.

248

Final Definition of Territory

While the southern boundary remained as defined, changes occurred elsewhere as late as 1926, when the status of the territory itself had been altered. In 1924, a treaty was signed between Britain and Italy whereby Italy was given a large tract of land including the Juba (Giuba) River in the northeast. This area was joined to what was then Italian Somaliland. In 1926, land between Lake Rudolf and the present boundary with Uganda was included in Kenya. Both changes involved the definition of geometric boundaries, which today still separate Kenya from Somalia and from Sudan. Neither change involved valuable land. The northeastern transfer of territory, especially, affected a dry and parched region, although the Juba River valley itself is of better quality.

The total area of Kenya is just under 225,000 square miles, of which a little over 5,000 are covered by lake water. This, however, is a misleading figure, because many thousands of square miles in the northeast are among the most useless in Subsaharan Africa, and many more in the north along the Ethiopian and Sudanese border are little better. Indeed, this north and northeast is one of the most sparsely populated parts of the entire subcontinent.

The Kenya Highlands

East of Lake Victoria, therefore, the British East African domain included much land which could at best be described as steppe. In general terms, only the southwestern quarter of the territory could be considered an asset; the administration of the remainder was a liability.

The railroad which was under construction from Mombasa toward the Lake Region reached the steep ascent to the higher areas of the territory in 1900. The initial object was to connect Mombasa with Kisumu on Lake Victoria, an achievement which occurred in

1903. The railroad had been built in view of future potentialities rather than existing opportunities, and at the time it was completely uneconomic. Its contribution in opening up the country and eliminating slavery, disease, and poverty were among the factors leading its construction, and British administrators sought means to reduce the drain upon the home exchequer.

Connecting Mombasa and Kisumu by the shortest possible route, the railroad crossed southwestern Kenya in its entirety, including the region which has come to be known as the Kenya Highlands. This is Kenya's most diversified area, and tropical Africa's most extensive highland zone, as the bulk of it lies over 5,000 feet. The soils are among Africa's best, derived in large part from volcanic rocks. There are extensive areas of rather flat land, and the climate is cool and sufficiently moist to permit specialized cropping. Depending somewhat upon the contour boundary selected, the Kenya Highlands cover some 60,000 square miles. This includes several extremely high sections, such as the Aberdare Mountains and Mount Kenya (over 17,000 feet above sea level), as well as the lower lands in the Eastern Rift Valley, whose floor nevertheless lies several thousand feet above sea level. Included also are steep escarpments and dense forests, but in general the land is of excellent quality for intensive agriculture. Areas such as the Kikuyu Plateau, the flanks of the Aberdare mass, and the Nyeri Plains support a dense population where occupied by Africans practicing subsistence farming and produce high incomes for plantation farmers.

None of this potential was evident when the railroad was being laid across the Highlands, which are divided into two sections by the Rift Valley. There was no dense African population on the fertile lands and, of course, there were no plantations. The lands had been occupied by many people in the past, as subsequent research has proved, but they were vacated just at the time Charles Eliot, first Commissioner of British East Africa, saw them. Eliot envisaged a thriving European farming community in the Highlands, economic prosperity, civilization—and a paying railway. He advised the British government

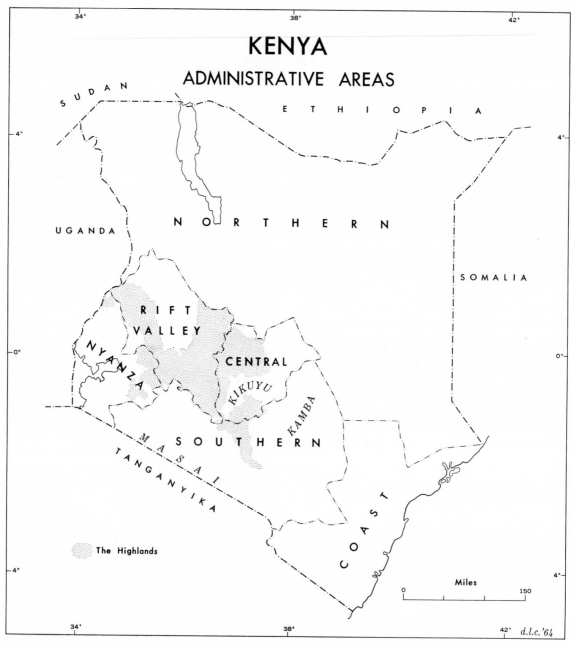

KENYA
ADMINISTRATIVE AREAS

Map 57

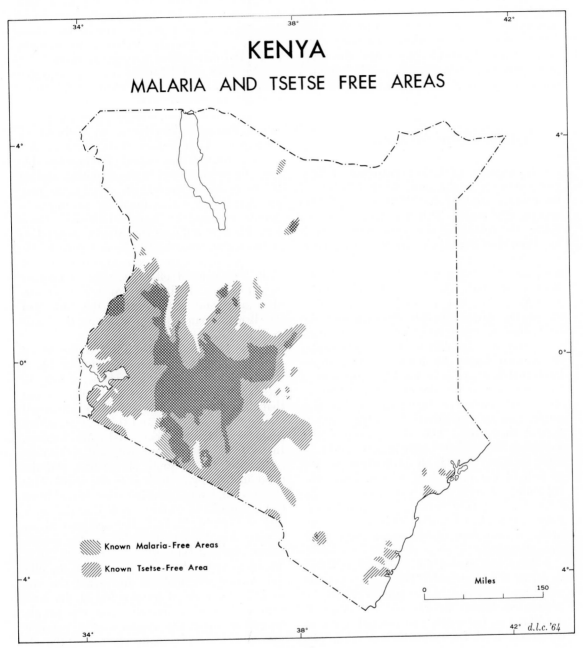

KENYA

MALARIA AND TSETSE FREE AREAS

Known Malaria-Free Areas

Known Tsetse-Free Area

Miles

0   150

42° *d.l.c. '64*

Map 58

to encourage white immigration into the protectorate. The first few settlers arrived before the turn of the century, but white immigration into Kenya really began in 1902. Initially occupying the land around Nairobi, the white settlers soon commenced to penetrate other parts of the Highlands. With this, the seeds of friction had been sown, to reach fruition a half-century later.

Land and the Africans

In response to the concentration of Kenya's resources in the southwestern sector of the country, most of the 7,500,000 people also occupy this region. This was true in Kenya before the coming of the white settlers, as it has been true since their arrival. It was, however, not true at the exact moment in history marking the first organized penetration by Europeans, and Charles Eliot saw British East Africa in a unique condition: the majority of the African people had vacated the lands they normally occupied and cultivated.

Land was granted to the settlers under the Crown Lands Ordinance, which stipulated that land not in beneficial occupation at the time was at the disposal of the Crown. Areas of sparse or haphazard cultivation might also be considered for settlement, as indeed they were. The area placed under European freehold or leasehold increased rapidly, in fact, out of all proportion to the growth of the number of whites. From the beginning, it must have been clear that the white settlers could never expect to farm the huge areas placed under their care. Eventually, no less than 16,700 square miles were thus alienated.

What had caused the African population to vacate the Highlands? The Kikuyu people, who occupied much of the land between the Aberdares, Mount Kenya, and the lands of the Masai to the south, had cleared much of the forest land for cultivation. Having displaced the Wanderobo hunters toward the end of the nineteenth century, the Kikuyu are said to have compensated the former with livestock for the lands they occupied. Prior to the arrival of the whites, the Kikuyu lived in an uneasy balance with their enemies, the raiding, cattle-herding, nomadic Masai and the spirited Kamba. In the south, some land may have been relatively empty because of the aggressiveness of the Masai, but these people were already declining in strength when the first whites penetrated there.

In 1898 and 1899, however, a sequence of events occurred which changed the situation drastically. In 1898, there was a great smallpox epidemic which ravaged the population, followed directly by an outbreak of rinderpest which decimated the livestock. Beginning during this period, an interminable drought persisted for many months, ruining the crops which might have saved many people, and while it was breaking, an unprecedented invasion of locusts followed. These four disasters reduced the African population of the region, and the survivors turned northward and fled back in the direction of Fort Hall. The general effect was the temporary depopulation of the eastern sector of the Highlands—and it was just at this time that the British commissioner first saw the lands as "empty."

The catastrophe also affected the Masai seriously and dealt them a series of blows from which these people never were fully to recover. It was through the lands of the Masai that the railroad was drawn before it reached the Highlands proper, and this was an added problem for these beleaguered cattle herders. In 1904, the Masai were confined to two reserves, one to the south of the line, and the other in Laikipia, which is to the north. This move completely emptied the Rift Valley from Naivasha to Nakuru, as well as the lands east of Nairobi. In 1911, the northern Masai reserve was closed, and the people moved across the railroad to the southern area, described as ample for their needs in the official documents involved. Just what the criteria were for the determination of the land requirements of a nomadic pastoral people dependent upon the vagaries of a variable climate never were made clear, but the effects upon the Masai have been obvious.

It is true, however, that the lands available to the various African peoples in the first decade of the present century were sufficient for their immediate needs, reduced as a result of their decimation. Of course, their confinement in demarcated areas did not immediately alter their methods of patch agriculture, and as time went on, the method began to reduce the capacity of the soil. Lands which were initially adequate eventually failed to provide the required yields, which the British administration ascribed to "wasteful and harmful methods" of African agriculture. Meanwhile, Africans who had left their section of the Highlands in 1899 began to return, either to overcrowd the lands set aside for African occupation or to find that the lands they left some years previous had been reserved for white occupation. ". . . Certain small areas of Kikuyu land had been alienated in all good faith for European settlement, (and this) led to the beginnings of agitation for the return of the 'stolen lands.'"[1]

As the reserves became areas of severe population pressure, many Africans made their way to Nairobi and onto the European settlers' farms in search of wage labor. By 1912, 12,000 were thus engaged outside their home areas, in 1927, 152,000, and in 1939 as many as 200,000.[2] As the number of settlers and their prosperity increased, Nairobi became the thriving center of a wealthy farming region. The town grew rapidly and attracted many unskilled laborers, for whom there were insufficient jobs and grossly inadequate housing. In contrast, there were less than 10,000 white settlers in the entire country in 1914, and under 30,000 in 1948. The white population of Kenya never exceeded 70,000.

Since the early 1920's, land has been the central issue in Kenya. After the end of the First World War, when a number of Kikuyu returned from service in other parts of the world, political organization among the Africans began to come about, and the oft-expressed aim was to effect a change in the government's land policies. Pressure rose, in response to which the Secretary of State for Colonies in 1932 appointed the Kenya Land

Commission (Carter Commission). The task of this body was to investigate the needs of the African population in terms of land and to consider every claim made by the local inhabitants. As a result of its lengthy deliberations, some hundreds of square miles changed hands, but basic policies (such as the reservation of certain areas on the basis of skin color) were not altered.

When, after the Second World War, African veterans received a work permit whereas whites obtained land concessions, the land crisis entered its crucial stages. African grievances were rife. There had been restrictions upon African cultivation of certain cash crops such as coffee and tea, the argument being that good quality was to be maintained and that Africans would cause a deterioration of the level of Kenya exports. In addition, the whites did not especially want the competition of African farmers, and, finally, African land was best put to use under staple crops. These practices, and the differences between wage scales for Africans and non-Africans, unemployment in Nairobi, segregation practices, and the need (for Africans only) to carry an employment registration certificate created increasing tensions. The return to Kenya of Jomo Kenyatta late in 1946 was followed by much political and illegal activity, and the Mau Mau crisis broke in earnest in 1950. The "stolen lands" issue plunged Kenya into an abyss of division as the Africans initiated an unprecedented campaign of murder and destruction.

Underlying the entire matter was the contrast between the white and black man's approach to the ownership and use of Kenya's land. The Africans, and especially the Kikuyu, viewed land as the only real security, something sacred, eternally the possession of the people who once occupied it and depended upon it. Communally owned, the temporary abandonment of such land did not change the situation at all, and when the Kikuyu returned to find the lands of their people occupied by settlers it was, indeed, from their point of view, stolen. The whites, of course, applied European concepts of land ownership to the Highlands they found nearly empty: it was parceled out, purchased, fenced, and partly cultivated. Many African squatters

---

[1] F. D. Corfield, *The Origins and Growth of Mau Mau* (Nairobi: Government Printer, 1960), p. 17.

[2] W. Fitzgerald, *Africa,* p. 258.

The Highlands, Kenya. Kenya's best farmland is concentrated in the Highlands, scene of many of Kenya's recent problems. The Highlands are connected by good roads to the capital, Nairobi (top), and in this farming area lie some of the largest and wealthiest estates in Africa (middle). These two photographs were taken north of Nyeri. Another aspect of the Highlands (below), seen between Thomson's Falls and Nakuru, shows a striking resemblance to the Machadodorp Highveld of South Africa's eastern Transvaal.

254

were permitted to live on the unused portion of such land, but they were compelled to work 180 days a year for this right. Thus reduced to servitude by the fact of their existence on lands they considered theirs, the Africans within the Highlands reserved for white ownership had their grievance, as had those in the African reserves.

Even if the area which became known as the "White Highlands" had been immediately parceled out among the African claimants, it would not have solved the problem of overpopulation. More far-reaching solutions are required for Kenya's unemployment problem and for the condition of African agriculture, and several strides were taken in this direction after 1948, when a violent crisis was already inevitable. African leaders exploited the land issue, as it was bound to provoke strong reactions among the people, and when the Mau Mau uprising was over, nearly 14,000 people had died, the economy had been dealt an almost irreparable blow, race relations were worse than ever, and Kenya's future was bleak indeed. But in 1953 a Royal Commission came to Kenya to study means of improvement, and in 1955 it reported that the policy of reserving land on the basis of race should be terminated. In addition, the Swynnerton Plan for the intensification of agricultural development in the African land units was adopted by the government. Swynnerton, an assistant director of agriculture, called for methods which would increase production without adding greatly to the area under cultivation—something which might have saved the situation had it been evolved earlier.

Land and the White Settlers

The white settlers of Kenya have been the economic mainstay of the country, as a result of their ability to exploit the most valuable resources. The alienated lands, at their maximum extent, covered less than 17,000 square miles in total. If the forested, dry, and otherwise unsuitable land is subtracted, the whites possessed about 8,000 square miles of the country's best agricultural land, of which over 40,000 square miles exist.[3]

Whatever the relative size of the whites' land in Kenya, it is on this area that the economy of the territory has been based. Kenya's tremendous ecological extremes permit the cultivation of a wide range of crops, and the European farmers quickly introduced several. Possessing the capital and technical skills required to establish plantation farms, and benefiting by the unquestioned asset of individual land ownership, these settlers began to introduce modern times into the territory.

Initially, the Kikuyu, among other African peoples, were not unfriendly to these efforts by the European invaders. The events leading toward widespread dissatisfaction have been discussed above, but the white, too, saw a need for change—in the opposite direction. As their number grew and Kenya developed, the whites desired more power in the decision-making processes affecting British East Africa than they held while the territory remained a protectorate. Thus, in 1920, the major part of the British East Africa Protectorate was proclaimed a colony. The new colony excluded Uganda and, along the coast, the strip of land which was once a part of the independent Sultanate of Zanzibar. It was named after the great volcanic mountain, Mount Kenya ("White Mountain"), on the eastern edge of the Highland region.

The white settlers introduced such crops as coffee (almost exclusively the arabica va-

[3] The various observers of Kenya's situation use many different criteria to present the situation, depending upon their individual sympathies. Corfield (op. cit.) points out that the whites' area included thousands of square miles of forest "being preserved for the benefit of the whole Colony," but concludes that 12,000 square miles were under farms and ranches. Brown, in E. W. Russell, ed., *The Natural Resources of East Africa* (Nairobi: D. H. Hawkins in association with East African Literature Bureau, 1962), states that the criterion is rainfall: about 41,630 square miles have an annual precipitation over 30 inches, and "less than one-fifth or about 7,560 square miles lie in lands alienated to Europeans and Asians." The alienated lands, whether comprising one-fifth or one-quarter of Kenya's good agricultural land, cover the heart of the Highlands, and much of the surrounding African land, though also of high quality, shows some of the effects of increasingly marginal location.

Views in Nairobi, Kenya. The capital of Kenya is East Africa's largest urban center, and its bustling, high-rise central business district reflects its growth and prosperity. Shown here are apartment buildings and stores above and government buildings below.

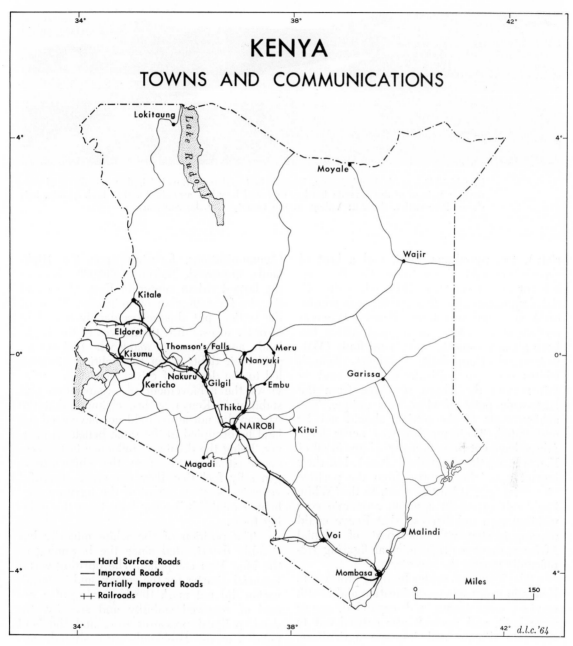

KENYA
TOWNS AND COMMUNICATIONS

Lokitaung

Lake Rudolf

Moyale

Wajir

Kitale

Eldoret

Thomson's Falls

Meru

Kisumu

Nanyuki

Nakuru

Gilgil

Kericho

Embu

Garissa

Thika

NAIROBI

Kitui

Magadi

Voi

Malindi

Mombasa

Miles
0   150

Hard Surface Roads
Improved Roads
Partially Improved Roads
++ Railroads

d.l.c.'64

Map 59

257

The Nairobi-Uganda Road, Kenya. Kenya's best and most traveled highway is the road connecting Nairobi to the Uganda border. Its initial length is asphalted and of high quality. It is shown here within the **Rift Valley**, in the vicinity of Lake Naivasha.

riety), tea, pyrethrum, sisal, and a host of cereals, vegetables, and fruits. The first significant export year was 1910, when the initial domination of coffee (which has continued) and sisal was foreshadowed. Whereas settlement by whites in tropical Africa has been attracted mostly by mineral finds (Witwatersrand, Copperbelt, Katanga), Kenya's whites came to cultivate the soil, and in this respect the Kenya situation, from the large-scale point of view, was unique. The achievements of the settlers should not be underrated. Their number was never large (there have not been as many whites in all of Kenya as on the Copperbelt alone), but their impact upon the country, from the positive viewpoint, was at least as great. In the "White Highlands" grew an agrarian economic core yielding such rich harvests that Kenya could develop in step with other parts of colonial Africa without a single mineral figuring significantly among the exports.[4]

The European settler brought progress to Kenya in many spheres. Education and health services were begun and expanded, towns were built, and research was carried out to eradicate disease and improve agriculture.

Communications, focusing upon the Highlands, improved. Nairobi (250,000) became the largest urban center in East Africa and the site for a number of industries. Many of the settlers put themselves deeply into debt in order to establish themselves in the Highlands, and there were many who had not repaid their debts when the political situation led to the decade of crisis. The white settler views the achievement of organization and stability in Kenya as his, claiming that the African did not and would not have used the land he occupied in the same beneficial manner. Being the dominant influence in the economic situation, therefore, the white settlers generally feel that they deserve a powerful voice in the government of the territory they helped establish, having long been the guiding force.

The position of the white minority has steadily deteriorated since the beginning of the Mau Mau campaign. The uprising was a financial disaster for the colony, and its termination did not mark the beginning of a period of renewed stability and security. Indeed, political pressures rose, and the land policies in the Highlands were altered, permitting persons of any race to purchase land in the area. African participation in the government also increased, and the settlers, losing their privileged position, saw their secur-

---

[4] Sodium chloride (salt) is gathered in the dried-up lakes of the Rift Valley and has been exported in some quantity.

ity threatened, prices decline, and competition arise. An estimated 30 per cent made their intentions to depart known in 1962.[5] In some instances, their farms have been taken over by African cooperative ownership and are continuing to function satisfactorily, but it must be expected that the transition will have detrimental effects for some years. Kenya's agrarian economy is at least as vulnerable to a lack of confidence in government as is that of mineral-based Northern Rhodesia, and restoration will take much time.

In spite of the British and Kenya governments' efforts to solve the land crisis in Kenya, violent reactions persisted into the 1960's. A Land Freedom Army made its appearance, proclaiming that it would not rest until all leaders in the country, white as well as black, came from LFA ranks and all land had been returned to tribal, Ghitaka ownership. Although insignificant in terms of its actual accomplishments, the LFA has had an important effect upon government in the territory. Since its major object is the ousting of white residents, several African members of the Kenya government have declined to denounce the organization for fear of repercussions in subsequent elections. This has led to charges of irresponsibility by the white settlers, who will need the government's support and protection if Kenya continues to depend upon her plantation crops. Noting the trend, more settlers left the territory, which faces a bleak future after the brief period of post-Mau Mau progress.[6]

[5] S. Wood, *Kenya: The Tensions of Progress* (Oxford: Oxford University Press, 1962), p. 129.

[6] For a survey of the situation see J. F. Lipscomb, *White Africans* (London: Faber & Faber, 1955).

Street Scene in Mombasa, Kenya. Mombasa is Kenya's only port, and it has a comparatively large Asian and Arab population in addition to the Africans and whites. Stores of the *duka* type are shown here in a nonwhite district of the town. (United Nations)

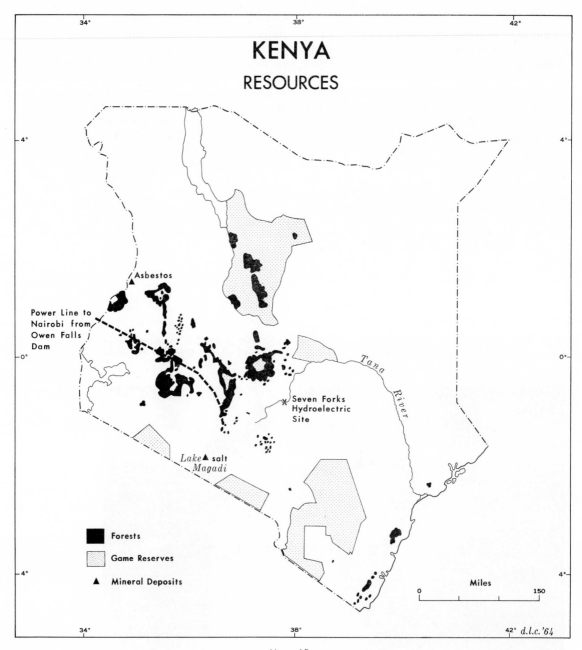

KENYA
RESOURCES

Asbestos

Power Line to
Nairobi from
Owen Falls
Dam

Tana River

Seven Forks
Hydroelectric
Site

Lake ▲ salt
Magadi

■ Forests

Game Reserves

▲ Mineral Deposits

Miles
0   150

d.l.c. '64

Map 60

260

The Asian Minority

In addition to some 70,000 white settlers, technicians, and government administrators, Kenya's population of nearly 9 million includes about 175,000 Indians, Pakistani, and Goans, and less than 40,000 Arabs, The white population has decreased in recent years, and the Asiatic minority has shared with it the fear of instability and insecurity.

As elsewhere in East Africa, the Asiatic population is highly urbanized, holds the majority of the skilled and semiskilled artisan jobs, and is found throughout the country in commerce and trade. The Asians possess much of the retail trade of Nairobi and Mombasa (145,000) and thus occupy a middle position in the economic order. As a result, the African finds himself competing first with the Asian for the jobs to which he can aspire. Here there is a conflict of interests, but otherwise the African and Asian share a history of inequality with their white cohabitants.

Asian influence in East Africa was felt long before that of the white man, and during the middle of the nineteenth century Asians controlled the commerce between Zanzibar Island and its coastal possessions. The spread of Asians into the East African interior came after 1895, when the British imported indentured labor for the Uganda Railway as they had in the 1860's in Natal for the sugar plantations. When the railroad had been constructed and the period of required labor was over, many Indians preferred to remain, and with diligence they proceeded to stake out a share of the economic life of the territory. While the Arabs remained concentrated in the protectorate strip along the coast, the Asians brought many of the amenities of modern life to distant parts, and wherever there is a settlement of any size, an Asian store is sure to be a part of the scene.

As in South Africa, the cultural impact of the Asians upon East Africa is considerable. Apart from the tangible influences such as the architectural peculiarities of Mombasa and parts of Nairobi, the Asians brought with them and retain their home religion, languages, and living habits. Like the Africans, they were restricted in their ability to occupy land, and their representation in Kenya's governmental affairs has been disproportionately small; yet they have not aligned themselves with African claims until recently. This is partly due to the cultural isolation in which many of the Asians continue to live (speaking neither English nor Swahili) and partly because of their need for political stability. Although accused Mau Mau leaders were often defended in court by Asian attorneys, the majority of the Asians were against the rebellion, and among Africans there are anti-Asian sentiments. The Asians are likely to adjust quickly to the new political situation, however, and may play an important role in a future Kenya.

The Remaining Assets

The liabilities of Kenya have been outlined above, and the prominent problems are socio-economic in nature. For more than a decade, Kenya has stagnated at a time when much of the rest of Africa is moving forward. Kenya needs long-term organization acceptable to the majority of all the people. There is little prospect that the dependence upon the agricultural resources of the Highlands will soon decline, but in tropical Africa they form an unparalleled asset. Like mines and industries, farming on a scale which will be a country's economic mainstay requires capital and large-scale operations, and if the plantations are to be fragmented, the encroachment of subsistence agriculture must at all costs be prevented, probably by means of controlled cooperatives. But whatever the means of production, Kenya's Highlands can be the foundation for rapid progress when stability returns.

Although the Highlands are the core of Kenya, there are additional assets. The southern part of the coastal belt is capable of sustaining certain crops such as corn and sugar cane, although the acreage is limited. In addition to a region of market gardening around Nairobi, livestock is reared widely across the territory and not only by the nomadic Masai.

261

Pastoralism in Kenya. Somali pastoralists sell their livestock in Kenya, usually driving their herds down the Tana River and beyond to Mombasa for sale. Both Somali herds permanently in Kenya and Somali from Somalia have sold cattle on Kenya's markets. A herd is seen approaching the end of the long trek (above). The market of Garissa is often the scene of goat and sheep sales (below). (United Nations)

The industry suffers from drought and disease problems, but is growing, especially dairying along the Kikuyu Escarpment. Hides and skins figure among the exports, and cotton cultivation is proving a success there as in Tanganyika.

The port of Mombasa-Kilindini serves a hinterland comprising not only Kenya but also Uganda. It is the best harbor in East Africa, and whatever development takes place in the interior will benefit this city, already the second largest in Kenya and third in East Africa.

Finally, there is the asset of Kenya's magnificent scenery and wildlife population. Tourism is a major contributor to Kenya's annual revenue, and the industry can be greatly expanded. Several game reserves have been established, and communications and accommodations are being improved. The preservation of this heritage is a matter of priority for any Kenya government, and the rewards of such a policy will be great and lasting.

In stressing the all-pervading importance of the agricultural sector in the country's rate of growth and in raising living standards, the Mission for the International Bank for Reconstruction and Development in its recent report strongly supported the continuation of the Swynnerton Plan.[7] Certain modifications, based upon the changed circumstances, are proposed, but the general terms of the plan —the improvement, through reorganization and modernization, of African peasant agriculture in the nonestate areas—continue to be upheld. In addition, stress is laid upon the need for the retention of Kenya's professional and technical staff, and those capable of running the Highland plantations, the major sources of revenue in this poor territory. This will require the restoration of confidence among the country's non-Africans, doubtless a difficult task. Meanwhile, government assistance to agriculture in the form of credit, crop and disease research, extension services, and marketing activities is needed.

[7] *The Economic Development of Kenya*, Report published by a Mission of the International Bank for Reconstruction and Development (Baltimore: The Johns Hopkins Press, 1963), pp. 301 ff.

13

UGANDA AND THE PROBLEM OF POLITICS

THE NORTHWESTERN SECTOR of former British East Africa is occupied by the state of Uganda, smallest (91,000 square miles) of the three major units and, with a population of some 7 million, by far the most densely populated. Landlocked Uganda partakes of the waters of Lakes Victoria, Edward, and Albert to the extent of about 14,000 square miles, and in addition there is much territory under swamps and marshes. The country lies largely on a plateau just under 4,000 feet above sea level, dropping to lower elevations toward the Sudan Basin in the north, and diversified by some great mountains west and east such as Ruwenzori and Elgon. The southern part of the country, especially, enjoys the ameliorating effects of elevation upon the tropical temperatures, and almost all of it receives over 30 inches of rainfall.

The compact territory of Uganda lies in a number of transition zones. By virtue of its location in the east-central part of equatorial Africa, its natural vegetation includes the savanna lands of the east and the forests of the Congo margins in the west. The swampy lake regions of the south give way to the dryness and rain-deficient conditions that characterize the Sudan Basin northward. Uganda also is situated astride ethnic transition zones: south of Lake Kyoga it is generally Bantu country, in the north it is mainly Nilotic, and in the northeast, Nilo-Hamitic. The south is dominantly agricultural, much of the north pastoral. From the east have come the Arabs, Europeans, and Asiatics, all of whom have made their impact in the country. And from the north came many of the po-

litical ideas out of which the strong traditionalism of present-day Uganda emerged.

Unity and Fragmentation

Uganda became an independent state in 1962, after a lengthy sequence of political difficulties was in some measure resolved. In spite of its compact shape and relatively small areal extent, the internal variety of this country, in terms of ethnic groupings, traditions, and degree of economic development, is very great. This is true of many other African countries, but in Uganda the spatial arrangements so strongly favor the southern part of the country, mainly Buganda Province, that the final political unification of the territory long administered by Britain as a protectorate presented deeply rooted problems. These involved two major centrifugal forces which, even when the desire for independence was the strong centripetal force, tended to dominate the country's internal political geography.[1]

The favored southern part of Uganda is inhabited in large part by the BaGanda people, who number about one-sixth of the country's total population of 7 million. These BaGanda, along with about 1 million non-BaGanda, live mainly in the province known

---

[1] The example of Uganda is an excellent corollary to R. Hartshorne, "The Functional Approach in Political Geography," *Annals of the Association of American Geographers*, XL (1950), 95.

as Buganda, where the traditional authority is the king or Kabaka. One major centrifugal force in Uganda's political geography was the reluctance of Buganda to lose its privileges by being merged into a larger Uganda, the modern state. A second was the reticence of many of the non-BaGanda peoples of the country to support an independent state in which most of the power would lie in the favored south. In brief, the problem was how to fit Buganda into a larger Uganda, and the centrifugal forces remained sufficiently strong to prevent the evolution of the most common type of state elsewhere in Africa, the unitary state. A complicated federal arrangement was the product of centripetal forces seeking to end colonial administration while desiring to retain certain amounts of separate autonomy.

In many respects, Uganda is almost the complete opposite of Tanganyika, and the comparison yields valuable insights. Uganda, although much smaller and far more densely populated, is primarily a country of peasant agriculture, plantations making a very small contribution to the export revenue. In spite of its dense population, Uganda each year has a sizeable annual surplus of farm produce, virtually the entire volume being derived from African smallholdings producing well over 80 per cent of the annual export returns.[2] Yet Uganda normally has a more favorable balance of trade than either Kenya or Tanganyika. The major contrast, however, emerges when the spatial organization of the countries is considered: while Tanganyika's development can still be best described as peripheral, and a core area, if recognizable at all, is in the initial stages of development in the northeast, Uganda has a core area that is as well defined as any. All factors seem to have conspired to make this so. When, after the European penetration, the modern phase of the country's development began, it naturally focused in the region which was at that time best organized. This, of course, was the Kingdom of the BaGanda, lying in Buganda Province on the shores of Lake Victoria. Had

the outlet of the country been north or west, it would have been necessary to construct transportation lines in that direction, with the result that the isolation of Buganda from the rest of the country would have been reduced. But, as it happened, the natural exit was southeastward, through Mombasa, and the modern transport routes, focusing upon Buganda, came from that direction. That meant that they failed to cut through any part of the former protectorate except Buganda and the southern part of the Eastern Province. Thus, Buganda's political eminence was supplemented by several additional advantages: the British set up their administrative headquarters in Buganda, and when cash cropping began, the most suitable areas in terms of climate and pedology were also those near the lake and railroad, all in the same province.

Uganda's core area evolved rapidly, but more economically and administratively than as the source of ideas and the center of national unity. As such, "a core area is neither sufficient nor essential to the evolution of a nation or state. What is essential is a common idea that convinces the people in all the regions that they belong together. Historically in certain states a core area may have played a major role in spreading that idea to other regions . . . but the common idea for a state may develop where no core area exists."[3] Uganda and Tanganyika are cases in point.

The Factor of Economic Geography

Economic development in Uganda has directly benefited a larger percentage of the population than in either Kenya or Tanganyika, but progress has differed greatly in the various parts of the country. Uganda has always suffered from her landlocked location, although the railroad from Mombasa reached Kisumu on Lake Victoria as early as 1901. At that time, goods were transported to the railhead by steamer, but the railroad was extended into Uganda to eliminate the water

[2] For an analysis of Uganda agriculture, see D. N. McMaster, *A Subsistence Crop Geography of Uganda* (Bude Haven, Eng.; Geographical Publications Ltd., 1962), p. ix.

[3] Hartshorne, *loc. cit.*

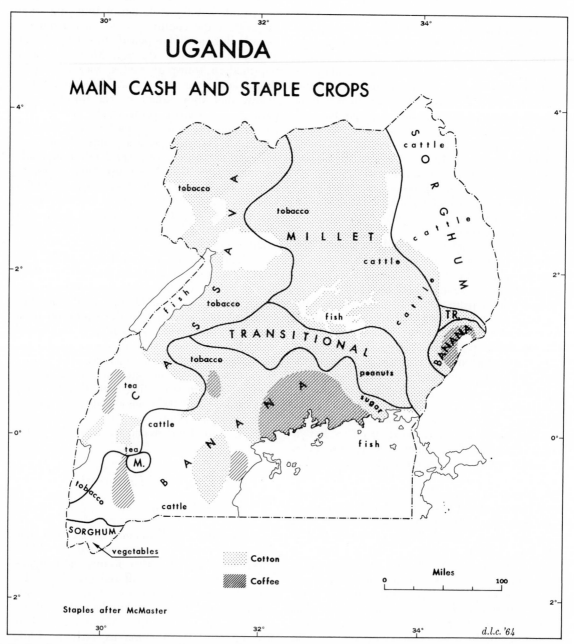

UGANDA

MAIN CASH AND STAPLE CROPS

Partly after D. N. McMaster, *A Subsistence Crop Geography of Uganda* (Bude Haven, Eng.: Geographical Publications, Ltd., 1962), p. 201.

Map 61

link. Development in Uganda has been closely tied to the expansion of the transport network, and a number of feeder roads to the central railroad and an increase in inland water transportation have been important factors. Further railroad construction into the northern regions (initially Gulu) is taking place.

Cotton was introduced during the first decade of the present century and proved to be a success, although the industry has been severely affected by fluctuating prices on the world market. After the Second World War, cotton cultivation rose sharply, partly as a result of the establishment of African cooperative unions and their participation in the cotton-ginning industry. Until then, this industry had been largely a non-African enterprise.

Well over 2 million acres are presently under cotton cultivation, and the highest intensity is in the Eastern Province, mainly Busoga, where conditions are good for the crop and where the distance to the railroad is not great. Cotton is cultivated in many other parts of the country, however, the most recent development being an area of cultivation along the southern foothills of Ruwenzori. Most commonly, it is grown as a rain crop, without irrigation, on farms which are less than five acres in size.

Uganda is the largest producer of coffee in the British Commonwealth. Initially, it was grown almost exclusively by the few white plantation owners and Asians; the Africans took an interest in this cash crop, however, and by the time of independence, about 30,000 acres were in plantations and some 600,000 in individual African farms. After the Second World War, coffee cultivation rose dramatically in Buganda, to the extent that the colonial government expressed concern about the possible replacement of cotton as the chief cash crop of the country.[4] The Ba-Ganda grow mainly the robusta variety, which is especially useful in the preparation of "instant" coffee, hence the ready market for this product. From the slopes of Mount Elgon comes the major part of the country's arabica harvest, grown in the Bugisu District and marketed through the Bugosu Cooperative Union. The acreage under robusta far exceeds that under arabica, but the combined acreage of these two varieties still is less than one-third of that of cotton. In terms of cash returns, however, coffee has exceeded the combined revenue for cotton, cotton seed, and cotton oil combined during the late 1950's. Thus, coffee is economical in its land requirements, although requiring more labor than cotton for its successful cultivation.

Cotton and coffee are by far the most important cash crops in Uganda, but the growing of corn as a cash crop has also become popular in recent years, and tea and tobacco (the latter mainly in the Western and Northern provinces) are likewise developing. The Uganda government is purchasing, for redistribution to African farmers, several of the remaining plantations. Sugar cultivation remains mainly in the hands of the Asians.

Somewhat less than one-third of Uganda's cultivated acreage is at present under cash crops, and in some parts of the country, notably the central area (between Lakes Victoria and Kyoga, in Buganda), the figure is as high as 60 per cent. In the northeast and southwest, food crops predominate to the extent that they occupy 90 per cent of the cultivated land, and in the Northern Province, 70 per cent or more of the land is under staples.[5] Thus, the population of the region which is politically and socially dominant in Uganda affairs also possesses the economic power of the country, being least dependent upon subsistence modes of life. The absence of a workable fuel deposit (other than wood), the discovery of copper deposits at Kilembe in the west, and the existence of a suitable site for water-power development at Jinja (35,000) combined to lead to the extension of the railroad to nearby Kasese, the large-scale development of the copper deposits (since 1953), and the construction of the Owen Falls hydroelectric project. In addition, a smelter was built at Jinja, and in 1960 Uganda exported nearly 15,000 tons of cop-

[4] *Annual Report of the Department of Agriculture* (Entebbe: Government Printer, 1948), p. 1.

[5] D. N. McMaster, *op. cit.*, map, p. 91. The main staple crops are bananas (Buganda), cassava (western Uganda), and millet and sorghum (north and northeast).

Cotton Cultivation in Uganda. Cotton is one of Uganda's chief exports, and many of the people are involved in the production of this commodity. A field of cotton is ready for picking (above, left, Department of Information, Uganda), after which the families of the village sort the bolls from the trash, which includes stalks, leaves, and so on (below, left). Then, the harvest is taken to a buying center, the one illustrated here being that at Rhino Camp (above, right). After the weighing, the cotton is put in bales and transported to the south and eventually via Mombasa to overseas markets. Until recently, water transport was important in this connection (below, right), but in recent years it has been disappearing in favor of the improving railroad system. (East African Railways and Harbours)

268

per. Although a number of other minerals are known to exist, and some are mined, including tin and cobalt, the mineral production of Uganda, compared to its agricultural output, is small. The significant point is that once again the main development has taken place south of the latitude of Lake Kyoga. Indeed, the people of northern Uganda (and the southwest) possess only one commodity they can export, in their case to other sections of Uganda, namely, livestock. Most of Uganda's 4 million cattle are concentrated in these regions, and beside their movement to Buganda, Busoga, and other markets within Uganda, they provide revenues in the form of exports of hides and skins to other countries.

Thus, there is a marked territorial concentration of the known wealth of Uganda, resulting in the development not only of several individual political arrangements but also of different economies, whose integration must be achieved. Similar situations have presented problems elsewhere in Africa. As a whole, Uganda's favorable balance of trade (with the United Kingdom the major trade partner) attests to the country's fortunate position among the political units of Africa. There is some danger that fluctuating world prices will at some time impede progress, and that the land of Uganda will not sustain the intensive modes of agriculture to which it is being subjected. In this, however, Uganda does not stand alone, and the state has given evidence of an awareness of these perils. Agricultural diversification is encouraged, the fishing industry (based on the many lakes, rivers, and 5,000 artificial ponds) is expanding, and communications are being improved. Meanwhile, Uganda, in spite of its situation and political diversity, may be described as an economically viable entity in Subsaharan Africa, and as such is unusual.

The Factor of Historical Geography

The political entity of Uganda was a creation of European colonialism, and the area prior to the first arrival of the Nyamwezi traders and the Arabs from the east in the late 1700's probably did not possess any elements of unity. Neither did it have the kind of contact with the outside world that marked the kingdoms of West Africa; for centuries no caravans reached the peoples of Uganda, no organized exporting of products took place.

The internal heterogeneity of the area of present-day Uganda, due in large part to its character as an ethnic transition area, was expressed in political ways long before the first European explorers reached the headquarters of Buganda in 1862. Clearly, some of the political ideas from the Nile Basin had reached Uganda, for there had been considerable progress in state organization, as exemplified by the kingdom of the BaGanda visited by Speke and Grant. This empire was by no means the only organized political area in the region, nor was it the first to have occupied a dominant position. The kingdoms of Bunyoro, Ankole, and Toro, whose areas also were incorporated in the Protectorate of Uganda, were similar in their organization, and had dominated the region centuries before.

Buganda was by far the most important of these politically organized units when the European invasion began, however, and in the period of colonial administration that followed, the kingdom played a leading role. But in precolonial Uganda, when there was no force binding the larger territory together, each of the kingdoms, and the tribal peoples of the more loosely organized areas elsewhere, had existed separately. Each had a physiographically rather well-demarcated territory: Buganda between Lakes Victoria and Kyoga; Bunyoro between Lakes Kyoga and Albert, the Victoria Nile, and the Kafu River; Toro on the eastern slopes leading from Ruwenzori north of the Katonga River; and Ankole west of Lake Victoria and south of the Katonga. These kingdoms had their times of greatness and decline; during the course of history, they had expanded at the expense of the less well-organized peoples around them and had encroached upon each other. The frontiers between them really were frontiers in the technical sense of the word: either they were undesirable lands, with swamps or

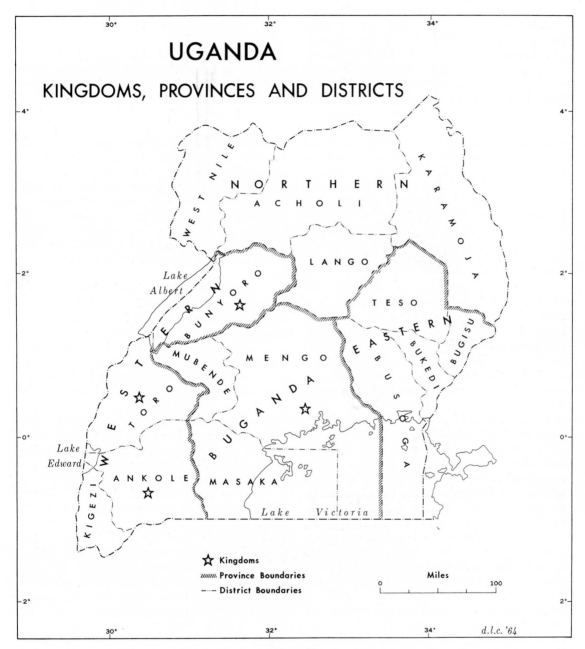

UGANDA

KINGDOMS, PROVINCES AND DISTRICTS

Map 62

marshes, or they were areas of conflict and attempted expansion.

When, during the middle 1800's, European contact was made, the Buganda kingdom was the largest, best organized, and most powerful in the region. The early explorers saw in Buganda a fertile field for missionary and trade activities, and it was situated in the southeast of the area beyond Lake Victoria, nearest to the coast from which penetration was to take place. But in the less organized parts of the region, the slave trade was still continuing, and where the Europeans were not exercising effective power and propagating Christianity, Arab traders were converting the people to Islam. Uganda, having been a meeting place of indigenous peoples, now became an area of competition between the proponents of these religions. Egyptian influences were felt in the north, European in the south. This conflict, and a real conflict it was, became superimposed upon the regional ethnic, political, and economic contrasts that already existed. In effect, the area was in a state of instability until after the establishment of a British protectorate in 1894 over the Kingdom of Buganda and its extension in 1896 over Bunyoro, Ankole, and Toro.

Thus, there was little to warrant the incorporation of so much diversity into a single political entity. It was natural that Buganda should be selected by the British as the headquarters of administration, for in the Uganda region, Buganda was the most powerful unit, and effective control there was the prime requirement for the establishment of order. Indeed, the BaGanda revolted against British overlordship not long after the establishment of the protectorate, and when the uprising had been put down, the kingdom was given special status in the Uganda Protectorate according to the Buganda Agreement of 1900. But then the British found themselves confronted by the task of forging a political whole out of the great variety within the country, in terms of the size, strength, competence, and desire to cooperate among the local authorities of nearly 30 distinct peoples, some of whom were being ruled on the basis of strong local customs and traditions, while others were still in the most rudimentary stages of tribal organization.

The Factor of Political Geography

The evolution of the state of Uganda provides an interesting illustration of Stephen B. Jones's unified field theory of political geography.[6] It will be recalled that the theory places "idea" and "state" at two ends of a chain, the model being political idea–decision–movement–field–political area. In the case of Uganda, the political idea, existing first in the minds of British administrators and later developing among African residents of the region, involves the eventual independence of colonies and protectorates in general, and Uganda in particular, the specific concept being the establishment of a united Uganda out of the diversity within the protectorate's borders.

In the case of Uganda, the final decision determining the nature of the political entity was preceded by a series of earlier decisions, including the 1894 and 1896 protectorates over Buganda and the other kingdoms, and the 1900 Buganda Agreement. Although the new state emerged more than a half-century later, the decision to foster self-determination in a future national state was implied by its protectorate status during that period, and was therefore made at that early time. Subsequent decisions were adjustments to the developments taking place within Uganda as the third phase—movement—took place.

In the application of the field theory model to Uganda, movement is seen to have taken several forms. Britain ruled Uganda from Buganda territory, and the administrative headquarters was located in Entebbe (whereas the traditional seat of the Kabaka has always been within a few miles of Kampala). In those areas where only the most rudimentary form of organization existed, it was necessary virtually to create and superimpose responsible local authority. BaGanda personnel were often used to staff adminis-

---

[6] "A Unified Field Theory of Political Geography," *Annals of the Association of American Geographers*, XLIV (1954), 111.

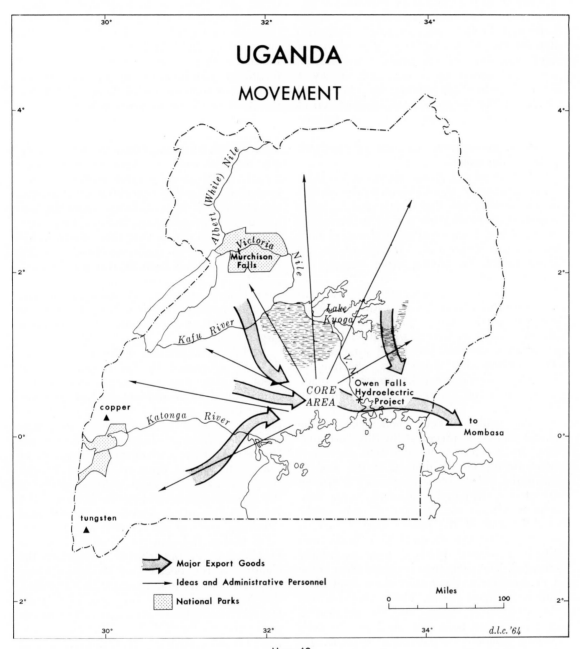

UGANDA
MOVEMENT

Albert (White) Nile

Victoria
Murchison
Falls

Nile

Kafu River

Lake
Kyoga

V. N.

CORE
AREA

Owen Falls
Hydroelectric
Project

copper

Katonga River

to
Mombasa

tungsten

Major Export Goods

Ideas and Administrative Personnel

National Parks

Miles

0   100

d.l.c. '64

Map 63

273

trative offices in such non-Buganda territories, perhaps the most striking single example of movement in the context of this model. But there were other instances. Efforts were made to imprint the Buganda pattern of administration on the other kingdoms. The nature of land ownership and occupance was changed, communal ownership being replaced by a form of individual holding by chiefs and headmen. This facilitated the introduction of a number of cash crops and accelerated the change from a subsistence to an exchange economy, an essential element of the field phase of the model.

Movement in Uganda, however, has been a slow process. It should be remembered that the initial idea was that of a united Uganda, requiring, of course, the partial submergence of tribal and local loyalties in favor of allegiance to a larger state. Movement, in the Jones model, is, among other things, the spread of a state idea. In several other countries (such as Tanganyika with its Tanganyika African National Union), strong national political parties have grown which have proved capable of fostering a national loyalty in addition to local and tribal attachments. This process has been less effective in Uganda, a factor which has inevitably made itself felt in the nature of the resultant political area.

The study of field phenomena in the model should be preceded, in this particular case, by a reference to the field characteristics already clearly defined at the time of the initial (idea) phase. Uganda's territorial extent was delimited, with only minor subsequent adjustments, at about the time of the establishment of the protectorate. Hence, it is not possible here to speak of a "field" from which a defined political area eventually emerged. The difference becomes clear upon a comparison to the model when applied to Liberia in West Africa. There, the idea was the abolition of slavery and the eradication of its consequences; the decision involved making available repatriation facilities for former slaves desiring to return to Africa; movement took place with the traveling of former slaves from several parts of the world to selected West African areas; and a field of settlement and governmental activity led to the political area, the state of Liberia. The point is that the field phenomena developed quite late there, with considerable adjustments after the state had already been proclaimed. In Uganda, on the other hand, the character of the field changed significantly— internally, that is—but there was no phase of territorial consolidation through war and expansion, as for instance in the case of Israel, the product of the idea of Zionism.

Furthermore, Uganda, even before it was Uganda Protectorate, possessed a core area, even though this area, Buganda, did not actually serve as such. In Buganda it possessed an area of advanced politico-territorial organization, considerable concentration of power, the beginnings of an exchange economy, and a degree of urbanization. But if a map were drawn of Uganda at that time, there would be no network of communications focusing upon this core area from the rest of the region, no integrating movement and circulation, no spread and adoption of ideas originating there. It required the initiation of the chain to forge there a functioning core area for a larger Uganda.

The special position of Buganda in Uganda was recognized by the Buganda Agreement of 1900 and was emphasized by the appointment of a resident in this province rather than a provincial commissioner. Uganda was divided administratively into four provinces of which Buganda was one; the Western Province included the kingdoms of Toro, Ankole, and Bunyoro, and the Busoga "kingdom" was the main political entity in the densely populated Eastern Province. The Northern Province included some of the least developed parts of the country, with its many small village and clan communities. Buganda Province so far outstripped the rest of the country as the decades of the protectorate wore on, and its individualism so intensified, that its function as the core area of a larger Uganda was actually impaired. The services performed by the Kabaka's government have been far more complete than those of any of the other local governments in Uganda. With the concentration of the country's productive capacity there, per capita incomes are larger than anywhere else in the country, the level of education is higher, its degree of urbaniza-

Elephants, Murchison Falls National Park, Uganda. One of East Africa's major tourist attractions is the variety of its wild life. If fewer people went to shoot, and more to see and learn, scenes like this one would be a permanent and incomparable asset to the region. Several African governments have shown concern recently for the future of their countries' wildlife heritage and have passed stricter laws against poaching, while limiting hunting licenses. (East African Railways and Harbours)

tion (with the capital and largest city, Kampala [75,000], located in Buganda) is greatest. Finally, Buganda lies at the center of the country's road and railroad network, virtually all roads leading to Kampala, and the railroad from Kasese to the eastern border (and beyond to Mombasa) crosses through the entire province.

The individualism—indeed, separatism—of Buganda has been a major centrifugal force in the political geography of this country. Uganda possesses many of the elements required for independence, the success of cash cropping has ensured economic viability, and a series of maps showing the urban centers, resources, communication grid, and core area would seem to support the assertion that the field phenomena are those of a state. But the old forces of fragmentation had not been submerged sufficiently, even in the independence year 1962, to permit the organization

of the political area—the final phase of the model—as a unitary state, for which its shape, size, and communications network seem to be so suitable. While Buganda Province possessed far more cohesion than any other part of Uganda, and political sophistication and levels of education were more advanced in this region, the total population of 2 million represented only about 30 per cent of that of Uganda. In an independent state with a government based on the universal franchise, therefore, Buganda could not expect to dominate politically as it dominated economically and socially. Thus, Uganda was faced with demands for secession and independence from the very core area upon which its future as a state was to depend.

The British government, in an effort to find a solution to this problem, in 1960 established an investigative body known as the Relationships Commission. In 1961, it recom-

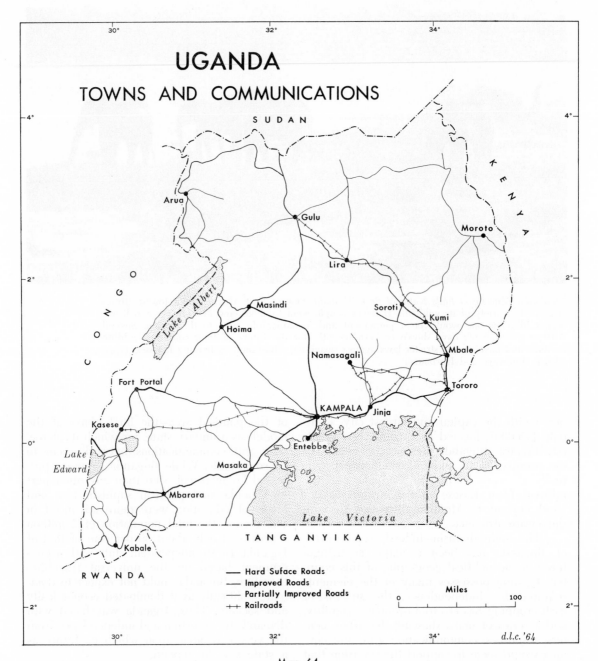

Map 64

mended that Uganda be served by a strong central democratic government, with Buganda in a federal relationship and Toro, Ankole, and Bunyoro in a semifederal relationship with the central government. Broadly on this basis, the political area became the state of Uganda late in 1962.

The East African Common Services Organization: Toward a Federation of East Africa

The territories in East Africa which have been under British control have for many years cooperated in a wide range of non-political activities. The pattern of interterritorial relationships in the economic sphere was developed by the British and is continuing after independence. In 1948, the East Africa High Commission was established to coordinate the approaches in the individual countries toward common problems. This commission, composed of the governors of the three territories with their advisory and executive staffs, had a legislative branch empowered to deal with matters relating specifically to the services involved. These included the railways and harbors, postal services, telecommunications, civil aviation, and customs.

Independence in East Africa, which came first to Tanganyika on December 9, 1961, required a revision of the High Commission's organization, and Tanganyika declared its intention to continue participation in the common services provided by the commission. Meanwhile, African leaders throughout East Africa (which has an area comparable to that of western Europe and a total population of 25 million) had begun to voice support for East African unity not only in the economic and communications fields, but also politically. Thus, in 1961, a conference took place in London, attended by representatives from each of the three major territories in East Africa and an observer from Zanzibar, in addition to a British delegation. At this conference, an East African Common Services

Organization was established, coming into formal existence two days after Tanganyika achieved independence. Superseding the High Commission, the Common Services Organization (also referred to locally as the Common Market) was constituted differently, with the three prime ministers forming the central authority in charge of general policy, and various ministerial committees concerned with the individual services involved.

The organization offers a number of advantages for East Africa as a whole. The customs union, for instance, has practically eliminated barriers to the interterritorial movements of goods and factors of production, and it has greatly reduced the need for administration: for example, goods entering the region at Mombasa and intended for Uganda need be processed only once, at the port. There is no need for further checkpoints along the roads or railroads between Kenya and Uganda, or, for that matter, between Kenya and Tanganyika.

The economic geography and the location of the areas of productive capacity of each of the three countries have resulted in different responses to the Common Services Organization and its programs. Tanganyika's Lake and West Lake provinces use the Lake Victoria and Kenya railroad as a means of contact with the outside world, while a considerable part of the trade of the Kilimanjaro–Meru region goes via Mombasa. But Tanganyika is the least developed of the three new states and requires the means to exercise an economic policy in support of its special needs; if it does not accept the fiscal policies of its wealthier neighbors, it faces a dangerous outflow of capital, but if it does, it will sustain losses in tax revenues. Hence, Tanganyika cannot without certain reservations participate in any economic union of East Africa. Tanganyika is also less well off than Kenya in terms of the relative location of the components of the Common Market. Kenya's core area lies in an excellent position with reference to the transportation system of East Africa and the distribution of population. In the northwest, the province of Buganda lies in close proximity, and the best port, Mombasa, is about as far to the southeast. Railroad connections now link Nairobi not only with the Kilimanjaro area, but also with Dar es Salaam and its hinterland. Industries serving the entire East African market, therefore, most probably would select the Highlands as their location. Moreover, Kenya's land shortage continues and intensifies, so that industrialization is essential. For this, among other reasons, Kenya needs the Common Services Organization more than either Tanganyika and Uganda, so that its policies are directed at the preservation of the unit.

The position of Uganda in the organization is a difficult one, at least at present, apart from the political aspects of the matter. Obviously, Buganda, having struggled for a privileged position within Uganda itself, sees that position endangered by any movement toward a greater East Africa. East Africa's modern nationalist leadership does not easily cooperate with the hereditary traditionalism of the Kabaka and his kingdom. But Uganda is a landlocked state and needs its only feasible outlet through Kenya, so participation is in its own interests.

From the point of view of economic geography, nevertheless, there are distinct disadvantages for Uganda in its cooperation within the Common Services Organization framework. Some of these it shares with Tanganyika, in that Uganda, with a primarily subsistence and cash crop economy, needs specially adjusted fiscal policies to foster development. Unless agricultural incomes within Uganda rise so much that the prosperity of the local market will justify industrialization, Kenya will remain the preferred location for East African industries, and Uganda will lag in this area. Such a rise in agricultural incomes will take much time, during which the organization is likely to put the country at a disadvantage.

Another disadvantage, also shared to some extent with Tanganyika, involves the loss of import (and export) duties. A common market protective tariff and industrialization in Kenya, coupled with more Uganda purchasing from one of the other two East African countries and less from foreign sources, result in two things. First, the prices paid by Uganda may be higher, and, second, Uganda loses the import duties once levied. In Kenya, where such duties are also re-duced (but by the growth of local production), the loss of income is replaced by revenues from taxes on the industries' profits. Uganda cannot replace this loss.

Thus, economic union in East Africa is not an unmixed blessing for all three of the territories involved, but eventually the advantages are likely to outweigh the liabilities. The common services are far superior to those any one of the countries could alone sustain, and the rate of growth of the unit as a whole has been more rapid than would have been possible for the separate territories individually. The difficulties of the initial phase, however, must have their impact upon the political blueprint for any East African Federation. Unity under a strong federal government would superimpose political problems upon the still maladjusted economic relationships. A larger East Africa is among panafricanists' prime goals. The first steps must necessarily be economic if such a unit is to have a strong foundation, and they are being taken. If and when the politico-geographical obstacles are also overcome, Africa will have taken a major step forward.

278

14

RWANDA AND BURUNDI:
LEGACY OF DEPENDENCE AND DISUNITY

RUANDA AND URUNDI, prior to the First World War, were among the most densely populated districts of German East Africa. When armed hostilities erupted in East Africa, Belgium participated, using Congolese troops to attack the Germans from the west. By September, 1916, Belgian forces had reached Tabora, in the central part of German territory, and one battalion actually penetrated to the Indian Ocean at Lindi. At the end of the war, the Belgians had captured not only Ruanda and Urundi, but also most of the District of Kigoma and parts beyond, and were thus in effective control of nearly a third of the people and territory of the former German sphere.

In 1919, the Supreme Council of the League of Nations, meeting at Versailles to consider the question of disposal of Germany's colonial empire, placed all of former German East Africa under British mandate. This decision aroused great resentment in Belgian circles, in view of the effort Belgium had expended in the East African war theater, and because the area captured by the Belgian forces contained land suitable for white settlement and for livestock raising, opportunities which in the adjacent Congo were rather scarce. Thus, Belgium expressed its desire to retain for occupation, at least, a section of the territory in question, and the matter was reopened for discussion. The League of Nations granted Belgium the right to solve the problem by direct negotiation with Great Britain, and an agreement was reached whereby Belgium received, under mandate, almost the entire area of the territories of Ruanda and Urundi. Boundary definition, delimitation, and demarcation (in part) took place during 1923 and 1924. In 1925, "Ruanda-Urundi" became an integral part of the Belgian Congo. As a result, Belgium came to rule the most densely populated region of former German East Africa, including over one-third of the total population of that dependency.[1]

Belgian Administration

An additional reason for Belgian interest in Ruanda and Urundi was the relationship of this area to Katanga, which was developing and where labor was needed—and in short supply. The Belgian government initiated large-scale transfers of the local population to the mining area, and soon found itself subjected to criticism, which also had accompanied the 1925 incorporation of Ruanda-Urundi into the Congo. Thus, the labor pol-

[1] *The Belgian Congo*, "Geographical Handbook Series" (London: Naval Intelligence Division, British Admiralty, 1945), p. 213. The sequence of events as described by a Belgian source: "In 1919, the Supreme Council of Allied Powers assigned the Ruanda-Urundi Mandate to Belgium and the terms of this agreement were confirmed in 1923 by the League of Nations and finally approved by the Belgian Parliament in 1924. . . ." Inforcongo, *Ruanda-Urundi, Geography and History* (Brussels, 1960), p. 71.

icy was altered somewhat, but the territories continued to provide large quantities of labor for Katanga until much later.

But in securing the administration of Ruanda-Urundi, Belgium inherited problems as well as assets. The area of the two territories combined is just over 20,000 square miles, and their total population, which today numbers some 5 million, already exceeded 3 million in the mid-1920's. Population pressure increased constantly, and resettlement projects became necessary, while the variability of rainfall (highest on the Congo-Nile watershed, lowest in the western lowlands) caused periodic famines in certain areas.

The Belgians faced an especially difficult problem of administration in Ruanda-Urundi, where an effort had to be made to impose a democratic form of government upon one of the best samples of what may be called feudal Africa. In substance, these problems were not entirely different from those faced by the British in Uganda, where access was easier and more living space available, however. Unlike Ruanda-Urundi, also, a territorial separation of the "kingdoms" and tribal peoples existed in Uganda.

The ethnic composition of Ruanda-Urundi's African population was such that three distinct groups occupied the territory, and the social system was based upon this situation. Perhaps 15 per cent of the total is WaTusi (Watutsi, Tutsi), the tall, proud pastoralists who are known for their great height. These people have long ruled the other population groups, including the numerically dominant BaHutu, who are related to other Bantu peoples in Congo. The BaHutu comprise perhaps 84 per cent of the total population of the combined countries, but they have been the serfs of the WaTusi. The remainder of the population consists of some thousands of BaTwa (pygmies), who in turn often served the BaHutu. In this organization, the omnipotent ruler was the king of the WaTusi, who delegated power to the chiefs of his people; there was, of course, no semblance of a democracy, and without education the imposition of democracy had little meaning. Ruanda-Urundi, therefore, was a country of vested interests (of the WaTusi) and

smouldering resentment, which often found expression in friction of a more or less serious nature along tribal lines. Although improving the material lot of the people within its mandate, Belgium found the obstacles in the path of educational and political progress insuperable. When it transferred sovereignty to Ruanda-Urundi in 1962, it saw the country fragment into two states and the social problems little reduced.

Rwanda and Burundi

The Republic of Rwanda and the Kingdom of Burundi lie in one of Africa's least accessible regions. Physiographically, the 20,000 square miles divided about equally between two states form part of highland equatorial Africa, with volcanic mountain masses reaching over 14,000 feet in the north, the Western Rift in the west, and a source area of the Nile River in the east. The area is dominated by the north-south-trending backbone of mountains forming the eastern edge of the great rift occupied by Lakes Tanganyika and Kivu, and most of it is in submature drainage conditions; river captures are taking place, poorly drained sections remain, and in some areas, the drainage is still aimless. Toward the major rivers, such as the Maragarasi and Kagera, slope incidence increases, and the general aspect of these countries is one of a plateau in the process of dissection, with prominent ridges and valleys over extensive areas. Communications are difficult, and in the absence of internal railroads, the railheads at Kigoma and Albertville on Lake Tanganyika are the nearest exits.

Rwanda and Burundi's inaccessibility is increased by the paucity of communication lines immediately westward toward the Congo routes to the ocean; only the poorest of roads (and no railroads) link Bukavu, the Congo town on Rwanda's border, with Kindu on the Congo River. Northward, the high Birunga Mountain chain, several lakes, and a national park combine to limit contact with Uganda (with its railhead at Kasese). Eastward, there is the densely populated West

Cattle and Herdboy, near Kitega, Rwanda. While the BaHutu people are mainly farmers, the WaTusi are pastoralists. As attitudes toward the sale and slaughter of cattle change, the pastoral industry will increase in importance, since the high areas are tsetse-free and permit herding. (United Nations)

Contour Planting, Rwanda. Cultivation on the steep slopes of Rwanda and Burundi requires careful soil management. Shown here is an area of proper contour planting. On the right is a conduit and small hydroelectric power station adjacent to the lake. (United Nations)

281

RWANDA AND BURUNDI

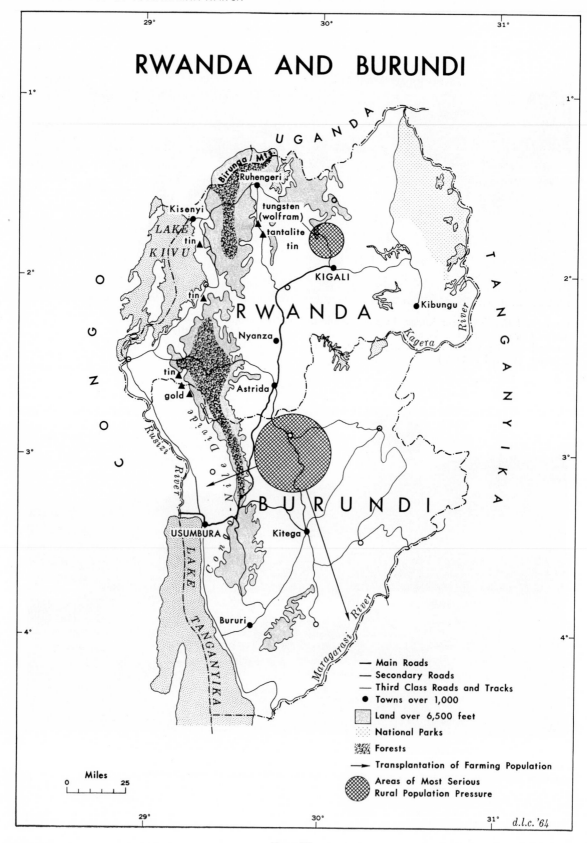

1°

29°　　　　　　　　30°　　　　　　　　31°

U G A N D A

Birunga Mts.

Ruhengeri

Kisenyi

tungsten
(wolfram)

tantalite
tin

LAKE

tin

KIVU

KIGALI

Kibungu

tin

R W A N D A

Nyanza

Kagera River

C O N G O

Rusizi River

tin

gold

Astrida

Nile-Congo Divide

B U R U N D I

USUMBURA

Kitega

Ruvuvu River

Bururi

LAKE

TANGANYIKA

T A N G A N Y I K A

Maragarasi River

—— Main Roads
—— Secondary Roads
— Third Class Roads and Tracks
● Towns over 1,000
Land over 6,500 feet
National Parks
Forests
→ Transplantation of Farming Population
Areas of Most Serious
Rural Population Pressure

Miles
0　　25

d.l.c. '64

Map 65

Pyrethrum near Ruhengeri, Rwanda. One of the cash crops grown in Rwanda is pyrethrum, an insecticide base. Note the up-and-down-hill rows on the slope in the distance. (United Nations)

Lake Province of Tanganyika, and then Lake Victoria, so that the easiest routes would appear to be southeastward and southward into Tanganyika. But only two roads, both mere tracks, lead from Burundi to its southern neighbor. This situation, of course, is a legacy of Belgian administration, but it also reflects the economic conditions in these countries. Naturally, the closest contacts were maintained with the Congo during the days of Belgian administration. But the transport pattern also reveals that Rwanda and Burundi have long produced and demanded relatively few goods.

ECONOMIC GEOGRAPHY

Most of Rwanda and Burundi lies at elevations between 3,000 and 8,000 feet, and in the upper regions lie some favored parts.

There, the dreaded tsetse fly is absent, soils are often volcanic and rich, and precipitation exceeds 50 inches annually. By contrast, many of the valleys in the peripheral areas are low, hot, and disease-infested. Thus, although these countries possess areas whose carrying capacity in terms of human population is very great, they do not by any means cover all of Rwanda and Burundi's 20,000 square miles.

Vertically, three main crop zones can be recognized, of which the lowest (2,500 to 4,500 feet) is favorable mainly to subsistence crops such as corn, beans, and bananas, although some coffee and cotton are grown. The middle zone (4,500 to 6,500 feet), covering the greatest part of both countries, is the most densely populated, and in addition to the subsistence crops normally grown at these elevations in equatorial regions, coffee and tobacco are cultivated. Finally, in the highest zone (6,500 feet and over), cash crops such as wheat, barley, tea, tobacco, and pyrethrum can be grown, and there some of the European settlers, who at the time of independence numbered over 8,000, established plantations. In each of the three zones, subsistence crops such as corn, beans, sweet potatoes, and a variety of cereals are grown, occupying the vast majority of the acres of cultivated land. There are two rainy seasons, a short one from October to December, and a long one from March to May. Coffee and cotton seeds are the major agricultural exports, but in the late 1950's African production of coffee was only between 30,000 and 40,000 tons, and that of cotton seed, less than 10,000 tons. The bulk of this produce went the long journey via Dar es Salaam on its way to the major market for the coffee, the United States.

Rwanda and Burundi are the most densely populated countries of Subsaharan Africa, and in addition they are among the least urbanized. Practically everyone in the two states lives directly off the land, of which 27 per cent is under crops and 40 per cent under pasture (the remainder is in forest, reserve, or lake, or is excessively steep and rocky). Thus, the average density of population on the arable land (including also pastoral areas) approaches 400, and individual sections of the countries far exceed this figure, especially north of Kigali and south of

Usumbura, Capital of Burundi. Usumbura is the largest urban center in either Burundi or Rwanda. It lies on the shores of Lake Tanganyika, in the Rift Valley (top). It is the major exit and entry for the minimal tonnage of trade leaving and entering the region, and its port was recently improved to permit easier lake communication with Kigoma (below). A shipment of hides is being lowered on the deck of a lake steamer in the port, which will take the cargo to the railhead at Kigoma (Tanganyika), whence it will travel to Dar es Salaam and overseas (right). (United Nations)

Astrida. An indication of the development of economic production is given by the sizes of the major urban centers: Usumbura, 50,000, is ten times larger than Kigali, the second town. These are today the capitals of the two states: Usumbura, formerly the headquarters of the entire Trust Territory, now is the seat of government of Burundi, and Kigali has become the capital of Rwanda. In Rwanda, only six towns have a population over 1,000, and in Burundi, only three. In 1957, the urban population totalled 63,000 for the two territories combined, of whom more than 30,000 were Congolese rather than natives of the Trust Territory.

Apart from subsistence agriculture, there are few activities the people of these countries can engage in. There are only a few minor mineral deposits (some tin and gold, mainly) and raw materials of all kinds are scarce in these overcrowded countries. The several peoples represented within the borders engage in their individual ways of mak-

ing a living: the WaTusi are essentially pastoralists, the BaHutu are agriculturalists, and the BaTwa are hunters and also make pottery. Since most of the opportunities for farming and pastoralism lie in the higher areas, the central plateau, running north and south along the eastern side of the Nile-Congo divide, is by far the most densely populated part of both countries. Toward the lower western slopes, population densities decrease considerably, and they are lowest in the disease-ridden valleys of the lower east. As part of their ten-year plan of the 1950's, the Belgians designed a program for the relocation of people, with the object of reducing the pressure where it had become most serious. But the task was a difficult one, for it meant a considerable change in habitat, crop possibilities, and climate for those who were transferred. The only empty areas in Rwanda and Burundi were the lower valleys, where tsetse and other pests had kept the population totals low. Having cleared some of these

areas for resettlement, the Belgians made a start with the alleviation of population pressure on the plateau.

All this, of course, can only be a temporary measure, for the population continues to grow, and the opportunities for additional land availability constantly dwindle. Perhaps, when attitudes toward cattle change, the pastoral industry of Rwanda and Burundi could become a major source of revenue. Presently, it is still retarded by the traditionalist tribal limitations on slaughter. But modern times demand more than a subsistence economy from a state's nation, and the resources of both Rwanda and Burundi appear very limited. Indeed, an expanded production of cash crops could find ready markets, for the range of possibilities is considerable. But any increased cash crop production requires a major increase in the acreage allotted to such crops, and that acreage, under present systems of land occupance, is not available. In a sense, Rwanda and Burundi may be indications of what the Kenya Highlands might have been had they not undergone organization into plantation agriculture.

Toward the end of Belgian rule in the Congo, disturbances broke out also in Ruanda-Urundi, where their cause lay in the long-standing social order and the consequences for the ruling minority of proportional representation in any future governments. Politico-geographical adjustments guaranteeing Wa-Tusi privileges could not, as in Uganda with the BaGanda, be made on a territorial basis. Eventually, both countries found a solution, Rwanda becoming a republic and Burundi a constitutional monarchy, both achieving independence in 1962. But the countries need progress in the economic sphere more than in any other, and their viability—and therefore their future—remains very much in doubt.

Part 4

THE NORTHEAST

15

ETHIOPIA AND AFRICA'S HORN:
PROBLEMS UNRESOLVED

THE "HORN" OF AFRICA, including the lands north of Uganda and Kenya and east of the White Nile, is an area of immense physiographic diversity. Its physical core is constituted by the vast Ethiopian Plateau, rising to over 13,000 feet in many places, rent by great rift valleys and cut elsewhere by spectacular declivities. Impenetrable and hostile, the plateau still effectively prevents modern communications from reaching all of the heart of the northeast. It is the source of the Blue Nile (at Lake Tana) and wrings from the air more moisture than any surrounding territory. It possesses excellent soils and good climates as well as barren wastes and inhospitable environments. Desert and steppe lands bound the plateau in all directions, separating it from the coasts of the Red Sea and Indian Ocean, from the valley of the Nile, and from the good lands of Kenya and Uganda.

The northeast is as diversified politico-geographically as it is physiographically. There, Arab and Bantu, Islam and Christianity, local and foreign empires have met. A modern political framework has been superimposed upon an area which retains many of the characteristics of its initial feudal condition. Today, this framework fragments the Horn into Ethiopia, together with Eritrea, with which it is federated, French Somaliland, and the Somali Republic (Somalia), consisting of the former Italian and British Somalilands. The present boundaries of the Horn are indeed superimposed, subsequent boundaries, and they are not, in several areas, approved by the local population.

Some 25 million people inhabit the Horn of Africa, of whom the great majority (22 million) reside within the Ethiopian sphere of influence. French Somaliland has a population of less than 100,000, and the coastal Somali Republic about 3 million. However, there are many more Somali people (from the ethnic, religious, and other points of view) than the population of the republic might suggest. Indeed, there are Somali people under French rule, under Ethiopian rule, and also under the administration of Kenya. Formerly, the Somalis were further fragmented by the Italian and British division of Somaliland.

Neither does the population of Ethiopia justify the term "nation." Apart from the Somalis living in (mainly eastern) Ethiopia, there are numerous peoples within the confines of the empire, which is itself the result of the amalgamation of a number of rival kingdoms, their consolidation under powerful leadership, and its subsequent expansionist policies. It is this expansionism which carried Ethiopian rule into Somali territory and the ensuing definition of the boundaries which created one of the major, perpetual conflicts in this part of Africa.

Feudalism and Imperialism

Ethiopia often is described as one of the oldest independent states in Africa. It is true that the territory of Ethiopia was not successfully claimed in the scramble of the 1880's by any of the colonial powers, although attempts at annexation were indeed made, and parts of the Horn that might have become Ethiopian territory did fall victim to the colonial powers. Ethiopia fell within the sphere of influence mainly of Italy, but the period of effective control over the entire country by the Italians was limited to the years preceding and during the Second World War, 1936–41.

These aspects notwithstanding, to describe Ethiopia as having been a sovereign nation state since before the arrival of the European intruders is most misleading. Less even than Uganda has the country progressed toward unification and internal consolidation. Being much larger and affected by severe physiographic obstacles to circulation, movement of all kinds in Ethiopia is very restricted. Until the late nineteenth century, the plateau and its periphery were occupied by a number of feudal kingdoms (whose essential structure was not very different from that of Buganda), sultanates (in the eastern margins), and tribal peoples. Only then did the first steps toward the modern state take place, with hundreds of years of almost total isolation finally coming to an end.

Several geographical factors have contributed to the evolution of present-day Ethiopia with its great complexity and heterogeneity. The area's relative location and physiography have played major roles. Mediterranean peoples made contact with the shores of the Horn when the Red Sea was the only sea route to the Indian Ocean; Greco-Egyptian and Roman excursions led to some landings and intermittent associations. At this time, the center of territorial organization in Ethiopia lay in the region of Aksum, and covered a part of Eritrea, the Ethiopian Province of Tigre, and a section of the Arabian Peninsula opposite. This Aksum Kingdom,

The Blue Nile, Ethiopia. Lake Tana is the source of the Blue Nile, which is seen leaving the lake region here on its way to the Sudan. (United Nations)

itself a successor of Nile Valley empires (Nubia, Cush), was supreme from the first to the seventh centuries A.D. It was in this period that Christianity was introduced to the region, as missionaries settled among the people of Aksum.

At this time, therefore, the main center of organization in the Horn was not as isolated from the outside world as some of the later kingdoms were to be. Aksum was located against the northern extremity of the Ethiopian Massif and extended to the Red Sea coasts. Nowhere else in the region was there the organization, architecture, art, and literature of this kingdom. But as Islam rose in the east, Aksum declined, and the period of contact with the Mediterranean (limited as it was) ended. However, Christianity had taken hold among the rulers of the empire, and when the remnants of Aksumite power withdrew into the protective interior plateaus, it was the beginning of a permanent strife between Christian kings and the proponents of Islam.

As the Moslem religion spread into the marginal areas, the Horn went through its dark ages. Not until the twelfth century did the Zagwe (Zague) dynasty arise in the interior, whose Christian rulers engaged in ceaseless battle with the Moslems. Except for the contact between the Moslems and the center of Islam on the Arabian Peninsula, there was total isolation; the kings in the highlands were no more in touch with the outside world than were the early kings of Uganda. They waged their wars against the Moslems with varying fortunes. At times, the Islamic forces penetrated deep into the plateau, while at other times the Christian kings expanded their area of hegemony at the expense of their enemies. Like Moshesh and his Basuto, they used the military assets of the highlands to good advantage, but by the sixteenth century, the tide began to turn decisively against them. The Moslems of the peripheral areas had begun to become politically organized, and a strong sultanate had arisen centered upon Harar. Before the middle of the century, a powerful sultan crushingly defeated the Christians, and it appeared that Christianity in this region was doomed.

The apparently final defeat of the Christians in Ethiopia, however, happened to coincide with the Turkish defeat of Egypt, so that the entire Red Sea seemed likely to fall under the domination of the Moslems. At this time, however, another European power with Mediterranean interests was involved: the Portuguese, who saw one of their routes to the Indies seriously threatened, decided to take action. Portugal sent armed forces to Ethiopia, which landed at Massawa in 1541 and advanced into the interior. There, allied with the remnants of the Christian kings' armies, they defeated the Moslems not far from Lake Tana. The victory was the turning point in the Christians' fight for survival against the encroachments of Islam. Although the Moslem threat was not terminated, the war effort had taken such a toll from both sides that neither was able to deal a final blow to the other.

One side might eventually have prevailed, were it not for the invasion, at this time, of the Galla people from the southeast. Hundreds of thousands of these Hamitic, pagan people (who showed, in their social organization, the effects of contact with the Bantu) flooded onto the plateau. Their previous location appears to have been the valley of the Juba River, but pressures exerted by the Somali probably caused their exit from this region. The arrival of the Galla on the plateau gave rise to a lengthy period of upheaval, political disorganization, and wars. The center of Ethiopian power withdrew to the north, and the Galla spread as far northward as the region of Lake Tana and beyond. They were, however, not united internally, and fought among themselves as they did against common enemies. Thus, a period of chaos resulted, and eventually no less than six "kingdoms" arose, each of which was ruled by a man who considered himself to be the emperor of all Ethiopia.

Confusion also reigned in religious circles during this time, as Jesuit missionaries entered Ethiopia's kingdoms and attempted to convert the people to Roman Catholicism. Repression and bitter strife over the religious issue further divided the hard-pressed leadership, and eventually a ruler arose who expelled the troublesome missionaries and executed those who stayed or attempted to enter the highlands. Furthermore, the Red Sea route to the Indies had lost most of its importance to Europe, as the Cape route became the most frequently used, and the Turkish Empire gained unprecedented strength. The result was a separation of Christian Ethiopia from Europe and, of course, Rome, and another period of deep isolation and internal decay.

Not until 1855 did progress begin once more, and in this year the phase which led directly to modern Ethiopia may be said to have begun. A leader named Kassa ascended to the throne, after having defeated several of the feudal rulers on the plateau and thus having made the first step in the direction of consolidation. As emperor, Kassa assumed the name Theodore II, and he initiated a series of administrative, social, and religious reforms.[1] Although he was not always successful in imposing them, his effort in this direction was the first to have been made in Ethiopia.

---

[1] For a brief summary of the history of Ethiopia, see E. W. Luther, *Ethiopia Today* (Stanford, Cal.: Stanford University Press, 1958), pp. 9 ff.

Meanwhile, hostilities against rebel chiefs, Moslems, and all who displeased him continued, and in addition Theodore had to deal with a new factor on the Ethiopian scene: a renewed, this time political, interest in the Horn on the part of Europe. Theodore made a fatal diplomatic error in 1867 by imprisoning the British consul in response to an alleged snub by the Foreign Office. Britain acted swiftly, sending a rescue force which landed at Massawa in 1867. The force was joined by tribesmen who had suffered the oppression of Theodore, and in 1868 the emperor's army was defeated.

Britain's first incursion was not permanent. Having achieved its objective, the force withdrew, leaving Ethiopia in renewed disarray. This coincided with the opening of the Suez Canal and unprecedented European activity along the entire east coast of Africa. Pressures upon Ethiopia increased from several sides. Egypt briefly entered the stage by taking the Eritrean coast and southeastern Ethiopia as far west as Harar, and in 1869 an Italian concern purchased the Red Sea port of Assab. The Mahdist rebellion in Sudan brought invasions into western Ethiopia.

Ethiopia's own internal division was a major factor endangering its survival. Emperor John IV emerged as the dominant figure out of the feudal chaos, and he repelled the Italian advances from the port of Massawa. But he had a rival, whose power in the south and west was on the increase while John was occupied with the war in the east. This feudal king, Menelik, was encouraged by the Italians to open hostilities against John, and to this end he was given arms. In return, he was promised the throne. Before these negotiations could reach their conclusion, however, John was killed in the war against the Mahdists, and Menelik became emperor in 1889.

Menelik immediately faced the aggressive forces of colonial imperialism. During the period of his accession to the throne, Italy occupied Eritrea and proclaimed a colony in that country. Immediately after becoming emperor, Menelik signed the Treaty of Ucciali, which was to become the first serious source of conflict between his regime and the Italians. The Amharic text of the treaty, which is the only one actually signed, states that,

should he so desire, Menelik could make use of Italian diplomatic channels for his business with other powers and governments. The Italian translation, on the other hand, states that Menelik *consented* to make use of such channels, and in these terms Ethiopia was virtually a protectorate of Italy. This, indeed, is what the Italians professed to believe, and the inevitable crisis arose when Menelik made direct contact with Queen Victoria. War ensued, and again the Ethiopian forces routed the Italians, extracting from Italy a new treaty recognizing Ethiopia's sovereignty.

Menelik now embarked upon his own imperialist campaign and used the European powers to his own advantage. He expanded the territory under his sway far to the southeast, south, and west, and signed treaties with the colonial powers defining the boundaries of Ethiopia much as they are today. He had founded the modern capital, Addis Ababa, in 1883, and followed Theodore's efforts to initiate reforms by making major efforts to modernize the country. He negotiated with the French, who had occupied the port of Djibouti (Jibuti), for the building of a railroad from this port to the capital. He also began a road-building program, and established schools, postal services, public utilities, and other modern amenities.

The decline and death of Menelik, who had consolidated Ethiopia and withstood European intervention at a time when most of Africa was being parcelled out by the colonial powers, again deprived Ethiopia of strong central leadership at a crucial time. Even before his death, France, Britain and Italy theoretically divided the country into their own desired spheres of influence, to take effect in case of the disintegration of the Ethiopian state. Italy desired to connect her two possessions of Eritrea and Somaliland across Ethiopian territory, France wished to safeguard her interest in the Addis-Djibouti railway, and the British wanted to protect the source of the Blue Nile and the region around Lake Tana. For some time after 1913, when Menelik died, it seemed as though this division would indeed take effect, as a lengthy leadership crisis arose. Menelik's grandson and proper successor was youthful, irresponsible, and leaned toward Islam, and his reign

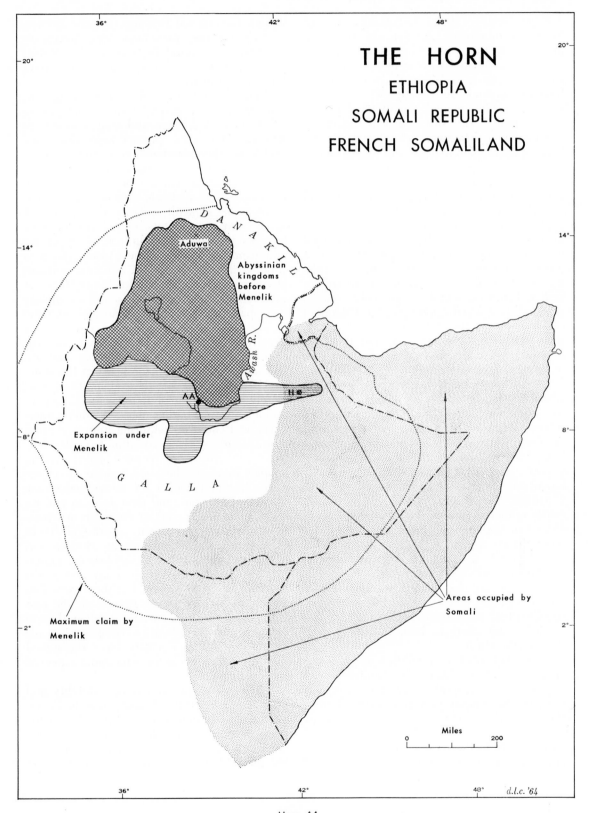

THE HORN
ETHIOPIA
SOMALI REPUBLIC
FRENCH SOMALILAND

Aduwa

Abyssinian
kingdoms
before
Menelik

D A N A K I L

Abash R.

A A

Expansion under
Menelik

G A L L A

Areas occupied by
Somali

Maximum claim by
Menelik

Miles

0   200

d.l.c. '64

Map 66

was predictably short. Eventually, one of Menelik's daughters, Zauditu, became empress, with the young Ras Tafari (Haile Selassie) designated as heir to the throne. A struggle ensued, and the divisive forces of feudalism again were strongly felt in Ethiopia as various chiefs gained in individual power.

Naturally, the situation was extremely detrimental to Ethiopia, and when Haile Selassie was crowned in 1930, the effects of two decades of stagnation were evident everywhere. But Haile Selassie had shown signs, even before his coronation, of desiring the end of Ethiopia's isolation. He had successfully applied for the country's admission to the League of Nations in 1923, and had engaged in treaties and cooperative projects with a number of European states. Under his rule, the country's first constitution was written, a first parliament assembled, and social reforms initiated. It is a reflection upon the Ethiopian situation that in the 1930's a new law against slavery had to be established, and that this law has not succeeded in eliminating the practice altogether.

In his attempts to unify and consolidate Ethiopia, Haile Selassie, like other rulers before him, faced an insuperable task. Ethiopia's relative location has made it a battleground between Christian and Moslem; its coastal fringes lie on one of the world's most important maritime avenues. Its high interior mountains afforded a haven for an island of Christianity amid an ocean of Islam, and its coasts attracted Moslem and European alike. But when modern times came, and boundaries were drawn around Ethiopia, the strife of ages had left a legacy of deep and fundamental division, too strong to be overcome in a matter of decades. The very physiography which once had helped ensure the survival of the Christian kings now became a major obstacle in the effort to build a nation state there in the Horn.

Viewing Ethiopia's politico-geographical characteristics of shape, the country would appear to have several assets. It is large, but compact. No lengthy proruptions extend from the country's main area (as in the case of Congo and South West Africa). The asset of its proximity to the coast is enhanced by several opportunities for port development, even

though the colonial holdings of Italy, Britain, and France long prevented direct access to the sea. The capital is located in a central position, which would appear to help bind the state together.

But apart from these politico-geographical features, everything seems to conspire to effect internal division and fragmentation in Ethiopia. The same physiography that once protected the kingdoms now continues to separate the peoples, languages, and religions within the state. Having once hindered the invasion of the plateaus, it now makes communications difficult, retards the spread of ideas from the capital, isolates communities from each other, raises the cost of importing and exporting goods. True, Addis Ababa is situated in the middle of a radiating network of communications, but the network thins out rapidly, roads become tracks and eventually mere paths (if they continue at all), and the greater the distance from the capital, the less effective the contact with it. And the less effective the contact, the less integrated are the outlying parts with the heart of the state.

If the result of these conditions was merely a limitation of movement, Ethiopia's problems would be like those of other underdeveloped countries requiring improved communications systems to stimulate development and foster a national spirit among peoples some of whom are located in remote areas. But in Ethiopia the consequences are much more serious, and their solution will require more than a better transport network. Strong actual and latent centrifugal forces exist within the state, with its Moslem and pagan majorities ruled by a Christian minority. The Islamic center of Harar and Addis Ababa seem worlds apart, but they are within 250 miles of each other. Peoples in the east look across the Somalia border rather than to Addis Ababa for solidarity. Divisive elements within the ruling minority have threatened the throne and reveal the semifeudal aspect of Ethiopian politics.

The period of comparative stability and progress under Haile Selassie was to be interrupted in a violent manner in 1935. In the previous year, during efforts to demarcate the boundaries in the region where Italian, British, and Ethiopian territory met, an incident had taken place at Wal Wal. Italian Somali forces had clashed with Ethiopian troops trying to control the area, and Ethiopia had taken the matter to the League of Nations. Italy massed armies on the Eritrean and Somali borders and invaded Ethiopia. The campaign ended before the middle of 1936, and Haile Selassie fled to Europe.

Italy's half-decade of rule in Ethiopia was marked by cruel repression of the local population, as Italy experienced the troubles of any authority attempting to establish effective control over the vast country. A vigorous program of road-building and economic development was initiated, which still has favorable effects today. Having interrupted Haile Selassie's reform program in 1936, the Italians were themselves unable to complete their plans, as British forces invaded Ethiopia in 1941 and, with the aid of patriotic forces, defeated the Italians. The emperor returned to his capital in the same year, and the sovereignty of the state was restored.

Since the end of the Second World War, one major change has affected the Ethiopian state. Having lost its colonies in the Horn, Italy yielded Eritrea, and in 1950 the United Nations decided that this territory should become federated to Ethiopia as an autonomous unit under the Ethiopian crown. Some minor territorial adjustments also occurred along the boundary with British Somaliland, but the boundaries of Ethiopia (except in Eritrea) have remained substantially the same since Menelik's days.

Although a sovereign state, no longer landlocked, and making progress in diverse fields, Ethiopia still faces major internal and external problems. Its essentially feudal character was again reflected by the attempted *coup d'état* of 1960, and by the writings of observers in the country. There still is no Ethiopian nation, and the unification of the country is still achieved to a large extent by force. The independence of the adjacent Somali Republic has brought renewed pressures upon the eastern boundaries and occasional border incidents. Over 90 per cent of the people of the country remain illiterate, and the ruling Amhara form a small minority. Many tribal peoples within the borders of Ethiopia (there are well over 100) consider themselves the victims of imperialism, as many others have under European colonialist rule; in the Ethiopian case, the imperialism is no less resented for being indigenous. Others continue to refuse recognition of the central government, not because the government is that of Ethiopia, but because the imposition of any state authority would be repudiated. Such are the Danakil people of the northeastern dry lands. These problems are not unique among those faced by the states of modern Africa, but Ethiopia with its history of feudal division, expansionism, ethnic complexity, and physiographic difficulties, faces unusually difficult obstacles in the path of progress.

LAND AND LIVELIHOOD

Ethiopia's problems in the economic sphere are as severe as those of its political geography. Once again, the initial impression is favorable: this is primarily an agricultural country, and it is comparatively well endowed with good climates and adequate soils. Estimates of the amount of arable land vary, but perhaps 10 per cent of the land area (excluding Eritrea) may be so classified, and no less than 30 per cent is capable of carrying livestock. But an agricultural economy, to rise above the subsistence level, requires adequate transport facilities and other forms of organization, and, again, because of the paucity of these amenities, current development falls far short of the country's potential.

The isolation of the agricultural areas is as great as that of its various peoples. It is hardly possible to describe the obstacles the topography puts in the way of communication, and the areas of arable land are for similar reasons widely scattered. Much of Ethiopia is under late youth and early maturity, and slope incidence is high. Areas of cultivable land, whether in the valleys, on gentler slopes, or on upland surfaces, often are separated by impassable declivities—and more important, they are also separated from the few routes to internal and external markets.

Three distinct environmental zones, which are actually altitudinal belts, are recognized

295

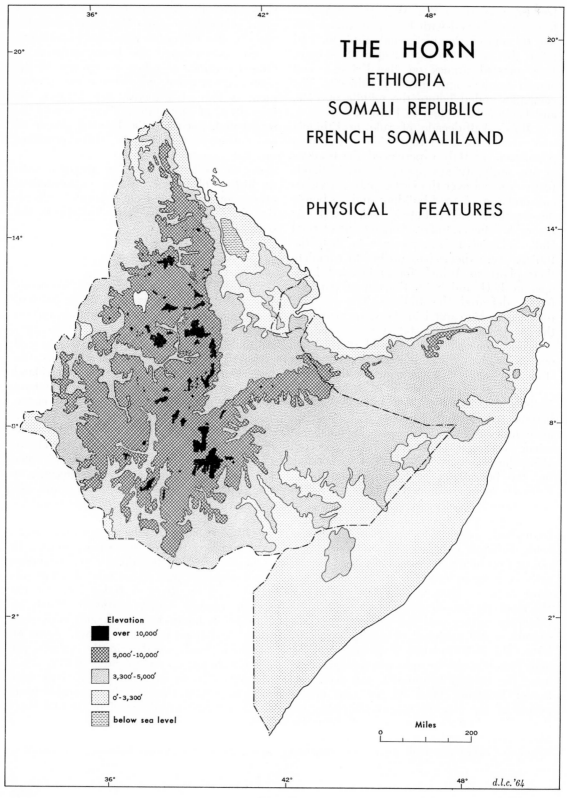

THE HORN
ETHIOPIA
SOMALI REPUBLIC
FRENCH SOMALILAND

PHYSICAL   FEATURES

Elevation
- over 10,000'
- 5,000'-10,000'
- 3,300'-5,000'
- 0'-3,300'
- below sea level

Miles
0   200

d.l.c. '64

Map 67

Farming in the Ethiopian Highlands. Peasants are seen here turning the soil with their huge, forklike farm implements. The rich, heavy soil may be difficult to work, in which case more than one man may handle the same "fork" in turning the lumps of earth. (United Nations)

in Ethiopia. In the hot lowlands is the kwolla, which reaches up against the valley and plateau slopes as high as about 5,000 feet. This is tropical Ethiopia, and includes also the deserts and steppe stretches around the foot of the highlands. There, bananas, dates, and other fruits thrive, as well as coffee in the higher parts. Above the kwolla lies the woina dega, or temperate belt, extending up to between 8,000 and 9,000 feet. Only about 7 per cent of Ethiopia is forested, and most of the forest areas lie in this belt, which also sustains a wide variety of crops. Cereals, fruits such as the fig and orange, grapevines, and other Mediterranean plants thrive there. There is much pastureland, and thus a large cattle and sheep population in this zone.

Highest is the dega, extending to the mountain areas of the country and including more pastureland and areas suitable for cereals such as wheat and barley.

This wide variety of conditions permits the cultivation of a large number of crops, and it has been said that Ethiopia's soils and climates make it possible to raise successfully "almost any type of crop with proper care and cultivation."[2] The limitations imposed by lack of communications, education, agricultural organization, modern implements, and incentive have retarded the development of a healthy agrarian economy. As elsewhere in plateau Africa, erosion is severe, and conservation practices are in their initial stages. Most of Ethiopia's farmers remain mired in a life of subsistence cultivation with some

---

[2] *Ibid.,* p. 76.

297

small local sales for cash. The main staple crop is a cereal, *teff,* but the country can produce far more than the population requires of almost every crop grown; indeed, it is often described as a future breadbasket of the north and Middle East.

Coffee is the most valuable export product of Ethiopia, often contributing half the total value of all exports. The manner in which this total is accumulated typifies much of what is problematic in Ethiopia's internal conditions. The country is extremely well suited for coffee of the arabica variety; indeed, this plant can be left untended and still produce well. There are veritable coffee forests in Ethiopia from which the beans are simply gathered, and if coffee seedlings are planted, they are often left without any form of care. The total harvest comes in large part from the wild forests, in addition to the production from the small plots of the local peasants and a relatively minor contribution from a few large plantations. The lesson of Tanganyika, where the establishment of cooperatives to coordinate the production, processing, and marketing of coffee has greatly stimulated the industry, appears especially applicable in Ethiopia. In 1957, a national coffee board was established with these aims.

Research has long indicated that Ethiopia can become a major producer of cotton, as the Italians recognized in the 1930's. Today, the growing of this crop is encouraged by the government, but progress—depending upon a certain amount of organization, incentive, adequate communications, and some capital—has been slow. The entire question of agricultural improvement in Ethiopia, as elsewhere, is one of education, which must bring an appreciation of the need for reform in land tenure and ownership, soil and water conservation practices, maintenance of irrigation and other structures and equipment, and seed improvement. The Ethiopian government has been accused of lethargy in this connection, and the gap between it and newly independent African states now embarking upon vigorous programs of this kind is evident.

Some export revenue is obtained from hides and skins. There may be as many as 20 million cattle in the country, and about the same number of sheep and goats. The livestock appears maldistributed in relation to the available pastureland. This is a function of the social conditions in the territory; especially large concentrations occur in the lands of the nomadic and seminomadic peoples of the lowlands. In the south, not surprisingly, a situation prevails which recurs throughout Bantu Africa: cattle are a source of wealth and are not slaughtered. Other cattle practices occur in various parts of Ethiopia, and although in much of the country they are used as animals of burden, slaughtered, and sold for meat and hide, elsewhere they are considered sacred. In the areas where precipitation totals are low, variability is great and the dry season lengthy and intense. As a result, many cattle are underfed in these overpopulated, overgrazed regions, and disease is rampant.[3]

The fact that Ethiopia does receive a certain revenue from exports is in no small measure due to the brief period of Italian occupation, for the Italians constructed a road system of over 4,000 miles, half of which were provided with an all-weather surface. As feeder lines to the Addis-Djibouti railroad, these roads brought some remote provinces into the economic sphere, facilitated the marketing of all goods, increased the effectiveness of governmental control, and contributed to the breakdown of the feudal situation still existing. Thus, in spite of the small quantity of its exports (only 10 per cent of the gross national product), Ethiopia in 1941 found itself in possession of an infrastructure on the basis of which her entry into the modern Africa could begin. Mainly as a result of the large market for coffee, the United States remains Ethiopia's major trade partner.

As elsewhere in East Africa, commerce is largely carried on by non-Africans. In Ethiopia, Armenian, Greek, Indian, and Arab merchants operate most of the retail establishments. Commercial activity is largely confined to the collection of farm produce from the peasants and its sale to export agents, and the resale of imports. Only a few towns have

---

[3] L. T. C. Kuo, "Ethiopia," *Focus,* V, No. 10 (June, 1955), 4. In the late 1950's, about 1½ million cattle died annually due to various diseases, especially rinderpest.

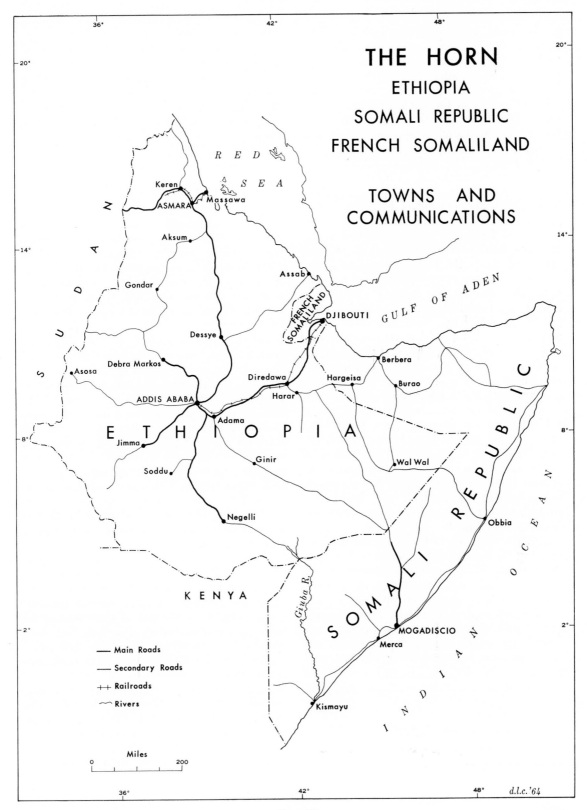

THE HORN
ETHIOPIA
SOMALI REPUBLIC
FRENCH SOMALILAND

TOWNS AND
COMMUNICATIONS

—— Main Roads
—— Secondary Roads
+++ Railroads
⌒ Rivers

Miles
0   200

d.l.c. '64

Map 68

real commercial districts in the Western sense of the word, and goods are still commonly distributed by pack animal (usually the mule), which carries them to the open-air markets in the smaller places. A retail district has developed in the capital, Addis Ababa (400,000), and in the capital of Eritrea, Asmara. These are also the only towns which have some industrial establishments of note (other than outlying sugar and coffee processing plants). The industrial sector of the economy is still negligible in terms of its contribution to the gross national product (about 5 per cent), employment of Ethiopia's laborers (under 50,000), and annual capital expenditure. There are several hundred manufacturing establishments, but the vast majority are small food and textile enterprises.

In a country as underdeveloped as Ethiopia, the size of the leading city, Addis Ababa, is a misleading indicator of conditions elsewhere. Addis has been described as "almost the only town" of any size in the state,[4] and as a mask, behind which the rest of the country is hidden.[5] The city has grown largely as a result of its governmental and administrative functions, in addition to which it possesses a good climate, central location, and is a focal point for communication lines. Ethiopia's second city is Dire Dawa, which lies near Harar and is the site of a few industrial establishments including a cement factory, but neither Dire Dawa nor Harar has a population exceeding 50,000. Harar, still the Moslem stronghold of Ethiopia, has a large Arab and Asian population.

With reference to the possibilities of increasing the rate of development in Ethiopia, the question of the country's mineral wealth is often brought up. Until today, the mineral output has been small, and opinions regarding the potential vary widely. Minor quantities of gold and some salt and platinum are mined, but other known deposits have not been exploited, including low-grade coal, nonferrous, nonprecious metals, and a variety of miscellaneous minerals. Geologic mapping,

prospecting, and exploration are still required, although the efforts of a major United States oil concern to locate petroleum have failed. In view of the obstacles faced by the mineral industry (which are among those confronting the entire country: capital, communications, etc.) there can be little reason for optimism with regard to rapid development in this sphere.

Federation with Eritrea

Eritrea became a politico-territorial entity in 1890, when Italy proclaimed the country a colony. By the Treaty of Ucciali of 1889, Menelik had recognized the Italian possessions on the Red Sea, and in subsequent years the Italians used the bases in Eritrea for attacks on the emperor's lands. This, and the controversy over the terms of the treaty, resulted in the hostilities of 1896, when the Italian forces were defeated near Aduwa, and the subsequent abrogation of the treaty. Late in 1896, Menelik and the Italians defined the boundary between their respective realms. In 1935, Eritrea again became a base for Italian military activity, and in preparation for the invasion of Ethiopia, the country was the scene of feverish activity. Roads, bridges, port facilities, and airfields were built, improved, and expanded, and thousands of Europeans entered the colony. The campaign was successful, but short-lived, and by 1941 Eritrea as well as Ethiopia had been wrested from Italian control.

After the end of the Second World War, Italy in 1947 renounced her rights to Eritrea, and the United Nations attempted to decide upon the territory's future. Several commissions were given the task of determining the most acceptable course of action, but none managed to produce a suitable blueprint. Eventually, the General Assembly itself recommended the federation of Eritrea with Ethiopia, the former colony retaining a considerable degree of autonomy. In 1952, this decision took effect. The Ethiopian government is responsible for commerce, finance, and defense, but Eritrea's own assembly continues to exercise control in domestic legis-

---

[4] L. D. Stamp, *Africa*, p. 361.

[5] D. Mathew, *Ethiopia* (London: Longmans, Green, 1947), p. 5.

lative, executive, and judicial fields. Eritrea, therefore, possesses far more power than any other part of the Ethiopian state. Indeed, in the sphere of constitutional development and, to a lesser extent, communications, Eritrea may be said to have been ahead of Ethiopia at the time of the merger.

The unification with Eritrea added some 49,000 square miles to Ethiopia's territory, perhaps 1 million people, two ports (Massawa and Assab), about 225 miles of railroad and nearly 2,000 miles of roads. The ports now handle as much as 60 per cent of the empire's external trade as connections between Eritrean and Ethiopian territory, begun by the Italians, have been improved.

Eritrea is not a rich country. It consists of two main physiographic regions, the coastal plain and the interior plateau. The former varies in width from 10 to 50 miles, and the latter is an extension of the Ethiopian Plateau. The descent from the highlands, which are mountainous in parts and reach 6,000 to 8,000 feet, is partly abrupt, as in the north, and elsewhere steplike. The lowlands are hot and dry, and in the highlands, rainfall may exceed 20 inches but is highly seasonal. Thus, the country is much less well endowed with agricultural possibilities than Ethiopia, and the latter supplies most of the food consumed in Eritrea. Overgrazing is a serious problem, irrigation a frequent necessity, and the available acreage capable of sustaining sedentary agriculture is small. Industrial development is limited to the processing of the country's small food production and the treatment of hides and skins. Asmara (130,000), located on the cooler plateau, is the capital and main manufacturing center.

Eritrea's population is as heterogeneous as is that of Ethiopia. In the highlands live Coptic Eritreans, in the coastal plain are several nomadic Arab peoples, and in the southwest are negroid peasants. In addition, there is an urbanized minority and a remnant of the once-large European population. Apart from the Europeans, these people generally share a low standard of living, high illiteracy, linguistic and religious diversity, and little scope for progress. They may also have inherited a potential political crisis. There have been criticisms in Eritrea of Ethiopian inter-ference in the country's domestic affairs, but the objections have been expressed by the small educated elite. If Ethiopian centralism results in the absorption of Eritrea before education and political awareness spread, the problem may be avoided. However, many Moslems came under Christian rule, and there has been some labor trouble. Like the Somali, some Eritreans consider themselves the victims of Ethiopian imperialism, and the political future of the Ethiopian Federation is not without latent problems.

The Somali Republic and Somali Irredentism

Along with the Italians, the French and the British also laid claim to a section of the coast of the Horn. The British obtained the southern coast of the Gulf of Aden and there established British Somaliland, a territory bounded by geometrical boundaries according to a treaty signed in 1894. British hegemony in this area dates from the early 1880's, but several adjustments took place before the turn of the century. The Italians, meanwhile, obtained a number of concessions from the Sultan of Zanzibar (including the important port of Mogadiscio) and from local chiefs, thus gaining control of Somalia. This area extended from Cape Guardafui to the Kenya border.

The boundaries between British and Italian Somaliland and Ethiopia soon became the source of almost continuous friction. Menelik's expansionism had carried Ethiopian rule far eastward, beyond the limits of the massif and onto the lower sections of the Horn leading to the coastal plain. These were, and are today, the grazing areas of the nomadic Somali herdsmen, and although boundary demarcation did not take place (other than at a few fixed points great distances apart), incursions by Ethiopian forces were common. British observers wrote that

as far as can be ascertained here, the countries in question have been so recently occupied that it is at present impossible to define the actual limits of Menelik's authority in these directions, but here, as on the south-

eastern frontier, raids on a large scale from the mountainous districts into the maritime plains would appear to be the usual methods by which the Abyssinians maintained their influence. . . .[6]

Menelik asserted that the Somalis had from time immemorial been the cattle-keepers of the Ethiopians and had paid annual tribute to their masters until the Moslem invasion, and that on these grounds, his assertion of hegemony over at least a part of the Somalis' lands was justified. The British, throughout the period of friction, showed an awareness of the problems facing the nomadic, pastoral people, who must practice a form of transhumance from the low plains to the foothill slopes and back in order to survive the rigors of the local environment. Menelik's actions and boundary demands prevented the migratory pattern from being followed, and the effect upon the Somalis was serious.

In 1897, further boundary definition (although very little delimitation and demarcation) took place, as Britain and Ethiopia signed an agreement which did not lead to any exchange of territory, but which terminated the nominal protection Britain had extended over certain Somali groups. Italy had likewise extended the territory nominally under her control well west of the defined boundary between Italian Somaliland and Ethiopia, and for several decades no real opposition occurred. Then the Wal Wal incident occurred when Britain finally attempted to demarcate the boundaries defined decades earlier. Haile Selassie was on the Ethiopian throne, and he recognized the encroachment of Italian rule over what Menelik had considered Ethiopian territory. The consequences are well known, for they were followed by the Italian invasion of the empire.

For some years (1942–47) the majority of the Somali people were under one administration. This was the result of war conditions, and although it was highly desirable to the Somali, the arrangement was terminated when the United Nations took charge of the frag-

mented Horn. Ethiopia made vigorous efforts to persuade the United Nations that the Horn should be unified under Ethiopian rule, while Somali representatives attempted to persuade the responsible bodies that the Somali people in the various sectors desired unification under Somali government. In the event, the boundaries as established previously were confirmed, and the only Somali unification that took place involved the merger of British and Italian possessions in the Horn under one flag as the Somali Republic (1960).

The Somali Republic consists of 246,000 square miles of relatively undiversified country, including areas which are among Africa's driest. In former British Somaliland, the coastal belt is hilly, whereas that of former Somalia is flat; in the northern territory the higher interior may receive over 20 inches of rain annually and contains, in Haud, some good grazing land. It is through this region that the Ethiopian boundary runs. Most Somali carry on a precarious nomadic and seminomadic pastoral subsistence, and they are thought to number about 3 million. Mogadiscio (Mogadishu) has become the capital of the country, although the focus of activity may shift to Kismayu at the mouth of the Juba River. Mogadiscio has an artificial harbor, while Kismayu has a rather poor natural site for port development. The small annual export production consists mainly of bananas, some sugar and cotton, and hides and skins, as might be expected from the economic condition of the country. Very little land is capable of carrying permanent agriculture, although there are opportunities in the Juba River valley and in a few localities in former British Somaliland.

Somali irredentism, in Ethiopia as well as French Somaliland, Kenya, and even Eritrea, remains strong. The Horn is one of the very few sizeable regions of Africa to possess some linguistic, ethnic, economic and religious unity, and in the Ethiopian region of Ogaden, for instance, conditions in practically every respect but legal administration resemble those in the Somali Republic. Indeed, the Somali on either side of the international boundaries which now divide them legitimately claim a certain amount of interdependence as, in several areas each year, they need

[6] *Public Records Office,* Rodd to Salisbury, Inc. Nos. 3–18, May 15, 1897, quoted from *The Somali Peninsula: A New Light on Imperial Motives* (Mogadishu: Somali Government Information Services, 1962), p. 52.

Mogadiscio, Capital of The Somali Republic. Mogadiscio, Somalia's largest city, does not have a modern port, and loading by lighters from offshore anchorage continues (top). This is a typically Arab town, as shown by the architecture (bottom). (United Nations)

303

Merca, Center of the Banana Trade, Somalia. The aspect of Merca, like that of other towns along the coasts of the Horn, is distinctly Arab. Although bananas form Somalia's chief export, the industry is hampered by the rainfall deficiency prevalent throughout the country. Development under irrigation is proceeding in the Juba Valley, and eventually the center of activity may shift south and to Kismayu, near the Juba mouth, the chief coastal competitor of Mogadiscio. (United Nations)

the land on the other side of the border. The Somali Republic has made it clear that it is not satisfied with the present arrangement and is attempting to gain support for a revision of the politico-geographical situation in the Horn.[7]

SOMALI IN KENYA

Sir Charles Eliot, who on behalf of Britain governed British East Africa for several years, in 1904 observed that

if it were possible to detach the districts inhabited by the Somalis, it would be an excellent thing to form them into a separate government, as they are different in population, economic and physical conditions from the other Provinces . . . but, unfortunately, they are too small [in number] to form a separate administration, and the adjoining Somali territories are not British.[8]

Initially, the boundary between the British and Italian spheres of influence in the equa-

torial part of East Africa was along the Juba River. This resulted in the division of the Somali people into British-administered Jubaland and Italian Somaliland. There were, in addition, many Somali in the region of the Tana River farther south, and in the interior far west of the area known as Jubaland. The situation was improved somewhat in 1924, when a new, geometrical boundary was delimited well to the west, transferring Jubaland to Italian control.

The lands of the Tana River and the northeastern section of Kenya's Northern Province, however, remained under British administration, and they are inhabited by a large Somali population. The Northern Province and Northern Frontier District have been administratively separated from the remainder of Kenya. This arrangement, which was legalized under the Special Districts Ordinance, was to facilitate the administration of a territory in which conditions were recognized to differ considerably from the remainder of the colony. One of its consequences has been the feeling of isolation, and, indeed, separatism among the handful of Somalis and others who have benefited from the very few educational opportunities offered in the outlying region.

THE ROLE OF FRANCE

Although France acquired but a small part of the Horn, it was a strategically important section. The French established a

[7] *The Somali Peninsula.*

[8] *The East African Protectorate* (London: Longmans, Green, 1905), Ch. 12.

permanent interest in the Obock area as early as 1862, when Danakil chiefs signed a treaty with the Paris government. After the Italians had claimed territory immediately to the north, further treaties with the Danakil in 1884 and the Issa in the following year expanded French-controlled Obock Territory somewhat. A subsequent rivalry between Britain and France led to the delimitation of the Anglo-French boundary approximately midway between the ports of Zeila and Djibouti, and in 1892 the capital of the territory was transferred to Djibouti.

The harbor of Djibouti (45,000) is large and well sheltered, and it is the obvious ocean port for Ethiopia. In 1896, Menelik formally recognized French Somaliland, and signed agreements with the French initiating the construction of the railroad to Addis Ababa. The first rails were laid in 1897, and the railroad was completed in 1917. For several decades, Djibouti was virtually the sole export harbor for Ethiopia's small external trade. After the Second World War and the Ethiopian federation with Eritrea, however, trade has increasingly been going via Eritrean ports.

French Somaliland has a population of less than 100,000, which is periodically increased and decreased as nomadic herdsmen cross the interior in their annual migration between the Somali Republic and Ethiopia and Eritrea. Estimates have placed the range of such temporary increase at between 10 and 20 per cent of the country's total population. French Somaliland's area is under 9,000 square miles, but this small region occupies much of the corridor between the plateau edge and the coast.

Perhaps 30,000 Somali and 35,000 Danakil live permanently in French Somaliland, the object of the Somali Republic government's drive for Somali unification. The country remains a French Overseas Territory within the French Community according to the vote (75 per cent in favor) and the territorial assembly's decision in 1958. The franchise is universal, and elected representatives are sent to Paris. It is a political situation which may not please outsiders, but which has permitted France to continue her rule.

The true wealth of French Somaliland has long been in its transit function. The land itself is desperately poor, and even pasture is rare. The production of locally consumed vegetables and fruits is achieved through irrigation. The water shortage is severe, but salt is plentiful; indeed, hides and salt are normally the only domestic exports. Even the profitable break-in-bulk function of Djibouti is threatened today, and adverse trade balances since the early 1950's reflect the results of increased Ethiopian use of Massawa and Assab. The territory has become a liability, having long been an asset. Its political as well as its economic future must be in doubt, since both Ethiopia and the Somali Republic have given evidence of desiring its incorporation.

16

SUDAN: BRIDGE BETWEEN AFRICAN AND ARAB?

THE REPUBLIC OF SUDAN is Africa's largest state, exceeding both the Congo (Leopoldville) and Algeria in total area (967,500 square miles). Sparsely populated by about 12 million inhabitants, the Sudan, bounding Egypt in the north and Uganda in the south, shares the peoples and cultures of Subsaharan Africa as well as the Middle East and Mediterranean Africa. Indeed, the Moslem north is the dominant region of the country in terms of size as well as population, influence in government as well as economic development. But the three southern provinces (Upper Nile, Bahr el Ghazal, and Equatoria) form a large part of the state and are of growing economic importance. The zone of greatest transition between the Arab north and African south lies along the twelfth parallel, below which physical conditions change also: emerging from the dry heart of the central basin, the country becomes moister and the vegetation denser, as the land rises to the North Equatorial divide.

Extending latitudinally over 1,200 miles, the Sudan does constitute a geographical link between cultural regions, perhaps to a greater degree than any other African state. No other transitional state is quite as sizeable and incorporates as large a population; although Ethiopia's total number of inhabitants is greater, that country does not penetrate black Africa to the same extent. Neither can Ethiopia really be called a bridge between Arab and African from the administrative point of view; Sudan is an Islamic country, and Ethiopia is not. Furthermore, the physiographic fragmentation and ethnic, religious, and linguistic heterogeneity of Ethiopia create a far more complex picture than that of the Sudan, with its low relief, unending plains, and basic cultural-geographical division.

Although a bridge in the territorial sense, the Sudan remains a divided country, with the south resisting the implementation of administrative decisions even before independence.[1] In part, this has been the result of the tenuous communications between the government and people of the north and those of the south. Just as the Somali of eastern Ethiopia look east rather than toward Addis Ababa, many southern Sudanese look south rather than to Khartum. The matter has been compounded by religious differences, for in the south many Africans have adopted Christianity and find themselves in a Moslem state.

The Politico-Geographical Entity

The Sudan is another of Africa's large, compact political units. All of its northern and northwestern boundaries (with Egypt, Libya, and northern Chad) are geometrical, and they lie in desolate, dry terrain for the greater part. In the east, the boundary corresponds more or less to the western limit of the Ethiopian Massif. The southern border shows some adjustment to physiographic conditions, running along divide areas between major drainage

[1] E. S. Munger, "Sudan Mutiny," *American Universities Field Staff Paper* (New York, 1955), p. 1.

306

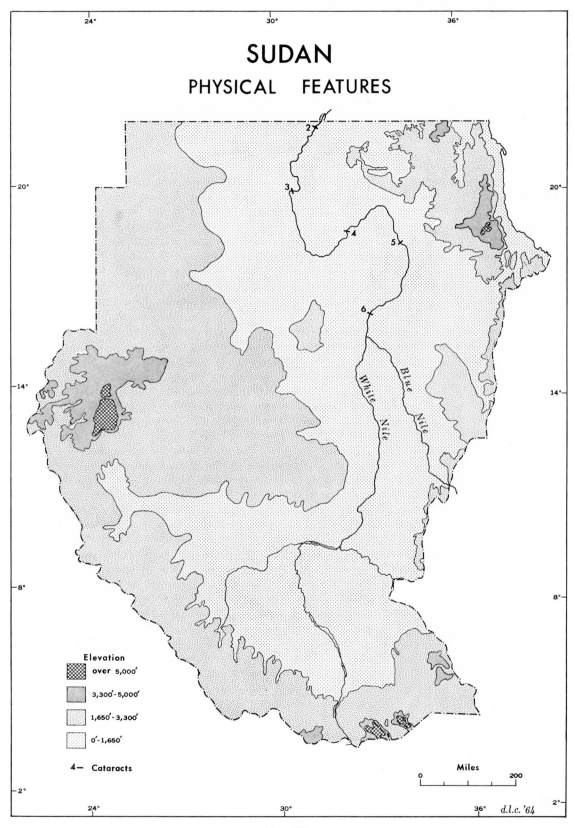

SUDAN
PHYSICAL FEATURES

Elevation

over 5,000′

3,300′–5,000′

1,650′–3,300′

0′–1,650′

4— Cataracts

Miles

0   200

White Nile

Blue Nile

d.l.c. '64

Map 69

Village in Southern Sudan. The peoples of the southern Sudan—Nilotic and Hamitic-Nilotic Dinka, Shilluk, Bari, and Latuka—engage mainly in subsistence modes of living in the swampy, forested south. But such villages as this one in Equatoria Province are beginning to feel the impact of government efforts to introduce rice, coffee, sisal, cocoa, and fruits as cash crops. (United Nations)

lines. The Sudan has its own seaport, Port Sudan, on the Red Sea, but although the state is not landlocked, parts of it are a thousand miles from that exit. The southern provinces are much farther from the railroads connecting the central Sudan with Port Sudan than they are from the Uganda railhead at Gulu, which is linked to Mombasa.

The orientation of the Sudan's physiographic belts is latitudinal, and a series of climatic zones can be recognized from the desert north to the moist savanna of the extreme south. North of the latitude of El Fasher, a vegetative cover is practically non-existent, and the average annual rainfall is below 10 inches. Across the Kordofan Plateau the total has reached between 25 and 30 inches, and in the southwestern margins it exceeds 50 inches. This east-west alignment of environmental zones has not promoted contact between the north and south of the

country, especially since the physiography of the south renders the building of modern transport routes difficult and expensive, and in places impossible. Hence, the factor of physiography is added to that of distance in the separation of the south from the northern regions.

The great longitudinal unifier, of course, is the White Nile. In the extreme south, the great river enters the Sudan via a series of rapids, all of which lie upstream from Juba. Below Juba, the Nile is navigable to Khartum, and over considerable stretches it forms the only possible means of communication. The gradient is very low as the river braids its way through the Sudd, re-entering a well-defined valley in the area of Malakal. In the latitude of the Sudd, the Sudan consists of swampland and marshes, and the road from Juba to Khartum, which traverses this region, is usable only part of the year. But the river is navigable all year round and continues to carry most of the traffic between the province of Equatoria and the northern parts of the country.

It is along the Nile that the "bridge" character of the Sudan between black and Arab Africa can be observed to some small extent. Not only have people of the south begun to adopt modes of dress that are normal in the north, but in the settlements, the square mud huts of the desert north and the round, thatched huts of the south stand side by side. The influence and control of the Khartum government are greater along and near the Nile than in the peripheral areas. But the river and the areas immediately adjacent to it form only a small part of the vastness of the Sudan, and interregional contact is much less evident in the distant areas.

In fact, the Sudan has also played a role in the east-west contact between African and Arab, involving peoples and ideas from beyond the boundaries of the present political entity. The savanna belt has been an avenue of penetration for Islam and a zone of transit by Africans on pilgrimages to Mecca. Some of the people involved in these movements settled in the region of the Sudan and made their impact upon local modes of living. Today, however, the modern state incorporates an area in which north-south diversification is greater than that from east to west, and if the Sudan is to form a real bridge between Arab and African, it must come through increased north-south contact and cooperation.

The republic has its origins in a turbulent past. As in the Horn, local as well as European imperialism played a part in the course of events, and the boundaries are in several places the result of the consolidation of colonial claims. The local imperialism is that of Egypt, whose interest in the lands to the south is as old as the state itself. The first exports of the Sudan included slaves, ivory, and ostrich feathers, and the Egyptians intermittently sought to extend their power over the source of these products. The invasion of Islam from the east isolated the pockets of Christianity which had formed during Roman days, and after various small Moslem states had formed and failed, a large Islamic Empire finally arose, centered upon Sennar on the Blue Nile. This empire thrived during the sixteenth century, and the region between the White and Blue Nile became a core area for the entire Sudan, a position it continued to hold through the tenure of several succeeding empires. The Fung Empire held the center of the stage for well over two centuries,

asserting its rule over far-flung tribal peoples, and in a sense it foreshadowed the rise of the modern Sudan.[2]

In 1821 the empire fell as a result of an Egyptian invasion, and an Egyptian government was established at Khartum in 1830. The entire eastern Sudan had fallen to the Egyptians, and the connection of Sudanese territory with the ports of Suakin and Massawa (the latter subsequently lost to the Italians) dates from this period. British influence was now beginning to be felt, and the slave trade was suppressed, as a result of which economic chaos developed; slavery had been one of the mainstays of the tribes in the transition zone between black and Arab Africa.[3]

Under these conditions, the country was ripe for revolt, which came in 1881, when Muhammad Ahmad proclaimed himself the Mahdi, a messenger of Islam who was to guide the people toward freedom from Egyptian rule. It must be realized that, although there was nominal British supervision, the Egyptians were the actual administrators of the Sudan, and it was against them that the revolt which the Mahdi fomented was aimed.[4] Support came from everywhere, and within a few years, the Mahdi's followers, the Dervishes, controlled large parts of the country.

General Charles Gordon was called back from assignment elsewhere to evacuate the Egyptian and British civilians caught up in the struggle and to organize the orderly retreat of the armed forces. This led to his famed stand at Khartum, which he decided to attempt to hold against overwhelming forces. He was besieged with his force of 7,000 men in 1884, the siege lasting 317 days

[2] See A. J. Arkell, *A History of the Sudan to A.D. 1821* (London: Athlone Press, 1955), for much useful information regarding this period.

[3] For a description of the first Anglo-Egyptian efforts to administer the Sudan, see M. Shibeika, *The Independent Sudan* (New York: Speller and Sons, 1959).

[4] The period is well described by H. C. Jackson in *Behind the Modern Sudan* (London: Macmillan, 1955), pp. 195 ff.

SUDAN

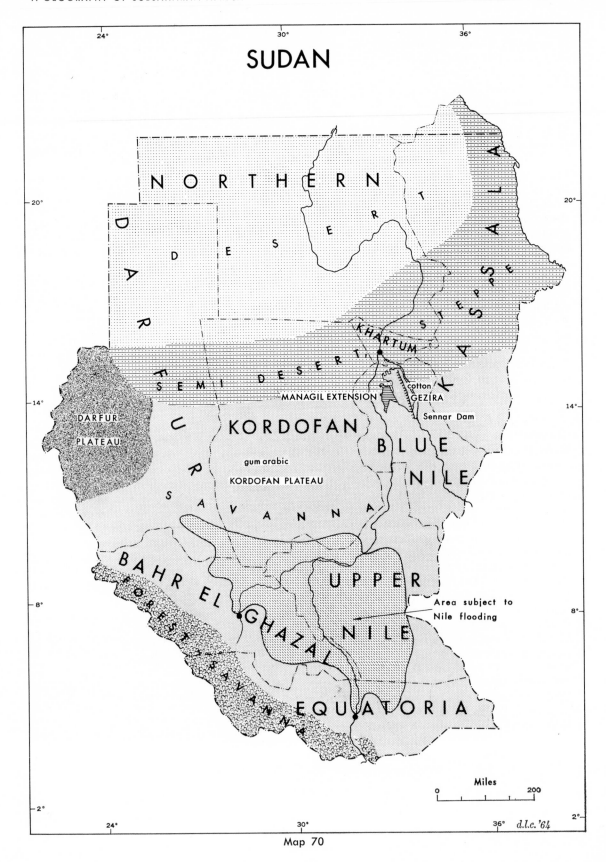

NORTHERN

DESERT

D E S E R T

DARFUR

KHARTUM

STEPPE KASSALA

SEMI DESERT

MANAGIL EXTENSION

cotton

GEZIRA

Sennar Dam

DARFUR
PLATEAU

KORDOFAN

gum arabic

KORDOFAN PLATEAU

SAVANNA

CURU

BLUE

NILE

BAHR EL

GHAZAL

UPPER

NILE

Area subject to
Nile flooding

FOREST SAVANNA

EQUATORIA

Miles

0   200

d.l.c. '64

Map 70

until January 25, 1885, when the Dervishes broke the defenses of the town and eradicated the entire army. Khartum was razed, and the relief force for which Gordon had waited almost a year arrived two days too late.

In the same year, the Mahdi died, but his successor Abdullahi carried on his rule. The Sudan descended into an abyss of disorganization and lawlessness, with slavery increasing to its former proportions and virtually no central authority to replace the administration that had been ousted. These conditions prevailed for 13 years, during which surrounding regions fell prey to colonial powers. France was expanding her dominions in the west and had a foothold in the Horn, as did Italy. German agents were at work immediately to the south. This concerned the British, who had had the initial interest in the Sudan and now occupied only Egypt. Thus, in 1896, British-Egyptian-Sudanese forces entered the Sudan and engaged Abdullahi's Dervishes in more than two years of bitter fighting.

H. H. Kitchener, who was in command of the invading armies, saw his campaign succeed very near the site of Gordon's defeat. At Omdurman, sister city to Khartum, the Dervish army was totally defeated and the Mahdist revolt came to an end in 1898. It was just in time. A week after this victory Kitchener sailed up the Nile to Kodok, on the tenth parallel, where he was able to dissuade a pioneer French party intending to occupy the Sudan from remaining in the area.

British control restored, the task of reconstruction was begun. The years of Mahdist rule had left the Sudan in a poor state. Disease was rampant, medical facilities out of order and unstaffed. Economic development was at a standstill, the livestock population was drastically reduced through lack of care and willful destruction, and general disorganization prevailed. It has been estimated that the population itself had been reduced from 8½ to 3½ million during the dozen years after Gordon's defeat.

Among the first steps taken by the British was the definition and delimitation of the Sudan's boundaries and the establishment of an administration under agreement with Egypt.

Italian control of the coast in Eritrea had been verified by boundary treaty as early as 1891, and since Uganda had become British territory no problems existed in the south. The northern boundary was defined in 1899 in the Anglo-Egyptian Agreement as the twenty-second parallel north, with the Sudan port of Suakin remaining an Egyptian enclave in Sudanese territory. That arrangement lasted only six months, and Suakin was subsequently transferred to the Sudan, which also obtained a small proruption along the Nile to Faras. Finally, an administrative boundary was superimposed over the legal boundary in the east, where tribal administration was thus facilitated.

The boundary with Libya was adjusted more recently. Initially, the Sarra Triangle, which today forms the southern sector of the state of Libya, was a westward proruption of Sudan containing important wells in very dry country. This arrangement originated in 1899, but was revised several times, the last in 1934. By the Italo-British-Egyptian Agreement of that year, the territory of Sarra was added to Libya and the present geometrical boundaries defined and delimited.

The late 1890's saw French efforts to connect their western and eastern possessions in Africa and British concern over the Sudan bring these two powers to the verge of war. In 1899, this danger was removed by the Anglo-French Treaty defining the boundaries between French Equatorial Africa and the Sudan, a treaty which was favorable to the British. Several French outposts, established while the British were engaging the Dervishes elsewhere in the Sudan, were abandoned in favor of Britain.

With international recognition of Menelik's claims and the close correspondence between Abyssinian political and physiographic boundaries in the west (i.e., with the Sudan), the territory of the country had been more or less established and consolidated politically. The Sudan incorporated the entire lower course of the Blue Nile and the bulk of the upper and middle courses of the White Nile. The vast country did not appear promising economically and presented some immediate problems of administration.

The Condominium

After the successful Anglo-Egyptian war effort in the Sudan, an administration was set up whereby both Britain and Egypt had a share of the government. The Egyptian khedive would appoint a British governor general, in whom the supreme powers in the country were vested. The governor general could legislate by proclamation and was the military and civil commander. Lord Kitchener, who had led the conquering forces, was the first governor general, and he established an administrative framework in which the policy-making positions were held by British, the majority of the civil servants being Egyptian. Egypt paid a large share of the costs of administration and control, and the country became known as the Anglo-Egyptian Sudan, although in effect it remained under British control.

Egypt, however, remained nominally a part of the Turkish Ottoman Empire, and when the First World War erupted, it found itself involved with both sides: with Britain in the administration of the Sudan, and with Turkey (which had joined the Axis Powers) in the war itself. Britain declared a protectorate over Egypt, solving the immediate problem but creating the basis for a new one. Egyptian nationalism arose against British overlordship, not only in Egypt, but also in the Sudan, over which the Egyptians wished to extend their sovereignty.

During the entire colonial period, the focus of activity, political as well as economic, was in the region north of 12° north latitude. The southern part of the Sudan, while under British administration, remained almost completely separated and isolated from such progress as took place elsewhere, and was little involved in the continuing administrative struggle among the Egyptians, northern Sudanese, and British. To the linguistic, ethnic, physiographic, and religious individuality of the south was added a form of administrative separation which had the character of a protectorate in all but name. Thus, rather than submerging the large-scale regional differences of the Sudan, British administration actually helped foster them, leaving the problem of actual integration and adjustment to the independent state. Under British administration, therefore, the Sudan did incorporate Arab and African under a single government, but the country did not really serve as a meeting ground between the two. The British deepened the division that already existed by supporting the spread of Christianity in the south while discouraging efforts to propagate Islam.

Contrasts between north and south also found their expression in the politico-geographical sphere before independence, the unifying factor of British administration notwithstanding. As early as 1944 an advisory council was constituted in Khartum, with representation from and responsibilities for the six northern provinces. The Christian and pagan peoples of the south, far removed from the mainstream of Sudan development, were not identified with the Sudanese struggle for independence, and they were not represented in the council. Neither did they feel the impact of Egyptian involvement in Sudan affairs: they were far removed from Egypt itself and from the scene of much of the Anglo-Egyptian-Sudanese friction, Khartum. The days of temporary solidarity between parts of the south and north, resulting from the Egyptian thrust southward in the early 1800's, were long forgotten. Deeper divisions, involving race and religion, and going back also to the days when the northerners were slavers and the southerners actual and potential slaves, remained. Indeed, it may be said that the southern peoples desired either British or Egyptian rule in the Sudan, but not Sudanese rule. In the decades before independence, the Egyptian crown did much to retard Sudanese nationalism and delay independence, partly because of its concern over the future use of the waters of the Nile. While the rift between the Sudanese and Egypt widened, the delay in the coming of independence was welcome in the south, where the replacement of British administrators by northern Sudanese officials was an unpleasant prospect. Thus, on the question of the attitude to Egypt, southern and northern Sudanese held entirely different opinions.

The internal fragmentation of the Sudan

was long minimized by the uniform quality of British rule, even though it could do little to wipe out regional differences. In the south, the British were unquestionably quite popular, since they were seen as security against the imposition of northern rule in the form of northern Sudanese officials. When independence came, and even before the actual date of its achievement, violence accompanied the withdrawal of British government and military personnel from the south and their replacement by Sudanese (of course, northern Moslems). In August, 1955, the Equatoria Corps of the Sudan Defense Force mutinied, and for some weeks held most of the south excluding the town of Juba, which remained in the hands of forces loyal to the Khartum government. Refugees streamed over the Uganda and Congo borders, both civilians escaping from Khartum rule and government officials seeking sanctuary. Belgium closed its Congo border, but among some Acholi leaders in northern Uganda there was talk of uniting the southern extreme of Sudan with Uganda. The British administration in Uganda negated these suggestions, but they were undeniably popular with a segment of the population of the southern Sudan.

Thus, Egyptian and British activities in this part of Africa have resulted in the establishment of a unique state, which is part of the Subsaharan African cultural realm as well as of the Middle East, internally divided in such a manner that people in the south consider themselves occupied by the north. Democratic government, predictably, has faltered, and military leadership has replaced it. Efforts to develop the south, to educate and integrate the peoples in the framework of the country are under way, but the process will be a slow and laborious one.

North, South, and Economic Development

The republic of the Sudan is primarily an agricultural country, and the climatic limits to cultivation are offset by opportunities for irrigation that are among Africa's best. The productive capacity of the country is concentrated in the region which once was the heart of the Fung Empire, between the White and the Blue Nile rivers. To be sure, this is not the only region capable of development, for possibilities also exist along the Nile River north of Khartum, along the Baraka River in the extreme east, and along the Atbara River. The south, also, can sustain sedentary cash cropping in certain areas, and there development has barely begun in the face of such major obstacles as poor communications, lack of education and incentive, and traditional subsistence modes of farming.

Depending mainly upon its agricultural industries, the Sudan is thus not without bright prospects. In spite of the country's reliance upon farming, it has enjoyed financial solvency practically continuously since 1913. This was first achieved through the export of gum arabic, of which the Sudan is the world's major producer. The Kordofan Plateau has been the main source area of this product, so that the south-central Sudan initially made the major economic contribution to the country. El Obeid, chief auction center for the harvest, was connected by rail (via Sennar and Kassala) to Port Sudan. But although this railroad was later extended to Nyala in Darfur Province, no southward line was constructed until the 1960's. Gum arabic, which is used principally in medicine, confectionery, and textile manufacture, is tapped from acacia trees. Indiscriminate tapping, resulting from the ready market and strong demand, has endangered the industry, which is now supported by the planting of trees. The region of production extends from Kassala Province through Blue Nile and Kordofan to Darfur, all "northern" provinces.

In the mid-1920's a cash crop, cotton, became the Sudan's leading export product, and has remained so ever since, annually contributing as much as three-quarters of the total export revenue. Its cultivation takes place throughout the country, under irrigation along both Niles and without it in the wetter southern provinces. Only the northernmost Nilotic peoples (Shilluk and Dinka) produce anything other than subsistence crops, including small amounts of cotton, so that the contribution of the south toward the annual cotton crop should not be overestimated. The south

313

Landowner at Work in the Gezira Area, Sudan. A farmer is seen plowing his lands in the traditional way, with oxen, prior to planting cotton. (United Nations)

Cotton Harvest in the Gezira Area, Sudan. Cotton, producing by far the bulk of the Sudan's export revenue, is produced largely on the lands of the Gezira Scheme. Here, pickers are taking their harvest to the collection point on another tenant's plot, whence it will travel to Port Sudan and overseas markets. (United Nations)

Cotton Bales Being Loaded for Transport to Gezira Ginnery, Sudan. Thousands of Sudanese families have benefited from the success of the Gezira Scheme, initiated by the British and today being expanded by the Sudanese. (United Nations)

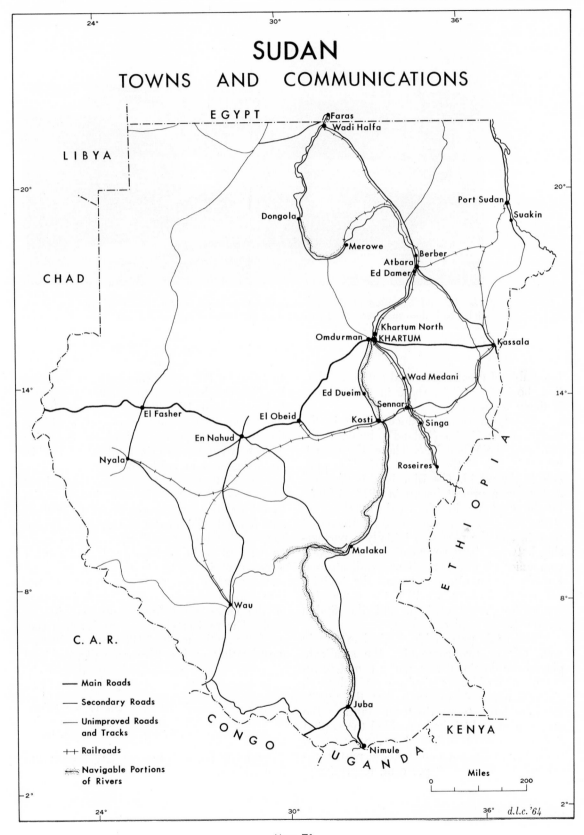

SUDAN
TOWNS AND COMMUNICATIONS

EGYPT

LIBYA

CHAD

Faras
Wadi Halfa

Port Sudan
Suakin

Dongola

Merowe
Berber
Atbara
Ed Damer

Khartum North
Omdurman KHARTUM
Kassala

Ed Dueim
Wad Medani

El Fasher
El Obeid
Kosti
Sennar
Singa

En Nahud
Nyala
Roseires

ETHIOPIA

Malakal

Wau

C. A. R.

Main Roads
Secondary Roads
Unimproved Roads and Tracks
Railroads
Navigable Portions of Rivers

Juba

CONGO
UGANDA
KENYA

Nimule

Miles
0   200

d.l.c. '64

Map 71

The Managil Extension of the Gezira Irrigation Scheme, Sudan. The Blue Nile lies at the right, with the canal permitting irrigation in the Managil area at the left. Note the extreme flatness of the terrain. The extension eventually will cover 830,000 acres of land. (United Nations)

is capable of greatly increased cotton production, however, and its share in the industry is likely to increase.

The great cotton-producing area in the Sudan is the Gezira ("island") between the Blue and the White Nile. There, the crop is grown in one of the greatest irrigation projects in the world. The Blue Nile is dammed at Sennar, a project begun in 1913, delayed by the First World War, and completed in 1925. The area was connected to the coast by rail, and the plan was initially a partnership between the government, two concession companies (Sudan Plantations Syndicate and Kassala Cotton Company), and the individual tenant farmers. In 1950 the concession companies' leases expired, and the Sudan Gezira Board replaced them.

The triple partnership worked extremely well. Of the two companies, the syndicate played the dominant role, and a complete reorganization of local agriculture was achieved. The arrangement was such that the profits were divided between the tenant farmers, the government (which had provided the capital and the cost of maintaining the irrigation works), and the companies, these parties receiving 40, 40, and 20 per cent, respectively.

In 1925, 240,000 acres were under cultivation; by 1938 this had risen to 850,000; and today it is well over 1½ million.[5] No expansion of the irrigated areas can be undertaken without the consent of Egypt, and of the 5 million acres between the two rivers, at least 1,750,000 are irrigable and cultivable.[6]

In 1950, when the role of the private firms was taken over by the Sudan Gezira Board and the scheme was therefore in effect nationalized, the profit sharing was altered somewhat. The tenant farmer now receives 44 per cent of the profits directly and another 4 per cent indirectly in the form of social services, while the government gets 42 per cent and the Sudan Gezira Board, in charge of the entire operation, is allotted 10 per cent.[7] The project continues to function successfully, with nearly 30,000 tenant farmers participating, each cultivating a piece of land

---

[5] A. Welsh, ed., *Africa South of the Sahara,* p. 60.

[6] L. S. Suggate, *Africa* (London: Harrap, 1960), p. 168.

[7] H. R. Jarrett, *Africa* (London: Macdonald Evans, 1962), p. 110.

Introduction of Organized Agriculture into Southern Sudan. In an effort to bring the distant south into the country's economic sphere, the Sudan government is introducing suitable crops on an organized basis to the southern provinces. Here, in preparation for a rice-growing scheme, land is being cleared and turned in Bar-el-Ghazal Province. (United Nations)

averaging about 40 acres.[8] Careful land husbandry practices have been enforced, protecting the soil. A rotation system has been developed whereby cotton is planted on a certain plot every third year. Following the cotton year, the soil carries a crop of millet or dura, and is then left fallow the next season. Nevertheless, yields per acre are very variable, and the total harvest is great mainly because of the enormous extent of the scheme. Average yields are, for instance, substantially less than those of Egypt, although the increased use of fertilizers is expected to improve this situation.

The central zone of the Sudan, therefore, makes the greatest contribution to the economy of the country, far in excess of the dry north and the dominantly subsistence south. This central belt lies in the "northern" provinces, and in an effort to involve the south

to a greater extent in cash cropping, the Sudan government initiated a cotton-growing project in the south in the area of the Zande (Azande) people, who were attracted to a miniature cotton project, there to be introduced to a new way of life. Compared to the investment in Gezira, the Zande project is a very insignificant one, but its importance as an example of social change is considerable. As in Gezira, planned villages were built, a money economy was introduced and some manufacturing, based on the cotton crop, developed. Elsewhere, in both northern and southern regions, development plans await execution.

The dependence of the Sudan upon its one-crop economy has steadily increased and is a matter of concern to the government. In the Sudan, the government dominates the economy, employing most of the country's labor, producing and marketing the bulk of the cotton crop, and owning the communications systems. The government has encouraged the growth of growers' cooperatives but continues to control them. Meanwhile, although the country is virtually self-sufficient in food crops, the dependence upon the annual cotton crop with its variable earning power entails serious risks. In the absence of the requirements for industrial development

---

[8] This figure (30,000 farmers) applied before the additional 400,000 acres in the Managil District, which became available in 1962, were settled. This recently available acreage was, however, included in the previously mentioned total of irrigated land.

and diversification, efforts are now directed to the balancing of the agrarian economy, and for this, the cooperation of southern peoples will be required. The Sudan environment becomes wetter southward, and the eradication of the tsetse fly could render the southern provinces capable of sustaining a sound pastoral industry. Among the major problems, however, remains the lack of adequate knowledge concerning the economic potential of large parts of the country. This is retarding investment from overseas at a time when local capital is virtually nonexistent.

Bridge and Barrier

Development in the Sudan has been concentrated in the northeast, with two major regions out of touch and lagging, although

for different reasons. One lies across the northern part of the country, where the dryness, absence of vegetation, and lack of resources have rendered tens of thousands of square miles practically empty and devoid of human activity. The important exception is the ribbon of habitation along the Nile River, although the Nile is interrupted by a series of cataracts, and railroad links have had to be constructed from Wadi Halfa and Kareima to Atbara and Port Sudan. The other region, of course, is the south, which is by no means empty but is the most remote part of the country.

The heart of the Sudan lies at the confluence of the two major arteries, the Blue and White Nile rivers; there is the largest irrigated region of cash cropping, the capital, Khartum, with its sister city of Omdurman (with a combined population of 500,000), the focus of the railroad system, and the northern limit of uninterrupted navigation on both Nile rivers. This also is the most densely populated area of the country, producing by far the bulk of the exported products. It has long

Port Sudan, Republic of the Sudan. Port Sudan is the country's only direct exit to the sea, and practically all external trade goes through this harbor. Shown here are the quays and loading facilities, including the terminal of the railroad from Khartum and beyond. (United Nations)

Market in Omdurman, Opposite Khartum, Sudan. Omdurman is Khartum's sister city, the entire urban complex having over a quarter of a million people. Note the modes of dress and the type and variety of items on sale—mainly cooking and other household utensils, baskets, etc. (United Nations)

been the focus of administrative, religious, and educational activity in the Sudan, and was the core area of the Fung Empire of old. It lies 490 miles by rail from Port Sudan (50,000), to which exports are funneled, and forms the major domestic market for the country.

The development of the Sudan has been concentrated in this region to such an extent that in 1964 the main town, Juba, possessed better connections with the Congo and Uganda than it did with the rest of the Sudan. The first railway line to penetrate the south, to Wau, was under construction in 1963. The physiographic barrier separating the south from the rest of the country, however, is all but insuperable, for when the seasonal flooding takes place, the area inundated may ex-

tend from the vicinity of Wau in the southwest to within a few miles of the Ethiopian border, making contact with the south possible only by steamer or aircraft. Although the problem in Uganda is less complex, certain similarities exist between the obstacles faced by Uganda in forging a unified state and those of the Sudan. In Uganda, the southern, dominating ethnic group is Bantu, whereas the northern peoples are not; in Sudan, the northern, ruling people are dominantly Arab, and the southern peoples are not. But Uganda is less than one-tenth the size of the Sudan, and contact between the outlying areas and Kampala is a great deal more effective than that between the southern provinces of the Sudan and Khartum.

In assessing the role of the Sudan as a

bridge between Arab and African, it should
be remembered that the southern Nilotic peoples are themselves not representative of
Bantu and Negro Africa, although linguisti-
cally they relate to central rather than northern Africa. Nor are the northern peoples
racially identical to the people of Egypt. The
transition from the heart of the Arab world
to black Africa along the Nile River, begun
in Egypt, ends in Uganda. Indeed, the most
obvious zone of ethnic transition lies across
the Sudan, but it would be a mistake to assume that the peoples of the northern and
southern parts of the country are part of
homogeneous Arab and African populations
living beyond. Nevertheless, any eventual
success on the part of the Sudanese in developing a nation out of the diversity of the
country's population will be the result of
education—and ideas in this country emanate
from the north; of economic participation—
and products must go to northern markets
and exits; of effective administration—and the
trained people in this field are the people of
the north; and modes of living which are
normal among the majority of the people—
again the people of the north. In other words,
the effort must be made by a strong central
government that is aware of the regional contrasts in the country and is prepared to make
certain sacrifices to promote internal unity.
As was stated earlier, the period of British
rule really only delayed the inevitable effort
to integrate the south with the north; it was
perhaps the only major British error in the
modern administration of the Sudan as a dependency. Since the year of independence,
1956, the country has had but little opportunity to begin the task. In a sense, the Sudan
still is two bridgeheads rather than a bridge,
the first connecting beam just being laid.

Part 5

WEST AFRICA

17

FROM COLONY TO REPUBLIC:
THE EXPERIMENT OF FEDERATION IN NIGERIA

ONE IN EVERY FIVE Africans resident in the Subsaharan part of the continent is a Nigerian. Although it is by no means the largest state on the continent (357,000 square miles), Nigeria's population is at least double that of any other country in the region here under discussion. Previous estimates of the population of Nigeria appear to have been low, and there probably are over 55 million people in this country—more, at any rate, than in all the countries of Southern Africa combined, as many as in all of equatorial Africa, more than in the Horn, and more than in the rest of West Africa. Nigeria includes some of Africa's most densely populated parts, and the variety of its peoples is considerable.

Several aspects of Nigeria's relative location, size, and shape should be emphasized. Though compact in shape (about 700 miles both east-west and north-south), the country extends from about 4° to 14° north latitude, thus incorporating a wide range of climatic and environmental zones. Indeed, Nigeria extends farther from the coast into interior West Africa than does any other coastal state in this region. It lies in the lower reaches of one of Africa's greatest river systems. The lower Niger River is navigable over hundreds of miles upstream from the delta, and the Benue River, its main tributary, carries goods from as far east as Cameroun. Nigeria is located in the "bend" of West Africa, and therefore lies closer to other regions of the continent than most West African states; its history is varied. African kingdoms and em-

pires occupied its coastal forests and its northern plains; caravans from the north brought trade and contact from the Arab world; pilgrimages to Mecca trekked across the country.

Although bordering forested equatorial Africa in the east and extending into Moslem Africa in the north, Nigeria is a distinctly West African country. Contact with its eastern neighbor has never been very effective, except with that part of former German Kamerun that became British mandate territory. From the coast to Lake Chad, only two good roads—one in the extreme south, the other in the north—cross the border. That in the south connects Douala with Mamfe and Enugu, and the northern route, linking Maiduguri and Fort Lamy, runs through Cameroun where that country is less than 50 miles wide. Elsewhere, only some tracks lead from Nigeria into Cameroun, and the Cameroun Highlands form a considerable physiographic obstacle to communications.

Nigeria is surrounded by countries under French influence, as it borders, in addition to Cameroun, the Republic of Niger in the north and the Republic of Dahomey in the west. Contact with these is little better than that with Cameroun. North of the road from Lagos along the coast to Porto Novo, Lomé, and Accra, surface connections between Nigeria and its western neighbors consist mainly of paths and tracks crossing the undemarcated boundary. Northward, roads lead into Niger from Kano and Katsina, but

The Niger River, Southern Nigeria. The braided Niger is shown near the place where distributaries begin spreading across the vast delta. Long a major transport route, the Niger-Benue system continues to carry a considerable volume of trade.

Nigeria's northern boundary corresponds approximately to the 25-inch isohyet, north of which the desert rapidly develops. Nevertheless, Nigeria is the natural outlet for the limited exports of the adjacent northern territories. As development progresses in the Lake Chad areas of Cameroun and Chad, and in the areas along the Niger in the Niger Republic, external communication links will improve.

Diversity

Nigeria is a country of immense internal geographic variety. The pivotal physiographic feature is the Niger River, which centuries ago was the natural boundary, in the northeast, of the powerful Yoruba Kingdom of Oyo. It is joined in the central part of the country by the Benue, after which it flows into the largest delta in Subsaharan Africa.

Together, the Niger and Benue form a Y-shaped system which fragments Nigeria into three areas. Both rivers, but especially the Niger, have figured importantly in the historico-geographical development of the political entity. When the Jihad (Holy War) waged by the Moslem Fulani of the north brought Fulani emirates to the Niger's banks, the river became the natural boundary between Yoruba and Fulani empires, although it did not stop the spread of Islam, which was adopted by many Yorubas in the south.

Although Nigeria does not possess such prominent physical features as East Africa's rifts or Southern Africa's Drakensberg, it includes a number of quite distinct physiographic regions.[1] Nigeria's highest elevations lie in the east, where the Adamawa High-

---

[1] For one example of their delimitation see R. J. Harrison Church, *West Africa* (New York: Wiley, 1961), Fig. 79, p. 460. A description of the regions occurs on pp. 452–88.

lands reach 6,700 feet (when the Southern Cameroons formed part of the country, Mount Cameroon, 13,350 feet, was the highest point and the Cameroon-Bamenda Highlands the highest region). The largest elevated region lies to the north of the Niger-Benue confluence, although it exceeds 5,000 feet in only a few areas. This is the Jos Plateau and its surroundings, the high plains of Hausaland. Together, these areas make up the core of northern Nigeria; toward the northeast, the land drops into the Chad Basin, and in the northwest into the valley of the Sokoto River and its tributaries. The Niger-Benue Lowland is separated from the coastal areas, including the extensive Niger Delta, by the Oyo-Yoruba Upland in the west and the Udi Plateau in the east, both regions lying mainly between 1,000 and 2,000 feet above sea level. In the south, the coastal plains decline gently toward a shoreline of spits and bars, lagoons and luxuriant mangroves.

Nigeria also possesses a wider range of climates than any other West African state.

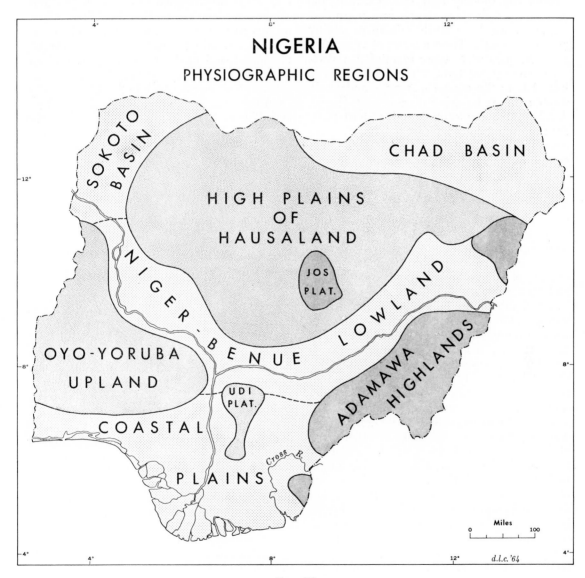

Map 72

Isohyets trend generally east-west across the country, and the extreme south receives over 100 inches annually, while the northern margins get less than 30. In the central part of Nigeria, including the southern portion of the high plains of Hausaland and the northern sections of the Oyo-Yoruba and Udi uplands, the rainfall is between 45 and 60 inches. Much of Nigeria, therefore, receives a large amount of rain by standards applicable throughout Subsaharan Africa; a comparison to two other coastal countries such as Tanganyika and Angola will quickly bear this out. Still, the northern periphery is steppe and thorn forest, and toward the north, rainfall variability increases rapidly. Thus, a series of vegetation zones lie parallel to those of rainfall, reflecting the increasing dryness from south to north. Inland from the coastal mangrove and freshwater swamps lie areas of rainforest (better developed in the central and eastern parts than in the west), which were formerly more extensive than they are today. This inner margin of the rainforest, as a result of human activity, has become a zone of forest and savanna, sometimes referred to as "derived savanna." North of this belt the country becomes more open, the bulk of it being covered by a savanna that is characterized by increasing dryness.

Nigeria's physiographic variety is paralleled by the diversity of its population groups, and their religions, languages, and modes of living. South of the Niger and Benue rivers, two peoples dominate numerically: the Yoruba in the west, and the Ibo in the east. To the north, the majority peoples are the Hausa and Fulani. Depending upon the bases employed for dividing Nigeria's population into tribal groups, however, perhaps 250 distinct units might be recognized, numbering from a few thousand individuals to several million. The region's history, like that of other parts of West Africa, includes alternate periods of local consolidation and tribal fragmentation; both the plains of the north and the forests of the south were the scene of efforts to create lasting empires. Some of these, like Benin, became powerful entities surviving several turbulent centuries, leaving their mark on the country to this day. Others failed in the feudal rivalries and were absorbed by more

successful contemporaries. From the north came the impact of Islam, as the Fulani, living in the land of the numerous Hausa farmers and traders, rose to power and established strong emirates. From the south came the impact of Europe, and slavery gave way to legitimate trade and to territorial control.

Nigeria, then, incorporates a more complete range of conditions—climatic, vegetative, pedologic, historical, demographic—than any other West African country. Some features are shared by several parts of the country, others are confined to one area. Sections of the south to the east of the Niger River, for instance, possess soils and vegetation, as well as climatic conditions, that are similar to those found to the west of the river. But in terms of their development, these two areas are quite different. And both differ greatly from the area lying to the north of the Niger and Benue. These regional differences were recognized by the British when in 1914 they unified the Nigeria Colony and Protectorate. They continued to be recognized while Britain aided Nigeria in its preparation for independence, and when, in 1960, sovereignty was achieved, regional interests were guarded by a federal constitution.

Emergence of Regional Individualism

Although political entities existed, in the area today occupied by Nigeria, prior to the spread of effective European control, there never was a unified state covering all of the territory. Nigeria, then, is a European creation, a piece of West Africa's physiographic and ethnic diversity around which boundaries were drawn and within which the course of progress has been one of constant adjustment.

The basic elements of Nigeria's internal division were already there before conquest and consolidation took place. Those divisions were not unique to the Nigerian part of West Africa; they relate to the environmental and locational aspects of the region. The peoples of the northern savanna plains traded with the far north and felt the spread of ideas from that direction. Their terrain permitted movement to a far greater extent than in the densely forested south, and their empires grew larger. They adopted Islam and propagated it vigorously, and they penetrated the lands of the southern peoples in search of slaves and tribute. The exposure of the northern peoples to Caucasoid, trans-Saharan elements also widened the gap in the somatic sense, and friction was frequent between them and their southern neighbors. It was the upheaval involving the Fulani, as well as

the desire to terminate the slave trade, that contributed much to the British decision to intervene in the interior.

The involvement of Europe, in Nigeria as in other parts of West Africa, changed the whole economic and social orientation of the area. Both the north and south had achieved political organization, both had engaged in the slave trade, but the north had long experienced more of the effects of circulation and contact with an outside world. In a sense, the south was a hinterland, separated

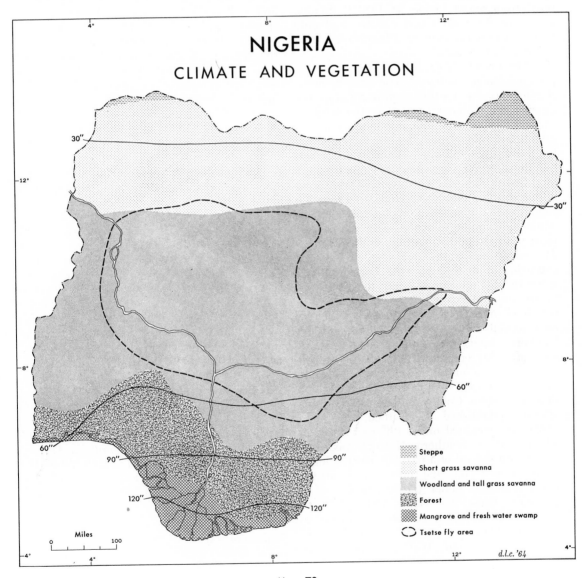

Map 73

327

from the north by a middle belt comprised of many larger and smaller pagan peoples sharing only a fear of domination by their more populous and powerful neighbors. British posts of trade and administration along the southern coast (which in Nigeria presented major obstacles to permanent settlement) began to develop in earnest toward the middle of the nineteenth century, and in 1861 the site of Lagos was ceded to the crown by King Dosunmu. But in the early years, Lagos Colony remained only a minor part of the British West African Settlements, administered from Sierra Leone; in 1874 it became a part of the Gold Coast Colony, and only in 1886 did it cease to be administered from another British post.

The decade from 1880 to 1890 saw important changes initiated. The British, desiring to end the hostilities prevailing in the interior, now intervened, and in the south, a rudimentary protectorate administration was established. Also founded were several chartered companies, of which the most important, the Royal Niger Company, did much to extend British influence northward. The process of penetration was completed by Frederick Lugard, who repelled French encroachment while subjugating northern Nigerian chieftains with the aid of locally drafted forces. The result was a British-controlled territory consisting of three parts: the Lagos Colony, a Southern Protectorate, and the Northern Protectorate. Actually, the two major parts remained practically separate, each under its own administration; in 1906, Lagos and the Southern Protectorate were merged. Lugard, soon after his conquest, advised the British government to unite the country, but only in 1914 did this step take place, at which time the Nigeria Colony and Protectorate was officially established. Even then, the south and north remained under different forms of administration. Southern Nigeria was governed with the aid of a partially elected legislative council, but the protectorate to the north remained under the jurisdiction of a governor. Thus, "the North and the South . . . remained almost complete strangers to each other. The . . . South was looking towards England and Western Europe. The

Islamic North fixed its gaze on distant Mecca. . . ."[2]

The political entity now consolidated, internal differences began to become increasingly well defined. The most obvious were those between the north and south; the Southern Provinces were not divided into an eastern and western section until 1939. The exposure of the south to European influence brought change there from which the north remained shielded. Most significant perhaps was the contrast in modes of administration. In the north, the Fulani emirates were left intact, and indirect rule prevailed. Traditional authorities and ways of life were little disturbed. Slavery was prohibited, but because the settling of Christian missionaries could take place only with the consent of the emirs, few mission schools—common in the south—operated there. In the south, on the other hand, colonial administration quickly led to African participation in government: as early as 1923, the legislative council included African members. Nigeria was the first British African territory to include African representatives in its governing body, but the important point is that this step was taken in southern Nigeria; little had changed in the north. The difference was to become ever greater, for political activity rapidly grew more intense in the south, which began to produce modern political leaders. These leaders came to demand changes in Nigeria's political situation with which the northern traditionalists did not always associate themselves.

Southern political sophistication and northern traditionalism inevitably emerged as one of the major centrifugal forces in Nigeria's political geography. Now, the north was the distant hinterland, and the south had contact with the outside world; surrounded by other colonial territories, the north to a large extent lost its access to the sources of its cultural and religious heritage. Having once propagated Islam to the south of the Niger and Benue, the Moslems saw Christianity gain in the lands of the coast, and with

[2] H. O. Davies, Q.C., *Nigeria: The Prospects for Democracy* (London: Weidenfeld and Nicholson, 1961), p. 92.

Christianity came a spread of education to which the north had no access. The difference, as reflected by literacy rates, became ever larger; as late as 1931, it was less than 3 per cent in the northern part of the country.

The developing transport network made the consolidation of the area possible, and it is one unifying element in the divided country. Prior to the arrival of the British, there had been trade across the Niger River between the Fulani emirates and the Yoruba kingdoms, and after the area had been paci-

fied, the importance of economic links in forging the whole was immediately recognized, as was the usefulness of good communications in effective control and administration. Hence, the railroad from Lagos to Kano was completed as early as 1912, with an additional link from that northern city to the navigable Niger River. Other railroads were built subsequently, from Port Harcourt to the collieries of Enugu (1916) and on to the Lagos–Kano line at Kaduna (1932). Several branch railroads were constructed in the north, and

Map 74

the effect was to stimulate enormously the production there of peanuts, cotton, hides, and skins, and to promote interregional trade and contact.

Improving communication links did not, however, eliminate the regional differences in the vast country. Economic development itself brought with it certain problems. Parts of the country obviously are better endowed with agricultural and other resources than other parts; some of the peoples are more fortunate than others. The demand for cash crops brought prosperity and progress to some areas, while others remained mired in subsistence patch cultivation. In the Oyo-Yoruba southwest, cocoa is the leading cash crop, and perhaps one-half of all the people in that part of the country are in some way involved in its production. In the southeast, on the other hand, the economy is largely based upon the oil palm, while in the north, peanuts form the major cash crop.

The areas of productive capacity in Nigeria lie in two rather distinct belts, one to the south of the Niger-Benue Lowland, the other to the north. The southern belt, corresponding approximately to the forest zone, extends from the cocoa-growing west to the palm-supported east. North of the lowland, the most productive zone lies east-west in the Kano-Zaria latitude, extending to the margins of the Sokoto and Chad basins. The two zones are divided by the comparatively unproductive "Middle Belt," characterized previously as having been a buffer between the north and the south. The Middle Belt is an area of tsetse fly, precluding the raising of livestock (except on the high Jos Plateau and in the Adamawa Highlands), and although its transitional location permits the cultivation of both the grain crops of the north and the root crops of the south, no important cash crops have been added to these staples. Thus, the Middle Belt, which covers about one-quarter of Nigeria's land, produces on an average about 10 per cent of its exports.[3]

----

[3] Harrison Church, op. cit., pp. 477–82. For a discussion of the Middle Belt and its relationships with the Northern Region, see K. M. Buchanan, "The Northern Region of Nigeria," Geographical Review, XLIII, No. 4 (October, 1953), 451–73.

The separation of the major areas of productive capacity, resulting from a combination of topographic and climatic factors and coinciding with a historico-geographical separation of the region's major peoples, has promoted regionalism. The road and railroad networks of Nigeria are best developed within the three major producing regions (the south, east and west of the Niger River, and the north), but connecting links have long been tenuous. Kaduna is 561 and 569 miles from the two seaports by the western and eastern lines, respectively, and the lines cross the unprofitable Middle Belt. In the mid-1960's there still was no railroad connecting the eastern and western parts of the south across the Niger River, and only in the early 1960's was a bridge constructed across the river at Onitsha, replacing a ferry. Bridge connections to the north were those of Jebba and Makurdi; all other cross-Benue and Niger traffic must use ferries. Thus, the Niger and Benue rivers have formed major obstacles to effective interregional contact. In the south, the Niger became an internal political boundary, when, in 1939, the Southern Provinces were divided into an Eastern and a Western Province. Although the boundary between northern and southern Nigeria never ran along the Niger and Benue rivers (above their confluence), but somewhat to the south, the divisive effect of these valleys remained. The core region of the north lies in the high plains of Hausaland, and it has always been separated from the Southern Provinces by the lagging Middle Belt, including the river lowlands.

As Nigeria developed economically and politically, the centrifugal forces of regionalism asserted themselves: they were sufficiently strong to play a major role during the time which in most colonial territories produces unity, the preindependence period. It is a measure of the intensity of regional differences, notably between north and south, that there were northern requests for delays in the attainment of sovereignty, which in the south was viewed as a national aim. In 1946 and 1947, the first real steps were taken in the creation of the modern political framework. A legislative council was established to deal with the whole of Nigeria rather than with the south alone, and regional legislatures were formed for the Northern, Western, and Eastern regions, as the former provinces were now called. The internal diversity of the country clearly called for a politico-geographical arrangement permitting a considerable amount of local autonomy; without it, the cooperation of most of the people of the north, and minority groups elsewhere, would have been lost. In 1954, a federal structure was put into effect, and after repeated adjustments, the country became independent in 1960. The Federation of Nigeria lasted, in name, just three years. Late in 1963 it became the Republic of Nigeria, although retaining the federal structure that is a legacy of enlightened colonialism and cooperation.

The processes of adjustment are not likely to cease soon. An additional region, the Midwest Region, already has been carved from the Western Region with its dominant Yoruba population; other peoples have indicated more or less well-founded desires for separate regional autonomy. Whatever the future may hold, however, the experiment of federation is unique in West Africa, and immensely significant because it involves so many people and a state so important in the entire continent.

THE WESTERN REGION

Prior to the separation of the Midwest Region (Benin and Delta provinces), the Western Region covered 45,376 square miles. The Midwest Region has taken about one-third of this area, including Benin City, capital of the old empire, and the towns of Warri and Burutu, where goods brought down the Niger and Benue are transferred to seagoing vessels. But the Western Region centers upon the largest city in tropical Africa and the second largest urban center in Subsaharan Africa, Ibadan (1,000,000).

The Western Region in many ways is ahead of its neighbors, and from some points of view is the heart of the whole country. Several factors have contributed to its progress, not the least important of which is its comparatively high degree of organization long before the penetration of European influences. Today, nearly one-third of the peo-

ple of the Western Region live in cities with populations over 20,000, and indigenous urbanization had created most of them prior to the European impact. Ibadan was founded toward the end of the eighteenth century and came under British domination only in 1893. By then, its population already was well over 100,000. The cities of the Yoruba performed the special function of affording protection for the residents in time of war. Yoruba cities, therefore, were walled cities, within which many people resided who would cultivate their lands miles away. They also were, and are, market centers, and Ibadan, capital of the Region, is also its most important commercial center.

In a sense, therefore, the cities of Yorubaland are very large villages, and the high percentage of urbanized population tends to give the wrong impression regarding the occupation of most people in the Western Region. The Yoruba are good farmers, and their movement to and from their lands, and the density of the population (over 300 per square mile in many areas) have led to careful and intensive farming and a relatively high degree of organization in agriculture. Furthermore, the Western Region probably is the richest part of Nigeria, containing good soils and receiving much rainfall. Thus, when cash crops were introduced, several factors required for success were present.

Cocoa, which was brought to Nigeria from Fernando Poo in the 1870's, came to occupy first place among the cash crops of the region, at times producing as much as a quarter of all Nigerian export revenues. Grown by peasant farmers whose plots average two or three acres in size, cocoa has long been the basis of the comparative wealth of the west, especially in the years after the Second World War. Actually, although the total production has never challenged that of Ghana, Nigeria began exporting cocoa earlier. The railroad from Lagos reached Ibadan, center of the industry, in 1901, and in addition to perhaps 200,000 farmers, many thousands of other Western Region workers are involved in the treatment, packing, and transporting of the product. The effect of the industry on life in the Region was to replace a subsistence economy with cash cropping involving not just a few plantation owners but a large cross-section of the farming population. Standards of living began to rise, however slowly; communication lines developed rapidly; long-isolated areas were drawn into the economic sphere; cooperative and other organizations were formed. Added to the pedologic, climatic, and topographic fortunes of the Western Region was its location near the coast and its major outlet to the overseas markets, permitting relatively easy exporting of the crop. Furthermore, internal trade was stimulated. As lands were put under cocoa, notably in the central part of Yorubaland, they ceased to be self-sufficient in food crops and required imports from other areas.

The Western Region also benefited more than any other part of Nigeria from whatever blessings colonial administration bestowed on the country. It was the first area to be connected by rail with the northern hinterland and to begin handling the exports from the interior. The administrative headquarters, Lagos, became the country's first port and second city, with a population of about a half million in the early 1960's. Modern port facilities were completed at Apapa in 1926 and improved subsequently; the city grew to become the country's largest industrial center. Lagos was the center of the old Lagos Colony, and in 1950 it was merged with the Western Region. The merger was short-lived, however, for in 1954 the federal arrangement necessitated the selection of a federal capital to be located on separate territory. Thus the city of Lagos, including some 27 square miles of land, was designated federal territory and became the capital of the emerging sovereign state.

The selection of Lagos (700,000) as the capital of the Federation of Nigeria did not meet with universal approval, for the relative strengths of the regional party representation in the federal parliament were of course related to the numerical strength of the populations in each Region. By separating densely populated territory from the Western Region, the Region's leading party lost a sizeable number of voters. Several grounds were put forward to justify the action, however: in the first place, Nigeria's administration had long been

Old and New in Lagos, Nigeria. The changing city of Lagos, federal capital of Nigeria, reflects the bustle of life in this progressing country. Modern buildings tower over the makeshift shacks still dominating much of the urban center; apartment buildings are arising in the suburbs as well.

headquartered in Lagos, so that it was by far the best-equipped city for the continuation of government. Secondly, the inclusion of the port facilities in the federal territory constituted an assurance for the Northern Region, which thus came to depend for its natural outlet upon a federal rather than a Western Region harbor. Thirdly, the selection of another western city would have had political consequences similar to those involved in the choice of Lagos, and the selection of any other city elsewhere would have meant that new facilities would have had to be constructed there. And Nigeria could afford the building of a new capital even less than Brazil.

In addition to Western Region opposition to the selection of Lagos as the federal capital, there has been a movement within the boundaries of the former Lagos Colony to establish a separate region consisting of the city and former colonial territory. The colony was divided, the 27 urbanized square miles becoming federal territory and the remaining, mainly rural, area being joined to the Western Region. The advantages of the transit function of the proposed region are obvious, but the move was opposed, for equally obvious reasons, by all major parties in the federal parliament.

The Western Region is the least populous of Nigeria's three major regions (between 8 and 9 million people), only the young Midwest Region having fewer inhabi-

tants. But its contribution to Nigeria, in terms of exports, industrial products for local consumption, skilled manpower, and an educated elite, far exceed what might be expected on the basis of numbers alone. The Western Region may be Nigeria's most favored region, but the progress it has made has been due at least in part to the industry and adaptability of its people. The old Yoruba cities have begun to take on a modern appearance. Standards of living have risen more rapidly than elsewhere in the country,

Map 75

Benin City, Midwest Region, Nigeria. A section of the capital, lying amid the forests of the south, is shown here.

and the Region has become a major internal market. Ibadan has become the country's most important university center. Over half of Nigeria's exports travel through the Region on their way to the coast, and in addition to exporting cocoa to Western Europe, the Western Region sends its products to other parts of the country, notably kola nuts and palm oil. It is in the process of diversifying its production further, and in addition to exports of palm kernels and some timber, tobacco and cotton are being tried. Among Nigeria's regions, the Western Region has made the longest stride on the path of progress.

THE MIDWEST REGION

The Midwest Region in 1964 was the smallest of the political subdivisions of Nigeria, and at the time of independence, it did not yet exist. Discussions leading to its establishment reached the point of decision in 1963, at which time Benin and Delta provinces, with a combined area of about one-third of the former Western Region, were given the right to secede. The Region is populated by a number of non-Yoruba peo-

ple, including a majority of Edo (well over a half-million), a very large Ibo minority, and smaller Ijaw and Itsekiri minorities.

Desire for a Midwest Region was by no means universal in this area. The Ibo living to the west of the Niger (representatives of the majority people in the Eastern Region) were divided on the matter; the educated Ibo favoring the new Region because they would take a leading role in government and administration, the uneducated Ibo desiring union with the Eastern Region rather than separation.[4]

The Midwest Region focuses upon Benin City (100,000), capital of the once-powerful kingdom. The city lies in the forest zone which forms the central part of the region, and is a rubber-processing center. To the north, the forest thins out, and the oil palm no longer sustains the local economy; there, root crops and rice are the staples, and some cotton can be cultivated. The majority of the Region's 2,750,000 people, however, live concentrated in the forest belt itself, and densities resemble those of the eastern forest belt, aver-

---

[4] R. J. Harrison Church, *Environment and Policies in West Africa* (Princeton, N.J.: Van Nostrand, 1963), pp. 84 ff.

aging between 200 and 300 per square mile and in places exceeding 400.

The south of the Region is covered by the delta's mangrove swamps, but nevertheless performs an important and sustaining function. The Niger's distributaries permit navigation, and the ports of Warri (35,000) and Burutu (10,000) handle goods shipped from as far afield as Chad and Cameroun. In fact, these ports handle shipments from every region in Nigeria as well, including peanuts shipped down the Niger and Benue rivers from the Northern Region, cocoa and timber from the Western Region, palm oil and kernels from the Eastern Region, and, of course, from the Midwest Region itself. Part of these exports go to Lagos, where they are transshipped for dispatch overseas.

The Midwest Region is perhaps the least favored of Nigeria's internal political divisions, in terms of its total assets and in view of its small area. The comparatively dense population it supports is largely engaged in subsistence agriculture. Apart from lignite deposits around Asaba on the Niger, it has no known mineral resources. The soils are leached and more sandy than those of the west, so that the region is not suited for cocoa. The Region does not have a population group that is a clear majority and a leading people in national terms. With the 1963 completion of the Niger bridge at Onitsha, contact with the Eastern Region's Ibo is likely to increase, for the Ibo have been moving into the west for a long time, and this process is now facilitated, not only through the improved communication line, but also from the political point of view. Although a relatively insignificant minority in the former Western Region, the Ibo strength in the new Midwest Region is considerable.

THE EASTERN REGION

Nigeria's most densely populated areas lie in the southeast, where over 12 million people occupy less than 30,000 square miles of forested land, including also a large part of the delta and its mangroves and an area of drier northern savanna. Like the Western Region, this part of the country is connected by rail to the northern interior, and it has, in Port Harcourt, Nigeria's second port. For decades, the Eastern Region has lagged behind the richer west in development, but the pace of progress has accelerated sharply during the past few years.

The economy of the Eastern Region has long been based upon the oil palm. Its average annual output of palm kernels has amounted to fully half the world total, and an estimated one-third of the world's palm oil comes from this area. Together, these products constitute about 30 per cent by value of all Nigerian exports, and the oil palm also provides the basis for a host of locally used materials. It is used as a building material for huts, provides fiber for the making of mats, and its oil is put to a variety of local uses in the form of soap, lamp fuel, cooking oil, and so on. Not only does the oil palm produce a significant volume of exports, therefore, but it also is a basis of subsistence in this Region.

Eastern Nigeria provides many strong contrasts with the Western Region. It is the only Region in the country not to have experienced a lengthy period of indigenous urbanization; there were no Ibadan or Abeokuta, no Kano or Zaria in the southeast, although some market centers such as Onitsha on the Niger did develop. Even today, the largest towns, such as Port Harcourt and Enugu, have populations of about 100,000. The capital, Enugu, for instance, was founded as recently as 1909 as a result of the discovery of coal deposits on the edge of the Udi Plateau, and owes its development to the exploitation and distribution of that commodity and to its selection as the administrative headquarters for the Region. Enugu was connected by rail to Port Harcourt, and the coal was shipped down to this delta port for export and redistribution by water to other parts of the country. Later, the railroad was extended into the Northern Region, so that Enugu found itself on one of the major arteries in the country. The sequence of events in the founding and growth of Enugu, however, is reminiscent of Southern and East Africa (Kimberley, Kitwe, and so on) rather than West Africa.

Unlike the Western Region, therefore,

View from the Udi Plateau, Eastern Region, Nigeria. Taken near Nsukka, this photograph shows the landscape in the transitional area where the forest thins out markedly.

the high total population of the east remains overwhelmingly rural. Whereas the percentage of urbanization (people in cities over 20,000) in the Western Region is well over 30, it is a mere 7 per cent in the east. Rural densities, in consequence, are extremely high, exceeding 400 per square mile in much of Onitsha, Owerri, and Calabar provinces, and reaching 2,000 in parts.[5] Food requirements, obviously, are very great, and the introduction of cash crops there is a far more difficult process than it has been elsewhere. The pressure on the land is too great, farming practices are in need of improvement, and soil erosion is a serious problem.[6] Nigeria's current National Development Plan, sequel to the 1946–56 ten-year plan under the Colonial Development and Welfare Act, aims to improve the situation. In the Eastern Re-

gion, one-third of the entire investment has been allotted to the agricultural sector. It is thought that a breakthrough in agricultural reform would lead to immense possibilities, for the productive capacity of the Region is considerable and can, with better organization, be realized to a much greater extent. Already, the cultivation of cashew nuts, rice, and rubber is increasing, and further diversification is envisaged.

Eastern Nigeria's major asset of the future, however, may be its mineral resource base. Having long produced sufficient coal (from the Enugu deposits) to supply its own needs as well as those of the Ghana and Sierra Leone railroads, a new source of power has been discovered just at a time when the coal-mining industry is in serious decline, due to the increased use on the railroads of the very commodity discovered in the southern part of the Eastern Region—oil.

The search for oil began as long ago as 1937, but was interrupted during the war years. In 1947, the exploratory efforts were resumed, initially through shallow drilling, until the geologic mapping of the delta area was completed in 1953. After that date, deep wells were sunk, and in 1956 the wells near Oloibiri and Afam, within the delta proper,

[5] The figure of 400 persons per square mile has been suggested as the level above which the land may be considered overcrowded. See A. T. Grove, "Soil Erosion and Population Problems in Southeastern Nigeria," *Geographical Journal*, CXVII (September, 1951), 302.

[6] See W. B. Morgan, "Agriculture in Southern Nigeria," *Economic Geography*, XXXV (1959), 138–50, for a discussion of these and other problems.

336

showed commercial oil accumulations. Several new deposits were subsequently located, and activity increased greatly in the whole region. Oil production in 1959 amounted to 4 million barrels, in 1960 it exceeded 6 million, after which it rose rapidly to 16 million barrels in 1961 and some 25 million in 1962. In 1961 oil displaced tin as the leading mineral export, and the prediction has been made that it may become Nigeria's leading export in any category by 1970.[7]

Meanwhile, the petroleum industry has provided some work for the excess labor force of the Eastern Region, which seeks work in other regions of the country and even as far afield as Fernando Poo.. There may be further developments in the mining sector, for in addition to the coal deposits in the Eastern Region, iron ores exist in the vicinity of Lokoja at the Niger-Benue confluence, and a plant producing pig iron could be established. Lead and zinc have been found lying east of Enugu. In addition to the need for agricultural reform, the Eastern Region needs industrialization to take people off the land. In fact, so many Ibo have left the Eastern Region in search for work elsewhere that in some noneastern urban centers they make up a majority, having long been prepared to do work for which few Yoruba or Hausa were willing to make themselves available. For many years, this process went on without creating serious problems, for the Yoruba and Hausa preferred the personal liberty of farming and trade, and job rivalry was very limited. But when political parties formed in the various regions, the Ibo residents of the non-Ibo regions formed opposition groups against the parties representing the dominant peoples there. The ensuing friction was an expression of one of Nigeria's strongest centrifugal forces and brought the country to the brink of civil war at one stage. It was this sort of expression of loyalty to the "home region" that led to the development of a federal constitution for Nigeria.

The heart of the Eastern Region, then, lies in the Onitsha–Enugu–Port Harcourt triangle, with an eastward extension into Calabar.[8] It is marked by features that are very different from those characterizing the Western Region core. Densities of population are higher in the east than in the west, the population is rural rather than comparatively highly urbanized, the area lies in the forest zone and the economy is based upon its products rather than upon introduced cash crops, and the degree of organization of farming is less.[9] In the peripheral areas, population is sparser, as in the north (which is drier and where the oil palm thins out), in the south, where the swampy environment renders habitation more difficult, and in the east, where destruction of the forest has taken place, and where grasslands now remain. On the slopes of the Cameroun Highlands, which begin in the eastern margins of the Eastern Region, the original rainforest still stands, forming part of the main cover of lowland equatorial Africa. This area, also, supports a relatively sparse population.

The concentration of the Eastern Region's productive capacity in the palm forest zone is reflected by the intensity of the road network in the Region's core area. By far the majority of the Region's roads lie within the Onitsha–Enugu–Port Harcourt area, focusing upon the export routes; very few roads connect with adjacent regions. Like the heartland of the west, Eastern Nigeria's core area is circumscribed by physical zones and features tending to reduce contact with adjacent regions, internal as well as external. The Middle Belt develops northward; the relatively empty area beyond the Cross River lies eastward; and westward, the Niger has

---

[7] Nigeria Federal Ministry of Commerce and Industry, *Nigeria Trade Journal*, X, No. 1 (January, 1962), 32. The prediction was made by R. J. Harrison Church of the London School of Economics and Political Science, in *Environment and Policies in West Africa*, p. 81.

---

[8] For a definition of the Eastern Region core, see J. R. V. Prescott, "A Geographical Analysis of Elections to the Eastern Region House of Assembly (March, 1957)," *Department of Geography Research Notes*, University College, Ibadan, No. 10 (June, 1957), pp. 8–15.

[9] K. M. Buchanan, "Nigeria—Largest Remaining British Colony," *Economic Geography*, XXVIII, No. 4 (October, 1952), 302–22. See especially the map on p. 320, showing the contrasting development of West and East.

Market Scene in the Northern Region. In many ways, the north is a world apart from the southern Regions of Nigeria. Modes of dress, house construction, city outlay, and social conditions all reflect the contrasting influences on either side of the Niger-Benue Lowland. (United Nations)

always been an obstacle to two-way contact, the massive emigration of Ibo people notwithstanding.

THE NORTHERN REGION

Most of Nigeria's land and people are in the Northern Region, which extends from the northern border to south of the Niger and Benue rivers, thus covering over 280,000 square miles. With a population totaling about 30 million, this Region, on the average, is the least densely populated of Nigeria's political divisions. However, its population is of the same order as that of all other Regions combined, so that in the federal political scheme, it is a dominant power.

Perhaps the most striking geographical aspect of the Northern Region is what Buchanan has called its dualism—its division into a comparatively unproductive, greatly underdeveloped, tsetse-ridden Middle Belt

(in the south), and a better-organized and more progressive north-central area.[10] The Middle Belt, in many ways, acts as a buffer, keeping separated the progressive core areas of north, east, and west. Adding to this the divisive character of the Midwest Region (between east and west in the south), the regional fragmentation of the country can be seen. In the north, the factor of distance is added: the Region extends some 700 miles from east to west and about 400 miles from north to south. The capital, Kaduna, is 480 miles from the Western Region capital of Ibadan, and not much nearer to Enugu, headquarters of the Eastern Region. And Kaduna itself lies near the transition zone between the Middle Belt and the heart of the north, is hundreds of miles from any important sections of its own Region, and is linked to the

---

[10] K. M. Buchanan, "The Northern Region of Nigeria."

338

outlying parts at times by the most tenuous of communication lines.

The dominant peoples of the north are the Hausa and Fulani, an alliance in which the Hausa are numerically superior but the Fulani supply the ruling element. The north has been described as a world apart from the other Regions, and with much justification: this is Moslem Nigeria, where the legacy of a feudal social system, conservative traditionalism, and resistance to change hangs heavily over the country.[11] Literacy there is lower than in the other Regions; per capita incomes, averaging $80 annually for the country as a whole, are a little over half that amount in the north. Proportionally fewer people have been drawn into the sphere of progress there than anywhere else in the country.

Yet the possibilities for development in the Northern Region are considerable; even the Middle Belt provides some basis for optimism. Rainfall, of course, is less there than in the south, and it is more seasonal and, in the northern margins, quite variable. Especially in the northwest (the Sokoto Basin) and the northeast (the Chad Basin), the lack of water has restricted settlement. But north of the tsetse area that covers much of the Middle Belt, the country affords opportunities for pastoralism. The absence of fodder in the south and the presence of diseases in the Middle Belt make northern Nigeria a vital area for the country from this point of view. As the commercial opportunities of pastoral industries are recognized and traditional attitudes toward livestock disappear, the importance of herding increases.

Neither are the agricultural opportunities of the north restricted to pastoralism. After the establishment in 1912 of modern communications to the sea, the production of the major crop, peanuts, rose sharply. Today, Nigeria is the world's second largest exporter of peanuts, accounting for about a third of the total annual world commercial production. Peanuts produce between 20 and 25 per cent of Nigeria's annual export revenue,

and in the north-central part of the Northern Region the crop provides a livelihood for nearly three-quarters of the people. The experience of the provision of good communications is being repeated elsewhere, for whenever a good road or railroad penetrates an area, it stimulates production. The latest expansion of the railroad network is the Bornu Extension from Bauchi to Maiduguri, and increased outputs of peanuts and cotton will no doubt be recorded. Communication lines have long focused upon Kano, however, which lies in the heart of the peanut-producing zone and is the leading shipping center.

The productive areas of Northern Nigeria, then, lie in close proximity to the transport routes and around the major urban centers. The urban tradition in this region is very old, and the cities form foci for extremely densely populated surrounding rural zones. Kano, for instance, has been a trading center for more than a dozen centuries. Like other cities in the Region, it has been the capital of a Fulani emirate and performed a defensive function, as evidenced by the surrounding wall. Its commercial importance reached great heights during the fifteenth century, when European goods reached it across the Sahara (in exchange for goat leather that came to be known as "Moroccan" in Europe), and today its population approaches 200,000. But the immediate surroundings of the city proper carry as many as 1,000 people per square mile to a ten-mile radius, and half that many to a distance of 40 miles away. Thus, well over a million people are concentrated in the immediate environs of Kano, cultivating every available patch of land, which is constantly fertilized with night soil brought from the city.[12] Satellite towns are developing within the surrounding "rural" belt, but the focus of the whole Region remains the city proper. Each day, the number of people within the city itself grows by several thousand as the rural people bring their products to the markets.

Similar descriptions could be given of many other urban centers in the Northern

---

[11] For a summary of Nigeria's regional characteristics as they relate to economic growth, see W. F. Stolper, "The Development of Nigeria," *Scientific American*, CCIX, No. 3 (September, 1963), 169 ff.

[12] For a discussion of Kano, see D. Whittlesey, "Kano: A Sudanese Metropolis," *Geographical Review*, XXVII, No. 2 (April, 1937), 184.

Region, such as Katsina, the Hausa trading and cultural center, Zaria, an old capital and handcraft center, and Sokoto, the headquarters of the Fulani, although none has the same degree of concentration of population in so wide a surrounding farming zone. Yet Northern Nigeria is the least urbanized of the country's three major Regions, only 4 per cent of the people residing in cities of over 20,000. These cities form the foci for the surrounding areas, and in the Nguru–Kano–Zaria–Kaura Namoda region, they are the major elements of the developing core area of Northern Nigeria. But the Northern Region is a vast territory, and beyond the productive areas, subsistence patch agriculture still prevails, the people are out of touch, and change is yet to come.

One of the changes to have affected formerly unproductive regions has been the spread of cotton as a cash crop in the Northern Region. Although less is exported than is used locally, the growing of cotton has proved a profitable undertaking, and in the early 1950's the acreage exceeded the million mark, most of it in the north. The area around and west of Zaria has produced most of the exported cotton, but a number of smaller areas in the north also contribute and should develop as soon as improved communications reach them. The Bornu Extension of the railroad system should have this effect in the northeast. Meanwhile, however, the concentration of activity in the "railroad belt" of the north is marked, lending further emphasis to the core aspect of the three north-central provinces (Kano and Katsina, the two most densely populated divisions in Northern Nigeria, and Zaria, including the capital of the Region).

In addition to its agricultural possibilities (which include also the growing of benne seed in the Middle Belt and tobacco in widely scattered areas, along with the staple grain crops) the Northern Region has long produced the bulk of Nigeria's mineral export revenues. Alluvial tin and columbite deposits on the Jos Plateau in some years have produced 90 per cent by value of the country's mineral exports, but the mid-1950's was a period of much fluctuation. Production was curtailed in 1958 in accordance with the In-ternational Tin Agreement, causing a 50 per cent decline in output from the previous year.[13] The agreement was necessary because of the very limited increase in world demand for this metal, at a time when demand for other metals rose rapidly. Tin and columbite have since been replaced by petroleum as the main mineral product.

The iron ores within 30 miles from Lokoja at the Niger-Benue confluence lie only a few hundred yards from the Niger River and 700 feet above it, so that exploitation would not be very expensive, and there are an estimated 200 million tons at 45 per cent purity.[14] This deposit, in conjunction with the coals of the Eastern Region, may form the basis of a small-scale industry. These iron ores, of course, lie in the Middle Belt section of the Region, where underdevelopment is at its most serious.

The Middle Belt also includes what is perhaps the best site for the development of hydroelectric power in Nigeria, that at Kainji, about 65 miles upstream from Jebba on the Niger. The site is to be developed during the 1960's, to be followed by other projects at Jebba and in the Shiroro Gorge on the Kaduna River. Requiring elaborate locks to permit continued barge traffic on the waterways, the projects will be very costly, and their justification, in view of the Enugu coal reserves and the delta petroleum and gas production, has already been doubted.[15] The Kainji project, it is hoped, will form the basis for a steel plant, using nearby limestones and, of course, the ready labor force of the Middle Belt. In fact, the development of the Middle Belt's hydroelectric power potential is planned with a view to stimulating development within the belt itself as much as it is in terms of the future electricity needs of Nigeria as a whole.

Thus, the Northern Region has potential, but its needs are several: the improvement of

---

[13] United Nations, *Economic Survey of Africa Since 1950*, p. 120.

[14] International Bank for Reconstruction and Development, *The Economic Development of Nigeria* (Baltimore: The Johns Hopkins Press, 1955), p. 419.

[15] For instance, by B. N. Floyd in "Gearing for Growth," *Africa Today*, IX, No. 6, p. 15.

340

communications, eradication of diseases in the Middle Belt, the replacement of traditionalism in politics, education, and agriculture by a more modern outlook, and, if the Region is to remain unfragmented, the elimination of the bases for separatist feelings among the non-Hausa, non-Fulani, non-Moslem peoples in the Middle Belt. The diversity marking Nigeria is especially characteristic of the vast Northern Region, where progress is really still confined to islands near towns and communication lines lying in a vastness of very slowly changing interior West Africa. The Region depends, both for the handling of its overseas exports and for the marketing of its domestic products, upon its three southern neighbors, each of which functions as an outlet for the north.

POSSIBLE FURTHER INTERNAL FRAGMENTATION

Frequent reference has been made to the separatist feelings harbored by various population groups in Nigeria; the Midwest Region is a consequence of such sentiments among minority groups in the former Western Region. A number of problem areas remain. While Britain administered Nigeria, the country was divided into 23 units—22 provinces and the colony of Lagos. When the regional boundaries were defined, these units of administration were retained, as they conformed broadly to ethnic units within the country. Some prominent Nigerian politicians have suggested a further subdivision of the country into 8 (Azikiwe) and 30 to 40 (Awolowo) units, each corresponding to an ethnic core region. Such suggestions appeared, however, to involve a reversion to the sort of tribalism the federal framework was intended to circumvent, and they were not adopted at the

Kano, Largest Urban Center of the North. The walled city of Kano is the principal commercial center of Northern Nigeria. Shown here is a section of the mud-constructed town, with its dense agglomeration of small dwellings. (BOAC)

341

conferences leading to the federal constitution. One positive aspect of further subdivision, however, would be the smaller degree of self-sufficiency of each, and thus the smaller likelihood of individual secession from the country. The proposals for further subdivision also dealt with some individual problems in each of the regions; the suggested separation of Benin from the Western Region eventually did become reality.

Centrifugal forces remain in each of the Regions, and in some cases they can be described as a kind of internal irredentism; the case of the Yoruba-speaking people in Ilorin and Kabba is a good example. These people, according to the federal framework, became residents of the Northern Region, but they have many ties with the Yoruba of the west. During the days of the Fulani-Yoruba hostilities, they requested Fulani help against Oyo and Ibadan, having revolted against Yoruba overlordship. The days of friction are long past, and the people have asked to be rejoined to Yoruba territory, a request based

Map 76

upon historical, racial, and linguistic as well as religious factors. Indeed, such requests have been forthcoming ever since the days of Lugard, but a succession of British governors refused them consistently on the grounds that the historical foundation for the demand was too distant to carry weight. In reality, any proposed boundary adjustment would create problems while solving others; many of the people of Ilorin, for instance, are neither Yoruba nor Christian and have accepted northern government for decades without objection. Thus, the request for boundary change was not granted, although a commission was appointed by the government which determined a set of conditions under which change could take place. These included the requirement of a binding plebiscite in the area affected and the stipulation that at least 60 per cent of the people involved would favor the proposed transfer of their territory to another region. The matter has not been resolved and remains a potential problem.

In the Eastern Region, the Calabar, Ogoja, and Rivers provinces are occupied by non-Ibo peoples, some of whom have formed a COR State Movement in an effort to separate themselves from the east. Support for the idea appears to be strongest in Calabar, and although it has been negated, the possibility of its eventual implementation, with all the problems that would entail, remains.

The Middle Belt of the Northern Region also is an area where peoples have separatist sentiments, especially the Tiv who live in the Makurdi area of the Benue Lowland and the Birom of the Jos Plateau. The basis of demands for a Middle Belt Region is a rather negative one, however. The main unifying element in the Middle Belt is an aversion to Islamic rule, but the nature of the proposed Region is a subject on which the prospective inhabitants are sharply divided. In any event, the Region would be a very poor one, and it would present major problems of administration. Furthermore, some of the peoples involved would prefer inclusion in the Eastern, Western, or Midwest Region rather than participation in a Middle Belt state.

This sort of problem, of course, must be expected in a country as large and varied as Nigeria, and others will no doubt present themselves. Difficulties of this kind are to be expected in a young federal state still in the process of internal adjustment and still under the stresses of strong centrifugal forces. Certainly, the obstacles to any proposed imposition of unitary government are emphasized; the regional identities are too strong, the historical traditions too diverse, the individual economic contributions too great.

Politico-Geographical Forces

The politico-geographical forces which played a role in the evolution of the federal state in Nigeria continue to influence the state today, although some now exert more influence than they did previously and others have declined in importance. The centrifugal forces that were strong enough to delay the coming of independence remain, and they are expressed in various ways. These include the separatist feelings of the peoples living in the peripheral zones around the regional core areas, for the fear of domination by the majority is strong among many of the smaller groups in all Regions. It will be noted that each example of separatism noted previously applies to peoples whose location can be so characterized. A measure of distrust between the Northern Region and the southern peoples (with their higher standards of living, greater political sophistication, and relative freedom from the bonds of traditionalism) remains and finds expression in the Regional and federal parliaments. The position of minority groups in the various Regions (when they are representatives of the majority in other Regions) has also reflected the divided state of the embryo Nigerian nation. Hartshorne, in discussing centrifugal forces that may affect the state, notes that physical barriers (in this case the Middle Belt and the Niger-Benue Lowland) and distance (in Nigeria, that between the three core regions) are important centrifugal factors, but "separation of regions by barriers or by divergence of outside connections are commonly less important than the centrifugal forces that result from diversity of character of the population. To secure voluntary acceptance of a single common organization requires some degree of mutual understanding; obviously this is easier in a population homogeneous in character. Further, where regions differ in social character, the tendency of the state to force some degree of uniformity of social life meets with resistance. Thus the very attempt to produce unity may intensify disunity. . . ."[16] In the case of Nigeria, a strong outside influ-

_____

[16] R. Hartshorne, "The Functional Approach in Political Geography."

ence helped consolidate the state, and it was able to submerge the actual and latent centrifugal forces to some extent. But the framework arrived at and imposed in Nigeria obviously suited some people better than it did others; after independence, the opponents began to assert themselves, and a powerful centrifugal force came to play its inevitable role.

But the centripetal forces binding the diversity of Nigeria together also have emerged more strongly. As Hartshorne has noted, the

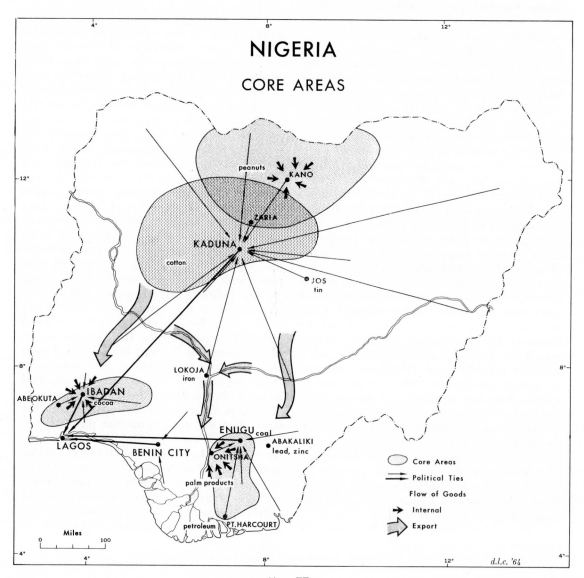

Map 77

344

basic centripetal force must be "some concept or idea justifying the existence of this
particular state incorporating these particular
regions." In Nigeria, the concept may, in the
view of some, not be clear-cut. But Nigeria's
greatest need is for accelerated progress in
the economic sphere, and just as such progress has come faster to a supranational unit
in East Africa than it could have to any single
entity there, so a united Nigeria will experience a more rapid growth than several separate entities would. The interdependence of
the Regions is constantly increasing, and interregional trade is growing; Nigeria has by
far the largest domestic market of any country in all of Africa. "Western" kola nuts are
sold in the Northern Region, "northern" cattle on Eastern Region markets, and "eastern"
products are handled by midwest ports, to
name but a few examples of interregional
economic transactions.

The important need in Nigeria is for the
spread of the "state-idea." Had Jones's field
theory model been applied there, some problems not altogether dissimilar from those of
Uganda would have been encountered. The
idea of the complex, Western type of sovereign state was introduced and first accepted
in the south, notably in the Western Region.
Although it was promoted there, little was
done to prepare the north for its application.
Even when independence came, that preparation really had barely begun. This major
obstacle was repeated in many localities and
on a smaller scale with minority peoples such
as the Tiv and Edo. The federal framework
did not permanently submerge these centrifugal forces, but it did provide possibilities for
repeated adjustments in the face of their
emergence. Meanwhile, the strengthening of
the centripetal factors—the interregional
bonds—reduces the likelihood of Nigeria's politico-geographical fragmentation.

18

GHANA: AN AFRICAN EPITOME

THE REPUBLIC OF GHANA is a dynamic state, among the most progressive on the continent, and one of the first to achieve independence after the Second World War.[1] Known as the Gold Coast until March, 1957, the republic was named after one of the ancient West African empires that flourished long before the European invasion began. Actually, although its territory in no way overlaps with that of old Ghana, it may perhaps be claimed that some of modern Ghana's inhabitants are distant descendants of people of the former empire. In any event, Ghanaians take pride in the positive aspects of West Africa's long history, and have sought to establish some ties with it.

Ghana is among Africa's smaller states. It is little more than one-quarter the size of Nigeria (92,000 square miles), but its population of 8 million is the seventh largest in Subsaharan Africa, after Nigeria, Ethiopia, South Africa, Congo, Sudan, and Tanganyika. Only Nigeria among these countries has a higher average population density. Yet compact Ghana extends only 400 miles from north to south and a mere 230 miles east and west.

In any assessment of the historical, political, or economic geography of Ghana, the relative location of the country should be taken into account. Ghana is centrally positioned along the West African coast and is flanked by several important African states. In the east, Nigeria (although separated from Ghana by Togo and Dahomey) dominates, and in the west Ghana's neighbors are Ivory Coast, Liberia, and Guinea. Ivory Coast is the wealthiest of the former French territories of West Africa, Liberia is the oldest modern independent black African state, and Guinea is a country of great political vigor. Like Nigeria, Ghana is surrounded by French-influenced countries. Ghana's eastern neighbor, Togoland, prior to the First World War was German territory and was split into a British and a French sphere. The western section was joined to the Gold Coast, and it eventually became a part of Ghana, just as a section of the Cameroons became a part of Nigeria.

Ghana's coast line provided some sites for early European settlement that were superior to many of those found both eastward and westward. Although better harbors could be found along the West African coast, settlement there certainly was easier than in the Niger Delta or in the stretch of coast from the Gambia River to Cape Palmas. But most important of all was the fact that it was interior Ghana that provided much of the gold taken by caravans across the Sahara. When the Portuguese arrived to establish, in 1482, the first fort and trading post on the "Gold Coast," this became the center of West African trade. Within a century, the coast had become the hub of European activity, several dozen forts and trading posts had been built, and keen international competition for the trade of the interior had developed, involv-

---

[1] In fact, it may be described as the first truly African country to become a sovereign state after the war; the Republic of Sudan, however, attained independence more than a year earlier.

346

Parliament House and Nkrumah Statue, Accra, Ghana. The government of Ghana has become highly centralized, and the country is the epitome of one-party rule; under the new system Ghana has seen rapid development. (United Nations)

ing the English, Dutch, Danes, and Brandenburgers, as well as the Portuguese.

The products upon which all this early activity was based—gold, ivory, pepper, and slaves—have long been replaced by others. But Ghana has maintained a leading position in the trade of West Africa, and with its comparative prosperity has come progress in other fields. Not only is Ghana's per capita income today higher than that of any other tropical African country, but in education and politics, too, it has forged ahead.

The Political Kingdom

The prominence of Ghana in Subsaharan Africa, then, is nothing new. The equalizing character of colonial control temporarily de-layed the emergence of this country as a leading political force in Africa, but the economic progress made there—also largely the result of colonial administration—foreshadowed its postindependence ascent. Long before effective colonial control was established, however, the elements of the present politico-territorial organization had evolved, although the center of power has shifted southward with the new economic orientation. When the Portuguese established themselves on the coast and began to alter the flow of commodities from northward to southward, central Ghana was producing much of the volume of exports leaving West Africa for northern markets. The success of the Portuguese in diverting the cross-Saharan trade was, in fact, due largely to the proximity of their Elmina trading station to this important supply area. Eventually, that area became consolidated

347

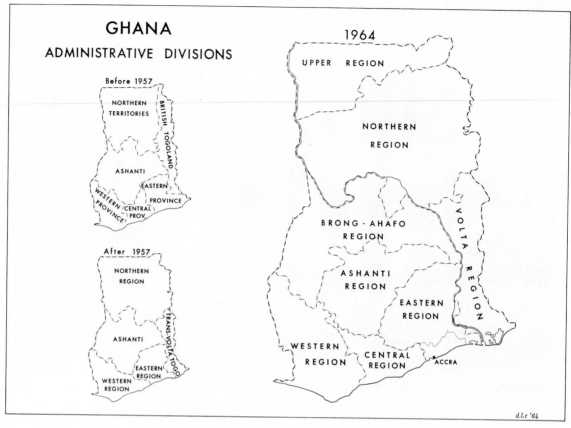

GHANA
ADMINISTRATIVE DIVISIONS

Map 78

politically as the Ashanti Union of Akan States. The people on the coast, the Fante, brought goods from the interior to the coastal trading posts, and thus a north-south flow of exports was initiated which has become a permanent feature of the coastal states of West Africa. The Fante middlemen jealously guarded their role in this trade pattern and resisted efforts by the Europeans to penetrate the interior themselves. Meanwhile, they bartered with the interior producers at one end of their route and with the Europeans at the other.

Consolidation in the interior began when a number of the Akan states in the northern margins of the forest formed the Ashanti Union. The first steps were taken in the 1600's, but during the eighteenth century the union became the most powerful political and economic unit in the region. Ashanti began to encroach upon the middlemen of the south.

Eventually, this led to contact with the Europeans, who failed to protect the peoples of the coastal states and tried to come to terms with Ashanti without success. The abolition of the slave trade and British efforts to eradicate its remnants brought economic ruin and strife to the region. Legitimate trade repeatedly was brought to a virtual standstill by intermittent hostilities. The Fante peoples tried to resist Ashanti encroachment by forming a Fante Confederation, but only in 1874, when the Ashanti army again crossed the Pra River—the traditional boundary—did the British retaliate. The Ashanti capital, Kumasi, was burned, and a treaty was forced upon the empire.

The events of 1874 did not end Ashanti imperialism in this area. Resentful of their defeat and the consequent liberation of the southern Fante states, the Ashanti rulers once again prepared for war, but the British in

1896 expelled the king and forestalled the outbreak of war by a show of force. At that time, Ashanti was made a protectorate, but in 1901 a new revolt erupted. When this outbreak was quelled, the British established a colony over the Ashanti Empire, and included the areas beyond the Volta River, the Northern Territories, in their possession as a protectorate.

Thus, the heart of African organization and power long was in Ashanti, and Ashanti expansionism was contained by the British, just as friction in Nigeria between the northern Moslems and southern peoples was terminated by British intervention. But in Ashanti, indirect rule did not work, and thus a colony was established there, while the Nigerian north became a protectorate. The definition and delimitation of the Gold Coast's boundaries (with the French in the west and north, and with the Germans in the east) took place mainly between 1896 and 1901; as elsewhere in Africa, there was little regard for ethnic units. In the southeast, the Ewe people were divided; in the west, the Nzima, among other peoples, were fragmented by the new political order. These divisions were to create future problems, but the incorporated area itself included many diverse African units which suddenly found themselves within a political boundary and part of a larger political entity. The Gold Coast thus faced the problems common to most modern political entities in Africa: there were perhaps over 100 distinct African states and chieftaincies, each with its own traditions. The British faced a formidable task in helping the inhabitants of the country forge a nation.

In this effort, the latent enmity between proud Ashanti, whose expansionism had been halted, and the peoples of the south formed an ever present obstacle. The south increasingly became the focus of activity in the Gold Coast, both administratively and economically. Like Nigeria, Ghana has a coastal capital, Accra. As in Nigeria, much of the development that took place as a result of colonial control occurred in the south, where education made most progress, communications were most rapidly improved, and the introduction of new crops proved most successful. Eventually, the country achieved sovereignty under mainly southern leadership and as a result of pressures exerted by southern politicians and citizenry.

In many ways, Ghana repeats on a smaller scale the regional differences of Nigeria. Like its larger neighbor, Ghana has a Moslem north and a dominantly non-Moslem south. As in Nigeria, where Fulani expansionism was halted by British intervention, Ashanti imperialism was contained by British control. Both states have a highly productive southern belt, which felt most strongly the impact of colonial administration. Political sophistication came to the south at a comparatively early stage, and pressures for independence rose there, while the far north remained little changed and under indirect, protectorate administration. Suspicions of southern designs on the part of inhabitants of northern Ghana were reflected by their desire for prolonged British involvement in their local administration. But there are important differences: unlike Nigeria, Ghana's northern regions do not have a majority population, and northern Ghana does not have a core region that is economically as significant as that of northern Nigeria. Southern Ghana leads economically and politically, which is reflected in the high degree of concentration of all types of communications in the southern third of the country; in the early 1960's there still was no railroad link anywhere north of Kumasi.

These differences are reflected also in Ghana's politico-territorial organization. Unlike Nigeria, which in response to its internal diversity adopted a federal constitution, Ghana became a unitary state with a highly centralized government.[2] Tribalism has been attacked, the power of chiefs reduced, education promoted vigorously, and tight control rigorously maintained. The effort is one of eradication of divisive politico-geographical characteristics within the country rather than adjustment to them. Ghana, from a geographical point of view, clearly lends itself better to this attempt than does Nigeria. The country and its population are much

[2] For an assessment of the Ghana experiment, see D. S. Rothchild, "On the Application of the Westminster Model to Ghana," *The Centennial Review*, IV (Fall, 1960), 465.

Unloading of Cargo by Canoe and Hand, Accra, Ghana. For many years, this was the main method of unloading vessels at the open roadstead port of Accra; the loss was considerable. With the new port of Tema under construction, Accra's port function will dwindle. (United Nations)

smaller; it has, for all practical purposes, one region where the main productive capacity, major administrative center, and best amenities for education and communication are all located. In other words, it has one rather than several core areas of activity. This is not to underestimate the country's internal variety, which may be as great as that of Nigeria. But all of Ghana focuses upon the productive south, the source of many of the political ideas being applied throughout the country, its main outlet and area of contact with the outside world.

A look at the political map of Ghana reveals the changes that have taken place in the internal politico-geographical organization of the country. Prior to independence, there

were three major divisions: the Southern Provinces (Eastern, Central, and Western), Ashanti, and the Northern Territories. British Togoland still was under League of Nations Mandate (until the Second World War) and United Nations Trusteeship. The coming of sovereignty brought several important changes. A plebiscite was held in British-administered Togoland in 1956 to determine the peoples' desires concerning the future associations of their country. The choice was between union with an independent Ghana and continuation as a British Trusteeship pending an alternative arrangement. A majority (58 per cent) of the registered voters favored a union with Ghana.[3] Hence, when Ghana attained sovereignty in the following year, British Togoland ceased to exist as a separate political entity in West Africa.

The inclusion of British Togoland in Ghana had several important consequences. The territory stretched along most of the Gold Coast's eastern border, the lower course of the Volta River forming the boundary in the south. Inclusion therefore made the lower Volta an internal river, and any plans to dam the waters and create a lake inundating large areas no longer would involve international negotiation. Furthermore, the British sector of Togoland was a landlocked territory, an extension of the Gold Coast's Eastern Province cutting it off from the sea. When it was incorporated in Ghana, it was split into two parts: the northern sector became part of the Northern Region of Ghana, while the south became a separate region including almost all the territory in southern Ghana east of the Volta River (and thus including the small eastern proruption of the Eastern Province that once cut it off from the sea). Initially, this new province was known as Trans-Volta Togo, but today it is called the Volta Region.

Inclusion of British Togoland in Ghana profoundly affected the Ewe people who live in the south. Colonial penetration and subsequent division of the land in this area fragmented the Ewe into three major groups, which in the 1950's numbered about 376,000

[3] J. S. Coleman, "Togoland," *International Conciliation*, No. 509 (September, 1956), p. 68.

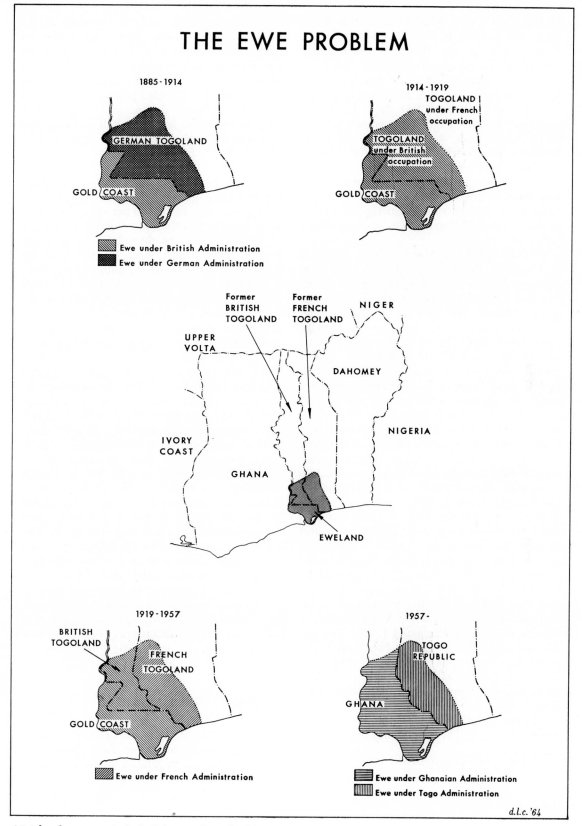

THE EWE PROBLEM

1885-1914

GERMAN TOGOLAND

GOLD COAST

☐ Ewe under British Administration
■ Ewe under German Administration

1914-1919
TOGOLAND under French occupation

TOGOLAND under British occupation

GOLD COAST

Former BRITISH TOGOLAND

Former FRENCH TOGOLAND

NIGER

UPPER VOLTA

DAHOMEY

IVORY COAST

NIGERIA

GHANA

EWELAND

1919-1957

BRITISH TOGOLAND

FRENCH TOGOLAND

GOLD COAST

☐ Ewe under French Administration

1957-

TOGO REPUBLIC

GHANA

☰ Ewe under Ghanaian Administration
▥ Ewe under Togo Administration

d.l.c. '64

Mainly after a map in J. S. Coleman, "Togoland," *International Conciliation*, No. 509 (September, 1956), p. 9.

Map 79

in the Gold Coast, 137,000 in British Togoland, and 174,000 in French Togoland.[4] The Ewe people, in the British Togoland vote concerning the merger with Ghana, voted two to one in favor of continued trusteeship by Britain, implying a desire for a future merger with French Togoland. But the over-all majority of British Togoland's voters favored union with Ghana, so that the Ewe were reluctantly joined with that state. Irredentist problems have arisen since the implementation of the merger, and relations between former French Togoland and Ghana have not been good. The Ewe question represents one of the major centrifugal forces in the political geography of Ghana.

When Ghana attained independence, it was initially divided into five Regions: the Western Region (including the former Western and Central provinces); the Eastern Region, Ashanti, the Northern Region, and Trans-Volta Togo. Since then, several changes have been made in the interests of more efficient government and with a view to historical and political realities. The Western and Central Regions have again been separated, the former centering upon the port of Sekondi and the latter upon Cape Coast. The Eastern Region has its headquarters in Koforidua, but the country's capital, Accra, also lies within its borders. Accra (400,000) and surrounding districts have been grouped into a separate administrative area known as the Ga-Adangbe District, which includes also the important developing port of Tema. Ashanti has been divided into two Regions: Ashanti Region, the core of the former empire, and in the north, the Brong-Ahafo Region, comprising areas which were once conquered by Ashanti. Ashanti still focuses upon Kumasi, and the Brong-Ahafo Region centers upon Sunyani. The capital of the Volta Region is Ho, the cocoa-collecting point for the Region. The area once known as the Northern Territories has been split into two regions, the Northern Region with headquarters at Tamale, and the Upper Region centering upon Bolgatanga.

Largest of the Regions of Ghana is the Northern Region, covering nearly one-third of the entire country, and the smallest is the Central Region in the south, which like Nigeria's Midwest Region is wedged between the Eastern and Western Regions. Five of Ghana's eight Regions have areas roughly between 8,000 and 10,000 square miles: Eastern, Western, Ashanti, Volta, and Upper. The Central Region is less than half as large. But population totals and densities vary widely. The Eastern Region, occupying less than one-tenth of Ghana's total area, has nearly a quarter of its population. The three northern Regions (Brong-Ahafo, Northern, Upper), although covering nearly 60 per cent of Ghana's area, include less than one-third of its people.

Ghana's Regions do not function, in the politico-geographical sense, in the way the Regions of Nigeria do. Administrative decisions made in Accra are implemented through the regional and district headquarters of the Regions; Sunyani and Tamale are not capitals comparable to Kaduna and Ibadan. Regional autonomy is at a minimum, but Ghana does not have the same set of checks and balances that produced federation in Nigeria. Nigeria's Northern Region is not only the largest in the country, it also has about half of its total population, and a majority voice in the Nigerian government. Ghana's northern Regions have neither economic nor demographic significance proportional to their combined size. In Nigeria, the majority people in one Region constitute the opposition in another, but in Ghana, the government has been dominated by the (majority) people of the south, and the opposition has come from the north. The demise of the opposition in Ghana has been due largely to the fact that it was tribal-regional in character rather than based upon policies and approaches to national problems; government became increasingly centralized, and Ghana today is the epitome of the one-party rule that characterizes so many other African states.

Assets and Liabilities

Ghana, like its neighbors in coastal West Africa, lies across several of the region's east-west climatic and vegetative belts. The coun-

---

[4] *Ibid.*, p. 13 (table).

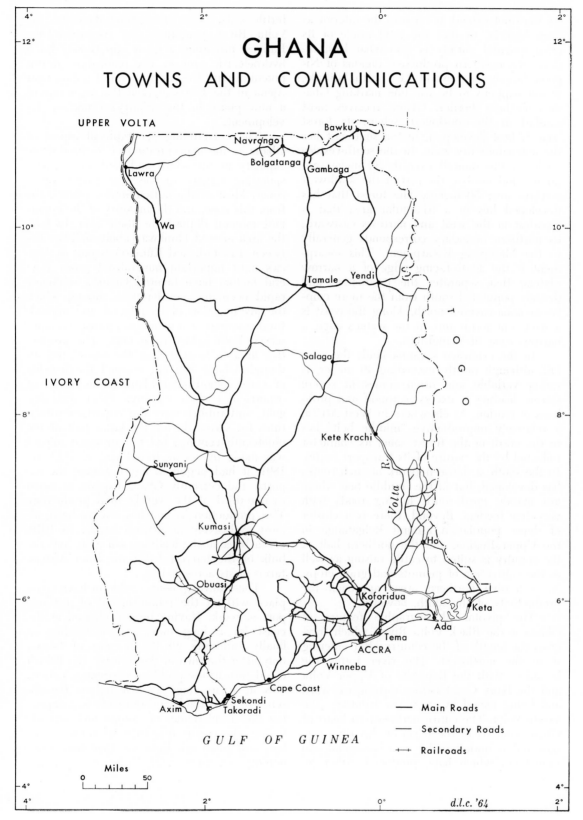

GHANA
TOWNS AND COMMUNICATIONS

UPPER VOLTA

Bawku
Navrongo
Bolgatanga
Gambaga
Lawra

Wa

Tamale   Yendi

T O G O

Salaga

IVORY COAST

Kete Krachi

Volta R.

Sunyani

Kumasi

Ho

Obuasi

Koforidua

Keta

Ada

Tema
ACCRA

Winneba

Cape Coast

Axim   Sekondi
Takoradi

GULF OF GUINEA

— Main Roads

— Secondary Roads

+ Railroads

Miles
0   50

d.l.c. '64

Map 80

try does not extend as far into the interior as does Nigeria, so that the total range of its environmental variety is somewhat less; indeed, the northern productive regions of Nigeria largely lie beyond 11° north latitude, which happens to be the line marking Ghana's northern border. Ghana receives most rainfall in the southwest, where its forest zone is best developed; in the southeast lies the anomalous dry zone. In the southwestern lowlands the rainfall exceeds 80 inches annually, and most of the rest of the southwest receives over 50 inches. The forest that has developed lies in a triangular area that is broadest in the west and narrows eastward; its northern boundary corresponds generally to the Mampong Escarpment. This escarpment is the south-facing edge of a narrow plateau that separates the productive and densely populated south from the more empty, savanna-covered north. Along the coast is a stretch of scrub and, at the water's edge, a narrow zone of mangroves.

In the extensive savanna lands the rainfall, although mostly exceeding 40 inches, is rather variable and often comes in severe storms, leading to excessive runoff and problems of erosion. As elsewhere in West Africa, a relatively unproductive "middle belt" lies to the north of the forest zone, its character reflected by the nature of its transport routes. In the south, a dense network of such routes has developed, but in the "middle belt" there are mainly north-south linking roads with very few feeders. Beyond, there is a cluster of dense population around Bolgatanga in the Upper Region, and the northern half of the country is suited to cattle raising as well as the cultivation of peanuts and grain crops. No extensive northern areas approach the productivity of the south, however.

The pivotal physiographic feature of Ghana is the Black Volta River, which traverses the length of the country after entering it in the northwest. The river forms the boundary with the Republic of Upper Volta and the Ivory Coast before turning eastward and being joined by its major tributary, the White Volta. The entire northeastern heart of Ghana consists of the basin of this river system and is underlain by near-horizontal, old sandstones which have produced rather in-

fertile soils. Prior to reaching its delta, the Volta River penetrates the Akwapim-Togo Ranges, providing a great opportunity for a hydroelectric project. The realization of this potential with the construction of a dam near Ajena in the 1960's marked the beginning of a new phase in the country's economic development.

The outstanding geographical aspect of Ghana is the concentration of its productive capacity in the south and southwest, corresponding largely to the area under forest cover. Most of the agricultural exports come from this zone, and the majority of the important mineral deposits lie there also. In fact, the area around Dunkwa (about halfway between Takoradi and Kumasi) is one of Africa's most important mineralized zones. Several factors have favored Ghana's relatively rapid economic development, among which the juxtaposition of its mineral and agricultural resources is a major one; transport routes served both industries at once. The productive area is located near the coast, and although Ghana has not enjoyed the benefits of a really good natural harbor, the volume of exports has risen steadily. Palm products, gold, and rubber were the important substitutes for slaves during the latter half of the nineteenth century, but the strongest impact was made by cocoa, introduced in 1879. By 1891, it had begun to figure among the exports, and currently Ghana exports as much as one-third of the world's total production. This production is, and has always been, almost exclusively in African hands. In 1910, cocoa became the leading cash crop, and the bulk of the harvest has come from African farms of six acres or less.

These developments could not have taken place without the establishment of a transport network. Having been contained at the coast for a long time, and succeeding in finally subduing all the peoples of Ghana only after the turn of the century, the British could turn to the problem of communications only at a late stage, by which time the absence of good roads and railroads was impeding the development of mining and was affecting the export quantities of rubber, timber, and palm oil. Between 1890 and 1900, mining companies exerted pressure upon the

Raking Cocoa Beans Drying in the Sun, Ghana. Ghana still depends heavily upon its cocoa harvests, although efforts to diversify the economy are in progress. Almost all the cocoa exported has been grown by African peasants, and the standard of living in the country has risen more rapidly than elsewhere due to the involvement of so many people in cash cropping. (United Nations)

Takoradi Harbor, Ghana. This western port long was the leading gateway of Ghana, and its facilities were modernized for the exports of cocoa and other products. It may be overtaken by the new, modern eastern port of Tema, under construction in the early 1960's. (United Nations)

View of Tema, Ghana. The modern port of Tema has been constructed virtually from the ground up, well planned, and ready to accept industry and trade. This view is of housing built in anticipation of industrial development, port expansion, and the general need for a labor force in the city.

government for the provision of bulk transport facilities, and the first surveys for projected lines were made during that decade. In 1898, the Sekondi-Tarkwa line was begun, and it was completed in 1901, connecting the goldfields at Tarkwa to the coast. Immediately, heavy use was made of the line, and its extension toward Kumasi, hastened by the need for rapid transport to the rebellious Ashanti capital, was finished by late 1903.

In the east, agricultural and forest production benefited greatly from the railroad begun in 1907 at Accra. By 1915 it had reached Koforidua, and carried no less than 40,000 tons of cocoa. The process of railway construction was interrupted by the First World War, but soon after 1918 it began again and in 1923 Kumasi and Accra were linked. Another line was started eastward from the Sekondi-Kumasi railroad, through the Central Region, reaching its terminal,

Kade, in 1927. A later phase of construction completed the triangle (1953–56), during which period the new, important port of Tema was linked to the system at Achimota.

Throughout the period of railroad construction and operation, and with the exception only of wartime periods of gasoline rationing, railroad transportation faced the competition of the roads. From 1923 to 1929, for instance, the percentage of cocoa exports carried by rail fell from 83 per cent to 63 per cent, "the heaviest competition (coming) from lorries (trucks) running parallel to the railway between Accra and Koforidua."[5] The road system expanded as the railroads were

---

[5] Details concerning the development of transportation in Ghana have been derived from P. R. Gould, *Transportation in Ghana*, "Northwestern University Studies in Geography," No. 5 (1960). The quotation is from p. 53.

extended, and, in addition, there always was the competition of the headload and the riverboat, the latter mainly on the Volta.

The ports of Sekondi and Accra both were roadsteads and for some time vied for the lead in handling the country's external trade. Originally, due to its position at the coastal terminal of the country's only railroad, Sekondi was the first port, until in the 1920's the Accra-Kumasi connection was completed. Soon afterward, the more modern port of Takoradi, near Sekondi, became operative, and the western terminal began to forge ahead of its competitors. Takoradi and Sekondi have virtually become a single urban concentration, the whole now possessing a population exceeding 100,000.

In the east, the construction of a new port at Tema, a mere 20 miles from Accra, is likely to change the flow of commodities. Opened in 1962 but still being expanded, the port of Tema has been connected by rail to the Accra-Koforidua-Kumasi line, and if the industrial development to be stimulated by the Volta River Project is to take place, Tema's future as one of Ghana's leading ports seems assured. It will take Accra's trade, but its function will, of course, depend greatly upon the location of the further extensions of the transportation network, and its share of the hinterland.

The effect of the transportation network in stimulating Ghana's economic development has been spectacular. In addition to gold, which until 1910 was the only significant mineral export, Ghana possesses mineable quantities of bauxite, manganese ore, and diamonds. Of these, all but the diamonds are found near the Takoradi-Kumasi railway; manganese near Takoradi and Tarkwa, bauxite near the terminal of the Awaso extension and in larger quantities not far from Kumasi itself, and gold near Tarkwa. Only the railroads could have provided the means to carry the heavy equipment required for the mining operations, and without them, the ores could not have been exported easily.

Equally impressive has been the effect of improved communications upon the agricultural industries, especially cocoa cultivation. Cocoa dominates the agricultural export list to the exclusion of practically all else, and contributes over two-thirds of the annual export revenue. Roads were initially improved (from bush tracks) to permit barrel rolling, later to carry truck traffic. Although sometimes cocoa cultivation already existed before adequate roads were pushed into a certain area, commonly the actual road-building process was immediately accompanied by the staking out of farms, while elsewhere the knowledge of plans for future road construction led to the preparation of such farms in advance.

In Ghana, the forest belt is the most densely populated area, economically the most important, and in terms of communications, by far the best endowed. Lying between the narrow coastal region of scrub in the south and the savanna region of the north, it covers most of the Western and Central regions, virtually all of Ashanti (although the forest thins out to the north) and extends into the northern part of the Eastern Region. As a result of the success of cocoa in this belt and the concentration of other economic activities there, population has moved into Ashanti from the north and even from the French-influenced countries adjacent to Ghana. With the rise of population pressure has come the destruction of large parts of the forest, soil erosion in serious measure, and the loss of the vegetative protection against the drying effect of the Harmattan. Urbanization has proceeded apace, Kumasi (110,000) trebling in population in 30 years (1931–61).

The forest was the economic focus of the country even before the suitability of cocoa in its environment was proved. From the forest came the initial exports of palm oil, rubber, and timber, and subsistence crops provided the food staples, a situation repeated in many other localities of lowland tropical Africa. With the introduction of cocoa, however, most of the land eventually was taken up by this cash crop, and so lucrative was the trade that food staples have had to be imported. In spite of the setback of swollen shoot disease, which struck with severity in the 1940's and threatened the whole industry, and government efforts to diversify the agricultural production of the country, the situation remains generally so today.

The Volta River Project

One hope for the future diversification of Ghana's economy lies with the implementation of the Volta River Hydroelectric Project. The project involves the building of three dams, of which the one at Akosombo (1½ miles south of Ajena) will be the major structure. Below the Akosombo Dam, a smaller barrage will be constructed opposite Kpong, and upstream a dam will be built at Bui on the Black Volta, not far from the Ivory Coast border.

The main dam at Akosombo will be 370 feet high and 2,100 feet in length, and it will inundate an area of well over 3,000 square miles, exceeding in size the Kariba Dam and thus becoming the world's largest man-made lake. It will extend some 250 miles up the Volta River and drown a number of settlements, but fortunately the population density in the valley is not high, and probably no more than 70,000 people will have to be moved. Moreover, the inundated area forms the heart of the sandstone-based Volta Basin, which is not fertile and therefore no great loss.

The benefits to be derived from the project, which is being financed by British, American, and Ghana government loans, are many. The generation of 768,000 kilowatts of electricity at the Akosombo Dam will make power available not only to existing towns and mines,

Timber Exports, Ghana. Although very dependent upon its cocoa exports, Ghana does produce sizable quantities of other goods, including diamonds, gold, manganese, and bauxite. Also exported is timber from the western forests, and logs are shown here before being shipped to Takoradi by rail. (United Nations)

GHANA
DEVELOPMENT

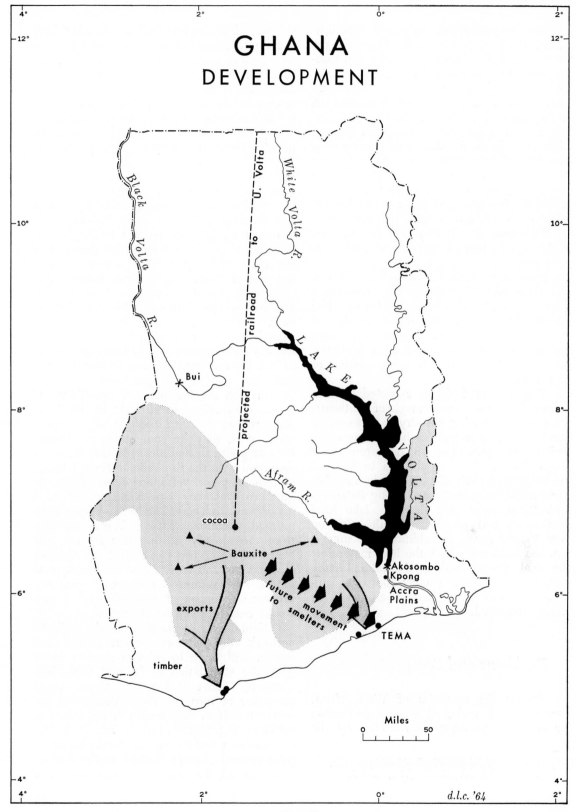

Map 81

d.l.c. '64

but also to prospective industrial establishments. Ghana's bauxite will ultimately be smelted at a plant presently under construction; initially, imported bauxite will be treated there. This is partly due to the problems and costs involved in the internal transportation of the required volume of the ore, and also to the interests of the corporations lending Ghana the funds for dam and smelter construction. These corporations mine bauxite elsewhere in West Africa (Guinea) and deem the smelting of those ores at the Ghana plant desirable. Doubtless, Ghana's own deposits will later be treated in large quantities also, at which time the country may become one of the world's four or five largest aluminum producers.[6]

Most of southern Ghana will be directly and favorably affected by the anticipated plentiful supply of cheap electricity. The Sekondi-Takoradi urban complex in the far west is well within the maximum possible distance of transmission, and, as in Rhodesia, the plan is to set up a growing network of supply lines.

The lake itself also is expected to have a favorable impact upon much of southeastern Ghana. A fishing industry is expected to develop with an annual catch that may reach 10,000 tons, providing an opportunity for people located far from the sea to improve the balance of their diets. The lake may become a transport route, and along its shores agricultural areas may develop: lake level fluctuations will permit rice cultivation on over 400,000 acres. In addition, the suggestion has been made that the lake may affect the local climate, making the rainfall more reliable and uniform.[7] Finally, the water supply situation of several interior areas will be greatly improved.

Problems and Prospects

Among the countries of West Africa, Ghana is well endowed with opportunities for economic progress, as reflected by the volume of its exports and a relatively high per capita annual income. The most productive region has been the hinterland of Sekondi-Takoradi, where the cultivation of cocoa has been most successful: the eastern areas have declined due to the dreaded swollen shoot disease and soil exhaustion. Furthermore, the minerals exported by Ghana lie mainly along the western railroad line to Takoradi, so that the focus of externally oriented economic activity has long been within a 150-mile radius from that port.

Efforts are now being made to change this situation and to create an industrial and transport complex in the east to supplement the agricultural and mining development of the west. The object of the construction of the port of Tema is not only to handle more effectively domestic imports and exports, but also to capture increasing volumes of trade from and to the interior. In 1962, Ghana signed an agreement with the Soviet Union for the construction of a railroad eventually to link the existing system at Kumasi to Ouagadougou, capital of Upper Volta.

In fact, the international significance of Tema, emphasized so strongly by President Nkrumah at the 1962 opening of the deepwater port, may be some time in coming. Present political conditions do not favor cooperation with the Republic of Togo, Ghana's eastern neighbor, yet a line across Togo and northern Dahomey into Niger would be a major boost to Tema. The Tema–Upper Volta railroad, if constructed, will face competition from the already existing line from Upper Volta to the Ivory Coast port of Abidjan. Upper Volta and Ivory Coast both participate in the mutual-interest entente, so that any proposed diversion of trade through Ghana would encounter major obstacles.

Nonetheless, expansion of the railroad network and the improvement of the road system will serve to achieve another major goal, the stimulation of internal trade. For instance, Ghana is the largest per capita consumer of meat in West Africa, but the southern half of the country is not suited to cattle raising. Cattle must be imported from the northern regions and, in larger numbers, from beyond Ghana's borders. In the absence of a railroad, the cattle are driven south and

[6] *Ghana Official Handbook* (1961), p. 128.
[7] Harrison Church, *West Africa*, p. 409.

Views of Accra, Ghana. The modern commercial center of the capital bears the imprint of British colonial rule, and many multistory structures have been added since independence. Within a few yards of each other, the main street and modern department stores (above) and busy street markets (below) can be found.

arrive in poor condition, fetching far less than they otherwise might. As industrialization and urbanization proceed in the southern parts of the country, along with specialized agriculture, the need for importing foodstuffs from the other regions will increase. Through the provision of better communications, the contribution to the national economy made by internal trade is expected to grow rapidly.

Ghana possesses opportunities for progress that many African states cannot match. In addition to its cocoa production, the bauxite deposits suffice to make this country a leading aluminum exporter. Iron ore from the Shiene Hills and manganese ores that already form a major mineral export may be used at a future steel plant in the industrial complex near the Volta Dam. The Accra Plains east of Accra permit farming under irrigation; the forests of the west provide timber and palm products, while rubber and banana production have recently shown increases. Grain crops and meat from the north will be required as the south develops. The incomparable asset of cocoa cultivation by tens of thousands of small farmers, stimulating commercial enterprise in the country and fostering the development of economic and political organizations, made the old Gold Coast an example in colonial Africa. With the new political direction has come a new desire to develop the country's other resources. Ghana appears to possess the ingredients to maintain its position among the leading states of black Africa.

19

SIERRA LEONE: PROGRESS IN POVERTY

Once the center of administration for British West African possessions, Sierra Leone became a sovereign state later than either Ghana or Nigeria. In April, 1961, the colony and protectorate, extending over some 28,000 square miles of West African forest and savanna land and inhabited by nearly 3 million people of great diversity, attained self-government within the British Commonwealth. Although possessing the oldest British-founded municipality in Africa, the first modern institution of higher learning, and a long history of political activity on the part of local people, Sierra Leone at the time of independence was less prepared for this event than either of her new sister states. Illiteracy in the country was in the vicinity of 95 per cent,[1] the per capita annual income about one-third of that of Ghana,[2] and political difficulties involving the imposition of proportional representation on a long-privileged elite were unsolved.[3]

Sierra Leone, so named by Portuguese navigators exploring the monsoon coast of West Africa in the sixteenth century, occupies the zone between the southern divide of the Futa Jallon Mountains and the coast. The descent, from over 6,000 feet to the embayed coastline, is accomplished by a series of steps representing, in the upper regions, cyclic erosion surfaces and, in the lower areas, raised marine terraces. Between the southern boundary of Senegal and the western border of Ivory Coast, the West African coast line trends northwest to southeast, thus lying directly in the path of the moisture-bearing air masses. The resultant precipitation is high (Freetown receives over 170 inches), but concentrated during the marked wet season (May to October). During the dry season, and especially from July to September, the dry, dusty Harmattan is very much in evidence. This, then, is the prime example of the monsoon coast of West Africa.

The vegetative response is the dense coastal forest, including mahogany, teak, and, of course, the important oil palm. In the south, coastal swamps exist in which a so-called swamp palm thrives which is economically important. This palm provides the fiber piassava, from which strong brooms are made. Sierra Leone is the world's leading producer of piassava. Toward the interior, the sequence recorded elsewhere is repeated, influenced somewhat by the rise in elevation toward the Futa Jallon crestline.

Considering its small size and compact shape, the environmental diversification and range of raw materials found in Sierra Leone are remarkable. In some cases, their exploitation has yet to begin. The fishing grounds off the country's shores may be the best of West Africa. The coastal regions, with their swampy lowlands, carry rice and could produce much more of this commodity than they do. Cocoa can be grown in the south-

---

[1] K. R. Schneider, "Sierra Leone: Profile and Proposals," *Africa Today*, IX, No. 6 (July, 1962), 10.

[2] Kimble, *Tropical Africa*, II, 502.

[3] T. R. Adam, *Government and Politics in Africa South of the Sahara* (New York: Random House, 1962), p. 93.

east, ginger in the south-central region, and peanuts in the north. While the hot, wet forest in the southwest is suitable mainly for extractive activities, the north can sustain a cattle industry. Cassava and kola nuts are grown, and coffee (robusta) has joined the list of exports. There are iron ore deposits (hematite) in Sierra Leone, and many river gravels are richly diamondiferous. Chrome ore has been located, and small quantities of this mineral are produced. Rutile and bauxite deposits exist near the coast in the southwest.

Yet Sierra Leone is a poor country, where communications, in spite of several railroad

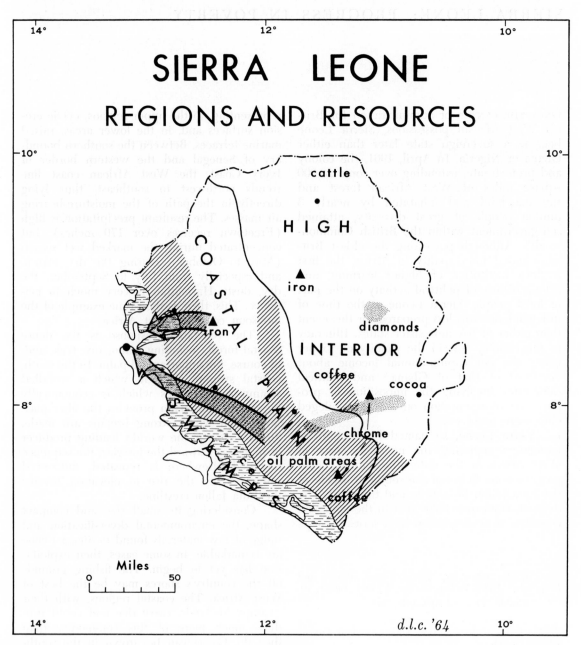

SIERRA LEONE
REGIONS AND RESOURCES

cattle

HIGH

iron

diamonds

INTERIOR

coffee

cocoa

iron

chrome

oil palm areas

coffee

COASTAL PLAIN

SWAMPS

Miles
0   50

d.l.c. '64

Map 82

364

View of Freetown, Sierra Leone. Freetown lies on one of the most favored sites along the coast of Sierra Leone, along hills and adjacent to a deepwater channel, one of Africa's best natural harbors. It is one of West Africa's older coastal settlements, having been founded before 1800; its present-day population is about 100,000. It is the focal point for the newly independent country and is connected by road and rail to the interior. (Courtesy of Hans Wolff)

lines, are still inadequate, power supply insufficient, education minimal, and the economy largely one of subsistence based upon rice. Industrial development, in effect, has yet to commence, and is presently confined to some plants processing palm oil, rice, and timber. Although it is the oldest British municipality in Africa, Freetown's population in the early 1960's was still under 100,000. Fourah Bay College, reconstituted in 1960 as the University College of Sierra Leone, and founded as early as 1827 by the Church Missionary Society, still had under 500 students. In the entire country, less than 100,000 pupils were attending schools.

Southern Sierra Leone is somewhat less underdeveloped than is the latosol-covered, repeatedly drought-stricken interior north. This is partly due to the pedologic and climatic factors, but the south has greatly benefited from the Freetown-Pendembu railroad, which has stimulated production and trade. There are also important differences—indeed, divisions—between the coastal region and the interior. These differences long found expression in their respective political status: the small colony was on the coast, the large protectorate was the almost untouched, traditional interior. This separation has its roots in historico-geographical developments which go far toward explaining the socio-economic condition of the present-day state.

The People: Kings and Creoles

The oldest numerically important residents of Sierra Leone appear to be the Temne people, who had settled the coastal regions of the country by the fifteenth century and with whom the Europeans made contact soon afterward. Calling for fresh water and other needs, the Portuguese and other Europeans found in Freetown West Africa's best natural harbor, and it soon became a trading center for slaves and ivory as well as a revictualling station. No continuous white rule was set up, however, and the resident traders came under the local African rulers. Meanwhile, the Mende people were settling in the north, and Sierra Leone did not escape the effects of the Fulani and Mandingo holy war, which spread Islam from the north, beginning in the early eighteenth century.

Both the Mende and Temne people were ruled by "kings" or chiefs, and at various times there have been between 100 and 150 chiefdoms in the area of Sierra Leone. When Granville Sharp, the British opponent of slavery, succeeded in establishing in Sierra Leone a small settlement for freed slaves in 1787, one of these kings gave his permission for the use of a section of his land for this purpose. "Province of Freedom," as the settlement was called, did not survive long, for the king's successor wiped it out. But in 1791, it was revived under the auspices of the Sierra Leone Company, sponsored by British abolitionists, and this time the effort had permanent success. The settlement was rebuilt and named Freetown, and freed slaves were brought there, not only from captured slave vessels, but also from the Americas, where some had gained their liberty by joining the British forces during the American Revolution and others had been emancipated in the West Indies.

Britain outlawed the slave trade in 1807, and in the following year the government took charge of the settlement as a colony, continuing the policy of making it a homeland for emancipated slaves. Freetown became an important base from which operations against the slave trade were carried out. During the half-century after 1808, an estimated 50,000 freed slaves were thus brought to Sierra Leone.

The first groups of slaves, who had come from the Americas, had in common some knowledge of the English language, and many were Christians. Those who arrived after 1807, however, never having made the Atlantic crossing, not having been exposed to Anglo-America, and coming from various parts of Africa, had little or nothing in common. As a result, an extremely heterogeneous community developed in Freetown and its immediate vicinity. The government now embarked upon a policy designed to provide these people with a common language, religion, and culture. Schools were built, missionaries sent to the colony, and much was achieved in a remarkably short time. It was during this period that Fourah Bay College was established. The new immigrants responded well, were active and very successful as traders, and began to settle in other parts of the general area of Sierra Leone.

These people came to be known as "Creoles," and they soon attained a privileged position in the embryo country, carrying on most of the trade, enjoying educational opportunities not available to the vast majority of the people in the hinterland of Freetown, sharing a common language which has come to be known as "pidgin English," and enjoying a position of influence in the administration of their part of the region. Indeed, they were responsible for the first efforts to expand the colony's influence into the interior, although they failed initially to interest the British in accepting the responsibilities inherent in this move. Eventually, however, this development did come about.

Colony and Protectorate

What led to the extension of British power into the hinterland was not the Creoles' desires, but French activities in West Africa and the realization that Freetown's strategic qualities would be endangered if French encroachment went unchecked. Hence, between 1890 and 1896, treaties were signed with chiefs in the interior, and in the latter year, boundaries were defined as agreed upon by the French and Liberian governments. While the coastal region remained a colony, the interior became a protectorate, and the administrative division of Sierra Leone had become a fact.[4]

The establishment of an expanded Sierra Leone did not have all the consequences desired by the Creoles. In the beginning, there was some strife between the British administration and the African chiefs, many of whom were not consulted about the establishment of the protectorate but who found themselves having to pay a hut tax to defray the government's expenses. The 1898 revolt was quickly terminated, however, and the British could set about the organization of their new possession.

In Sierra Leone as elsewhere, the protectorate status of the bulk of the country required the introduction of the principle of indirect rule, and so the chiefs remained in power, traditional ways were encouraged, and few modern amenities were introduced. But the Creoles, who had been involved in government in Sierra Leone ever since the colony obtained a legislative council in 1863, found their influence waning rather than increasing after the protectorate had been established. British district commissioners and administrators governed both the protectorate and the colony, and Creoles were gradually removed from those offices they held.

In 1924, when a new constitution was drawn up, the legislative council consisted of a few elected Creoles and, for the first time, protectorate representation in the persons of nominated chiefs. It foreshadowed independence and eventual proportional representation for all citizens of Sierra Leone, which inevitably meant the loss of privileges and the end of cultural isolation for conservative Creoles. The process reached its conclusion in 1961, when a predominantly protectorate party won the elections and

formed the government of the new state. This was not accomplished before internal political differences had led to rioting, and even today, although there is some evidence that the original differences are becoming somewhat blurred, they are continuing to hamper progress in this country, which so greatly needs unity of purpose on the part of its people.

The Consequences

Several centuries of neglect and a half-century of indirect rule left the interior of Sierra Leone far behind the accelerating rate of development in other parts of West Africa. It also caused important differences between the coastal colony and its hinterland, as mentioned above. The Creoles remain concentrated along the coast, as evidenced by several towns with names such as Waterloo. Although primarily an agricultural country, well over half of Sierra Leone's annual export revenue is derived from minerals. The fact that over 80 per cent of the people remain farmers indicates the degree to which the subsistence mode of life still prevails in spite of the range of exports. The country has seen careless administration; in 1935, a British company was granted a 99-year concession over the entire territory for diamond mining. A wave of illicit diamond digging and smuggling took place, especially during the poverty of the Second World War. Sierra Leone's diamonds are over 50 per cent gem stones, and the country lost perhaps one-third of the returns for its most valuable product. Eventually, the government stepped in (1955), limiting the company to 450 square miles. But incalculable losses had already been sustained. Indeed, illegal digging and smuggling of diamonds continue on a large scale today.

British policies before independence, although sympathetic to extractive industries willing to invest in communications or other necessary facilities (such as the 3-foot-6-inch gauge railroad from Lunsar, near Marampa, to Pepel, opposite Freetown, laid by the company mining the iron ore), did not in-

---

[4] The area actually administered as a colony is variously given as a few hundred square miles (269 square miles according to Suggate) to as many as 4,000 square miles (Fitzgerald). The estimate depends upon whether only the Freetown peninsula is considered Creole territory, or whether it is assumed that all areas along the coast to which the Creoles moved as traders became part of the original colony. The important aspect is the coastal, exterior location of the colony, irrespective of its precise area.

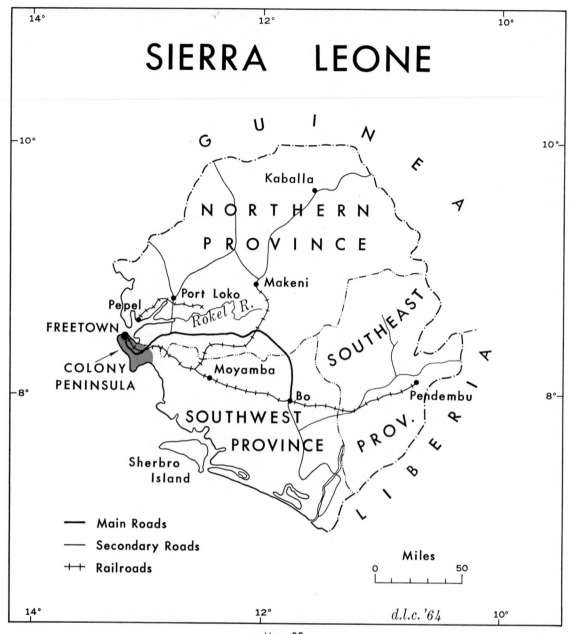

SIERRA LEONE

Map 83

clude any programs of vigorous economic development. The result has been an utter lack of planning in this direction, and a lack of acquaintance on the part of Sierra Leoneans with the necessary techniques. What has been accomplished has not even begun to form a foundation for a state facing the economic and social problems of its newly won independence. The railroad connections (2-foot-6-inch-gauge) between Freetown and the northern trading center of Makeni, as well as the diamond mining center of Kenema in the southeast and Pendembu farther east (via Bo, the former capital of the protectorate), were essential to the external trade of the country. This government railroad was the first line to be laid by the British in West Africa, and brought some tax revenues to administration coffers. Many parts of the country, however small it may be, are not served by railroads or feeder roads. Indeed, "95 per cent of the Africans . . . have not shared significantly in progress in the past."[5]

The consequences of Sierra Leone's particular condition are that the real problems of independence, which have given rise to so much strife elsewhere in the continent, have in effect yet to come into political focus. The transition, from the historical point of view, has been accomplished with remarkable tranquility, which has led some observers to ascribe this British success to the maturity of the Sierra Leoneans of the former colony and protectorate alike. Indeed, the Creole-indigenous problem was a major obstacle successfully overcome. But at the time of independence, the people of Sierra Leone were thinking about immediate problems, the choice of leaders and so on. Planning the economy, improving all conditions in the distant rural areas, stimulating industry—actually, creating the organization in all spheres that is a requirement of the politico-geographical definition of the sovereign state— has yet to begin. Meanwhile, the country continues to rely upon British loans and grants, and upon such organizations as the Sierra Leone Development Company, formed in 1930 to mine the iron ore deposits and a major contributor to government finance. Political self-determination has come to Sierra Leone, but economic independence appears yet a distant goal.

---

[5] Schneider, *op. cit.*, p. 11.

20

LIBERIA: THE PRICE OF SELF-GOVERNMENT

LIBERIA IS the only African state that has never been colonized or overrun by a European power. Like Sierra Leone, parts of this country served as a haven for freed slaves, in this case from the New World, but unlike its western neighbor, Liberia has existed as an independent political entity for well over a century. The two countries share many characteristics. They have roughly the same range of environmental conditions and produce similar agricultural products. They are in the same general size category, Liberia with its 43,000 square miles possessing a somewhat lengthier coast line. Although a reliable population census of Liberia is not yet available, the country may have approximately 2 million inhabitants, or about the same number as Sierra Leone. Liberia's economy, like that of Sierra Leone, has been transformed by recent expansion of mineral exploitation. But politico-geographically, there are vital contrasts between the two states, relating not only to the long-term dependence of Sierra Leone upon Britain, but also to the degree of participation of all population groups in the modern government.

In the area of present-day Liberia live some 28 distinct tribal peoples, speaking a variety of languages but sharing a dominantly subsistence agricultural economy. Many of these peoples, such as the Kru, Gola, and Vai, who were among the early arrivals in this area, were there long before the evolution of the country in modern terms began. Some were affected by the spread of Islam; most were involved in one way or another in the slave trade, for the sale of captured enemies was a lucrative business. With the advent of the Liberian state, these people have experi-

enced a remoteness from the progress and changes in Africa, political as well as economic, that is equalled in only very few other parts of the continent.

Liberia owes its origins to the movements aimed at the abolition of slavery and the slave trade prevailing in America around the turn of the nineteenth century. In 1818, representatives of the American Colonization Society crossed the Atlantic in search of African land to which freed slaves could be repatriated. These agents first visited Sierra Leone, where a similar experiment was in progress, and, not surprisingly, selected adjacent territory for the same purpose. An initial attempt to found a settlement there failed as a result of an outbreak of disease among the repatriates, but a second experiment was successful. This was the settlement, founded in 1822, on Providence Island on the site of present-day Monrovia, the capital of the republic. Gradually, by purchase and conquest, the settlement expanded under the guidance of white governors and with aid from American organizations and individuals.

The rate of progress, nevertheless, was slow. The first 25 years of repatriation saw relatively few "colored Americans" arrive in the area, and frequent hostilities involving African tribesmen consumed much of the energy of the settlers.[1] Meanwhile, the bur-

---

[1] Estimates concerning the number of repatriates vary widely. Stamp (*Africa*, p. 292) suggests that only 3,000 settlers arrived during the years from 1822 to 1847, excluding those who went to the separate "African State of Maryland." Yancy (*The Republic of Liberia* [Cairo: Middle East Publications, 1955], p. 33) claims that by 1840 there were over 32,000 colonists.

Monrovia, Capital of Liberia. Although the city has changed much during the past few years, Monrovia remains one of Africa's least well-appointed urban centers. This view, showing the city from the roof of the new Ducor Palace Hotel, shows the limited vertical development and haphazard occupation of city blocks.

den of administration and financial support was becoming too much for the American Colonization Society, which in the 1840's indicated a desire to withdraw its administrative assistance. In response to these developments and to pressures from within what essentially was the colony of a private society, President J. J. Roberts in 1847 proclaimed the settlement independent.[2] Thus began the fight for survival of the tiny state in turbulent Africa.

Stagnation and Survival

Liberia did not solve many problems by attaining sovereignty. Indeed, from several points of view the situation deteriorated. The support from the American Colonization So-

ciety was terminated, and efforts to collect duties on goods exported had little success. In addition, European interest in the African west coast was on the increase, and frontier disputes with the French in the Ivory Coast and the British in Sierra Leone were frequent. The "Independent African State of Maryland" in the east was absorbed by Liberia in 1857, but the problem of effective national control remained. The African tribal peoples of the interior retained their traditional ways of life and religion and did not pay allegiance to the new rulers on the coast. This induced Britain and France to bring pressure to bear upon the Liberian government to cede certain areas, and boundary treaties were signed with Britain in 1885 and with France in 1892. These treaties notwithstanding, Liberia lost still more territory as recently as 1910, when the French, claiming Liberian failure to exercise control over certain peoples, took 2,000 square miles of the nominally Liberian interior.

Independence, and less close ties with

---

[2] A major factor in the decision to proclaim the settlement independent was British refusal to pay customs duties to a colony of a private society, thus depriving Liberia of a source of income.

371

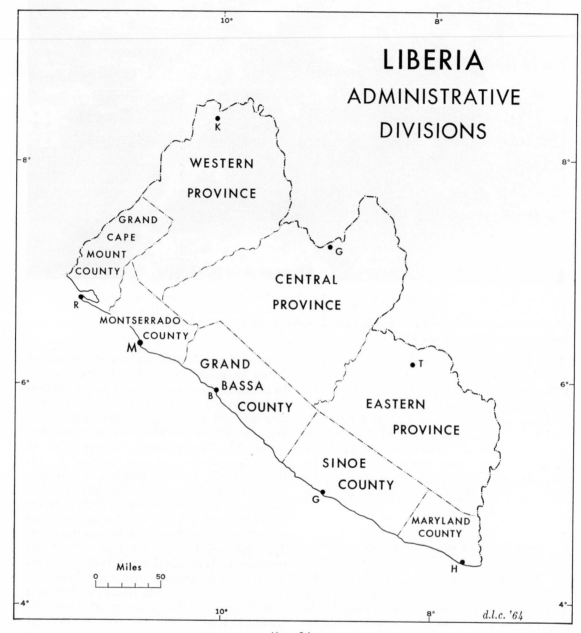

LIBERIA
ADMINISTRATIVE
DIVISIONS

K

WESTERN

PROVINCE

GRAND
CAPE
MOUNT
COUNTY

G

CENTRAL

PROVINCE

R

MONTSERRADO
COUNTY

M

T

GRAND

BASSA

COUNTY

B

EASTERN

PROVINCE

SINOE

COUNTY

G

MARYLAND
COUNTY

H

Miles

0   50

d.l.c. '64

Map 84

Street Scene in Monrovia, Liberia. Much of Monrovia still looks like this, with corrugated-iron-roofed, dilapidated structures standing helter-skelter along streets which often do not have sidewalks. Improvement is taking place, but slowly; European colonialism did not endow Liberia with a shining capital, for Europe never ruled here.

America, also meant that Liberia failed to obtain the material advantages of colonial rule. The failure of the colonists to control the interior was a function of the absence of communications, and even in the twentieth century Liberia was one of the poorest countries in Africa from this point of view.[3] Urban development was extremely slow (the capital, Monrovia, still has less than 100,000 inhabitants today), and the provision of modern utilities was long delayed. Monrovia obtained a partial sewerage system, electricity supply, adequate water, and surfaced streets long after most other West African cities.

What Liberia did have was obtained largely through loans, and the country found itself in constant debt, which gave rise to internal political instability. The forest products (palm oil, kernels, piassava) did not supply the necessary revenue, especially in view of the inadequate policing of the coast. But the country survived at a time when it

might easily have been absorbed in the colonial scramble for the continent.

An important factor in the country's political evolution has been the attitude of many of the returned Americo-Liberians. Having long lived in America, these people were often almost as foreign to Africa as were the European colonists elsewhere. They may have adapted more quickly, but they separated themselves from the tribal peoples who were indigenous to the country. Neither did these peoples desire to cooperate in the development of the Liberian state. The division between the settlers and the local people came to be expressed politico-geographically, the Liberian government ruling a coastal strip to about 40 miles inland, but being ignored—and unable to have much impact—in the interior. Meanwhile, some of the repatriates gave expression to their feeling of superiority over the local people, which was not calculated to enhance the prospects for unity. Although these mutually hostile sentiments are still not completely eradicated, the differences are now, after more than a century of independence, growing less.

---

[3] G. W. Harley, "Roads and Trails in Liberia," *Geographical Review,* XXIX (1939), 447.

Politico-Geographical Organization

The cultural, linguistic, religious, and economic differences between the Americo-Liberians (who by 1867 probably numbered about 19,000) and the indigenous peoples led to the establishment of two individual politico-geographical regions in the state of Liberia.[4] The coastal belt was delimited to a distance about 40 miles inland and fragmented, for administrative purposes, into five counties (of which Maryland County, the former "independent state," is one). The interior was divided into three provinces and nine districts, but for a century after the arrival of the first colonists, there was little tribal participation other than by those tribesmen who had come under the immediate influence of the new settlement, within which they resided. In 1946, the people of the hinterland for the first time elected three representatives, one from each province, to sit in the House of Assembly in Monrovia. Only since 1954 has the Liberian government made serious efforts to involve the indigenous population in the political affairs of the country.

The county-provincial division and its implications are indicative of the problems of forging a nation state out of the varied population of Liberia, which has not seen the advantages of an enlightened colonialism nor the unifying effect of the nationalist response to foreign rule. The relationship for many decades was one of intermittent war, but the enmity was among black people, one sector among whom "always looked back across the sea for their answers."[5] American political ideas were copied, the flag imitated, and the English language made the official medium

Rubber Plantations, Liberia. The beginning of modern development came to Liberia with the establishment of Firestone's extensive rubber plantations. A section of the older plantations is shown here.

of communication by the colonists, actions in which the indigenous people had little or no voice. Beginning with the Tubman regime, the integration of the interior into the national sphere has progressed, and with it the effectiveness of an increasingly authoritarian rule over the entire country.

The Twentieth Century in Liberia

The general area of which Liberia forms a part was known, during past centuries, as the "Grain Coast," because of the occurrence in the forests of amomum pepper, the "grains of paradise." The Liberian forest is a varied assemblage, in which several varieties of

---

[4] P. W. Porter, "Liberia," *Focus,* XII, No. 1 (September, 1961), 4. Porter's figure (18,858 settlers) agrees exactly with that of East and Moodie, who in *The Changing World* ([New York: World Book Co., 1957], p. 735) state that 13,136 settlers had gone to Liberia by 1867, in addition to which 5,722 were sent by the U.S. Government or put ashore by the U.S. Navy.

[5] Porter, *loc. cit.*

374

LIBERIA
TOWNS
AND
COMMUNICATIONS

SIERRA LEONE

GUINEA

IVORY COAST

Kolahun
Voinjama
Mano River
St. Paul River
Mt. Nimba
Ganta
Bomi Hills
Bong Mts
Gbarnga
Cape Mount
Robertsport
Clay
White Plains
Kakata
Harbel
St. John R.
MONROVIA
Buchanan
Cestos River
Tchien
Cavalla River
ATLANTIC OCEAN
Greenville
Harper Cape Palmas

— Main Roads
— Secondary Roads
++ Railroads
++ Proposed Railroad

Miles
0   50

d.l.c. '64

Map 85

375

coffee grow wild (liberica, among others), and the kola tree is also indigenous. The palm producing piassava grows in the coastal areas, and of course palm oil and kernels are plentiful and have long figured among the country's exports.

The stagnation experienced during the nineteenth century, resulting from internal strife, colonial competition, and a lack of effective communications, was not confined to the field of politics. Economically, the settlers sought, and failed to find, a stable export product, and the consequences are well known. The piassava industry faced the competition of easily accessible supplies in Sierra Leone (notably Sherbro Island). Coffee exporters could not compete with the rapidly expanding industry of Brazil. Liberia by the end of the nineteenth century was debt-ridden and had few prospects of emerging from this condition.

In the years prior to the First World War, the country appeared on the verge of losing her sovereignty. American loans were provided, but under condition that Americans should be in charge of customs duty collections, Americans should train a frontier police force, and an American should "advise" the Liberian government on all monetary matters. Meanwhile, the government was exploring the possibility of granting concessions of land to foreign companies, as was happening elsewhere in Africa. Thus, from 1904, foreign companies inspected Liberian possibilities, and in 1906 a British company established a sizeable rubber plantation near Monrovia.

The major breakthrough did not come until 1926, when an area of 1 million acres was leased to the Firestone Company for a 99-year period. Previous investigations had proved Liberia to be very suitable for rubber cultivation, and the company laid out extensive plantations, began to employ thousands of Liberian workers, and spent much money within the country. By the mid-1930's, rubber began to occupy a place of importance in the list of Liberian exports, and in 1940 it attained the dominant position. Ever since, rubber has been the leading export product, the peak year (in terms of percentage of the annual export revenue) being 1950, when

rubber accounted for well over 90 per cent of the total export revenue.

Once again, the power of foreign interests within Liberia caused a threat to the country's sovereignty. Having been a signatory to the League of Nations from its inception, Liberia in 1928 found herself facing charges of slavery by members of that very body. The question involved the transportation of several thousand young workers from the interior to the Spanish island of Fernando Poo with the acquiescence of the Liberian government. The League of Nations, over Liberian protests, proposed the replacement of the Liberian government by a League representative acting as administrator. Several parties, including the Firestone Company, revealed their support for such a move. Voices had long been raised in support of an American takeover in Liberia. The Liberian government resisted all attempts with tenacity, however, and survived this crisis as it had those of the past.

Economically, Firestone's presence continued to benefit the country. A large number of local plantations producing rubber were established (in 1963 some 2,600, of which 1,600 were in production), Firestone purchasing the harvest. Communications were laid, modern amenities provided, and the country experienced something of a boom. Firestone's own plantations now cover over 100,000 acres, producing over 100 million pounds annually, while the local plantations extend over more than 60,000 acres, producing some 15 million pounds per year.

The period after the Second World War has seen even greater progress, due to a number of circumstances. In 1947, the modern facilities at the free port of Monrovia (begun during and largely as a result of the war) were put into operation, and in the early 1950's the government liberalized the conditions under which foreign companies could obtain concessions. In addition to rubber, Liberia can produce cocoa and coffee, bananas and sugar, among other crops, and a number of European companies, hampered somewhat by a labor shortage, have obtained land for agricultural development.

More important than these new agricul-

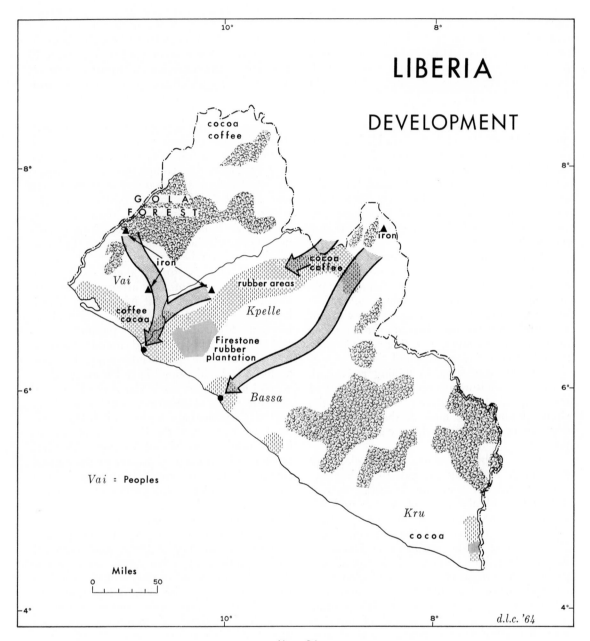

LIBERIA

DEVELOPMENT

cocoa
coffee

G O L A
F O R E S T

iron

Vai

iron

rubber areas

cocoa
coffee

coffee
cacao

Kpelle

Firestone
rubber
plantation

Bassa

Vai = Peoples

Kru

cocoa

Miles
0   50

d.l.c. '64

Map 86

377

tural plantations, however, has been the development of the mining concessions. As in Sierra Leone, the interior hills of Liberia contain important iron ore deposits, and since 1951 the output of ore has increased. A special railroad, 40 miles in length, was constructed from Bomi Hills to Monrovia, where the American company mining the ore (Liberian Mining Company, Republic Steel) has special loading privileges. Further discoveries have resulted in the construction of additional railroad lines, the expansion of the port of Monrovia, and the establishment of modern facilities at Buchanan.[6] Bridges are being laid, communications improved, communities planned and established, and the interior opened up. In the early 1960's, the value of the annual iron ore production rivaled, and seemed likely soon to exceed, the returns from rubber.

Despite all these developments, Liberia in the 1960's still remained a dominantly subsistence agricultural country. Some people are engaged in diamond mining and a few in the winning of some of the country's alluvial gold. Iron ore may become the country's major export product, but there is virtually no industrial development, and the participation of the labor force in mining is limited. Shifting agriculture occupies the majority of the peoples of the interior, and rice is the staple product over most of the country except along the coast, where cassava is important.

Thus, Liberia's pace of development picked up markedly around 1926, but the stimulus did not come much earlier than it did in the colonial parts of Africa; and the country started from an inferior position. Liberia after the end of the Second World War had few of the attributes of Ghana or Kenya. The long history of independence prior to the arrival of the wind of change in colonial Africa had not been accompanied by economic progress, and Liberia's position at the beginning of the period of political turmoil leading to independence was, if anything, poorer than that of most of the colonies. The first development plan in the history of

the country was drawn up in 1949, when with United States cooperation a five-year program was envisaged. To this, four years were added in 1953, when the plan was revised. Stress was laid upon the need for major improvements in the condition of agriculture in the interior. Aside from rubber, less than 10 per cent of the total annual export revenue is provided by agricultural products in a country where more than 80 per cent of the people practice agriculture as a means of living.

The focus of activity in Liberia is very much in the western part of the country, although the central section will develop more rapidly after the completion of improved transport links between the port of Buchanan and Mount Nimba iron deposits in the interior. The most important road has long been that linking Monrovia, Ganta, and neighboring Guinea; it lies through the heart of the region where palm products are exported. Coffee is grown along coastal and interior stretches of this artery, and cocoa, although not yet of great importance, also is being tried in both the coastal areas and the interior. Firestone's largest plantations lie just east of Monrovia and mainly between this city and the major international airport at Roberts Field, some 50 miles away, along a good all-weather road. The Bomi Hills area lies due north of Monrovia and again in the port city's immediate hinterland; further railroad construction to the Bong Mountains and into Grand Cape Mount County will serve to increase the nodal character of the capital. But in addition to communications permitting the more efficient exploitation of the country's resources by the extractive industries, Liberia needs transport routes connecting various parts of the country with one another. A glance at the map of towns and communications indicates to what extent the road and railroad pattern is coast-oriented and how rudimentary are the internal connections. Only in the embryo core region in the immediate hinterland of Monrovia are there interconnecting routes; thousands of square miles of interior, especially in the east, do not enjoy the benefits of even a passable road. Liberia's rivers do not serve as country-wide communications, for they are obstructed by rapids: the St. Paul River is navigable from its mouth at Monrovia to White Plains, about

[6] Bureau of Natural Resources and Surveys, *Annual Report* (Monrovia: Government Printer, 1962), p. 3.

River Boat and Village, Liberia. Although Liberia's rivers are not navigable for very great distances, their lower courses form transport routes in some cases. This illustration shows a boat passing the Firestone plantations, inland from Marshall, about 50 miles southeast of Monrovia.

15 miles inland; in the east, the Cavalla River is navigable for 50 miles from its mouth, but was ceded to the French in 1892. In any event, the rivers run directly from the interior to the coast and thus parallel the existing transport routes.

Whatever the political indignities of colonial rule, it cannot be denied that colonialism did bring certain material assets to many African territories that are lacking, or long were, in Liberia. The American Negro settlers and their descendants have in many respects remained as divided and separated from their indigenous countrymen as did the whites elsewhere, but without bringing to Liberia the techniques, capital, and experience of the Europeans. The pattern of the country's development, political and economic, in many respects resembles that of, say, Angola. Economic activity is aimed at the exploitation of the raw materials, the involvement of the majority of the local people in government has been minimal, the internal economy has not had much of a chance. But there is no Luanda (or Lagos, Accra, Abidjan, Dakar) in Liberia, nor are there as many of the other amenities colonial rule helped bring: agricultural research stations, schools, hospitals, and so forth.

All this cannot, however, be ascribed only to the historical circumstances of Liberia's politico-geographical evolution. Liberia's land and climate present tremendous obstacles to progress, perhaps the greatest in all of West Africa. The coast line is difficult to negotiate, swamp-ridden, and excessively moist; its soils are leached and poor. The country has always been far from the mainstreams of activity in West Africa, as it was when the first settlements were established; of all coastal West African countries of any size, it has perhaps been most isolated from contact with its neighbors both along the coast and in the interior. When development came to Liberia, it came on terms more or less dictated by those desiring to exploit the country's raw materials; the Liberians had little choice but to welcome whatever benefits accrued. Unlike much of the remainder of Subsaharan Africa, Liberia did not experience the salutary efforts of a colonial power attempting to "prepare" the country for independence while instituting development plans and building dams, roads, and airfields. There was not the centripetal effect of a rising anticolonial nationalism releasing energies which elsewhere, with independence, have been put to excellent use. In many ways, Liberia suffered many of the negative, divisive effects of colonial rule, although not by Europeans, without receiving a share of its benefits. Such, for the majority of the country's inhabitants, has been the legacy of Liberia's particular brand of independence.

21

FRENCH INFLUENCE IN WEST AFRICA:
THE ENTENTE AND THE COMMUNITY

ANY CONSIDERATION OF former French West Africa as a whole inevitably leads to references to areas which cannot be viewed as part of Subsaharan Africa. This is also true of similar discussions covering the Sudan and the Horn, but each of these areas extends well into Africa south of the Sahara. A choice becomes necessary: either the former French sphere of influence in West Africa is fragmented, and only such entities as Ivory Coast, Guinea, Togo, and Dahomey are considered, or the French Community in West Africa, having long been administratively unified, is viewed as a whole. Both approaches, from the geographical point of view, contain undesirable elements. But during the period of French administration as well as the present, such states as Mali, Niger, Chad, and Upper Volta have continued to look south rather than north. Economic and political alliances within and outside the French Community have stressed "Subsaharan" association, and although not all have succeeded, they have revealed the desire for identification with Africa rather than the Arab world. Former French West Africa is much less a "bridge between African and Arab" than the Sudan Republic.[1]

In addition to Chad (itself about a half-million square miles in extent) former French West Africa covered some 1,800,000 square miles. Today, this area is occupied by 9 separate states (including Togo), populated by a total of between 25 and 30 million people. Except for Guinea, which in 1958 voted to remain outside the proposed French Community and thus became immediately independent, each of these states attained its independence during 1960. None has a large population, and few have a bright economic future. Several (Mali, Niger, Upper Volta, Chad) are landlocked and partly or largely desert and steppe. Except for Guinea, the political independence of each is tempered by the continued domination of France in economic affairs, and, in some cases, an all-pervading dependence upon France for financial support.

With the exception of Chad and of Togo, which from 1922 was a French Mandate and, subsequently, a United Nations Trust Territory, all political entities here considered were from 1904 until 1959 united in a Federation of French West Africa (Afrique Occidentale Française). Upper Volta did not emerge until 1947, prior to which most of it was administered as part of the Ivory Coast. Having been labeled "colonies" under the Third Republic and "overseas territories" under the Fourth, those units which chose to join the French Community of the Fifth Republic became "autonomous republics" within this framework. In 1959, therefore, the federation ceased

---

[1] The island Malagasy Republic is excluded from the following discussion, to be considered separately later. Included, however, are two countries, one of which was formerly part of French Equatorial Africa (Chad) and the other not a member of either the Community or the Entente (Guinea).

Fishing Village on West Africa's Lagoon Coast. On the bars closing off West Africa's coastal lagoons, many villages have developed, precariously perched upon the narrow strip of sand. This particular one lies on the Dahomey coast.

to exist, the empire having been federal in name rather than in reality.

Although perhaps only 10 per cent of the local population speaks French, few would deny that the intensity of the cultural and political impact made by France in West Africa justifies the continued application of the term "French-influenced," even after independence. The governing elite is French-speaking, the political machinery is based upon French example, and virtually every modern institution in each country is based upon French models.[2]

Frequent reference has been made to the brevity of the actual period of effective European control in Subsaharan Africa, and French-influenced West Africa is no exception. Coastal settlements were established as

early as the seventeenth century, but the penetration and subjugation of the interior took place there, as elsewhere, during the last fifteen years of the nineteenth century. This part of Africa had a long history of complex political organization before that incursion took place, and the degree of superimposition of French cultural expression is all the more remarkable when it is seen against this background.

The Federation Established

French lines of penetration into the interior of West Africa were to some extent controlled by the consolidation of British, German, and other interests along the coast. Eventually, the French obtained five corridors between the coast and the inland areas: Dahomey between German Togoland and British

---

[2] T. Hodgkin and R. Schachter, "French-speaking West Africa in Transition," *International Conciliation,* No. 528 (May, 1960).

Nigeria, Ivory Coast between British Gold Coast and independent Liberia, Guinea between Liberia and Portuguese Guinea, and the stretches on either side of British-held Gambia, now combined in the Republic of Senegal.

The first decree with the aim of establishing a central government for French West African possessions was issued in 1895. At this time, Senegal, Guinea, Soudan, and Ivory Coast were placed under the jurisdiction of the Governor of Senegal, where France's oldest West African colonial settlement was located. Dahomey was added in 1899, but there was much competition between the administrations of the various individual colonies, preventing the introduction of an all-encompassing budget, a step that Paris regarded as an essential element in French West African unity. The system of administration that was to survive until the late 1950's was established by a new decree issued in 1904, by which time central control had become more effective. Dakar became the seat of the governor general of the federation, and as such the capital of the vast French West African realm. The city has grown to become former French Africa's largest.

The 1904 decree, however, by no means ended the French campaign for the consolidation of its West African empire. Mauritania was subdued as late as 1908, military rule was necessary in Niger until 1921, and Chad was finally pacified in 1913. These territories were brought into the federation, but the First World War revealed the incompleteness of French control. Several serious uprisings, mainly in the regions north of the forest belt, followed the withdrawal of French forces, fanned by the efforts to recruit local males and by the deteriorating economic situation.

Even after the First World War several important changes took place. Upper Volta presented a problem of administration which was solved in 1932 by the fragmentation of the colony for division among Ivory Coast, Soudan, and Dahomey. In 1947, the territory was re-created. Dakar and immediate surroundings were separated administratively from Senegal in view of the city's function as the federal capital; it has since reverted to Senegal. Several boundary adjustments took place, the last one being finally confirmed by a Franco-Libyan treaty of 1955. New boundary disputes arose after independence, Mali and Mauritania settling theirs in 1964. Although never actually a part of the federation, Togo in 1922 became a League of Nations Mandate partly under French administration.

During the Third Republic, when the countries of French West Africa were "colonies," French colonial policy first tended toward what was called "assimilation." This was especially true while the French colonial empire was still rather small and consisted of the few coastal stations in such places as Senegal. The legal aspect of this system was that African residents of such colonies were the equals of Frenchmen, and were represented in Paris by a member in the French Chamber of Deputies.

When, however, the French African empire was extended over several million square miles in Africa alone, and over several dozen million people, the policy of assimilation became impracticable, and made way for "association." This concept was a direct outgrowth of imperialist philosophies then dominant in France, and according to its prescriptions, Africans within the French empire became "subjects" of France and had no such representation in government as did the residents of the coastal towns in Senegal. Indeed, until after the end of the Second World War, the situation in French Africa was reminiscent of that in Portuguese Africa prior to 1962, in that the privileges of citizenship were reserved for "citizens," persons qualified for such status through education, wealth, and so on. French administrators possessed almost as much power as their Portuguese counterparts, forced labor could be recruited, and the elite among Africans was one of "acculturated" blacks best described as *assimilados*. This situation incorporated the roots of the problems which emerged after the Second World War. There was a new spirit of assimilation among the victorious French, who actually proposed that the African territories join with France in a French union of their own choosing (a proposal which formed part of the first, rejected draft of the constitution). Some reforms actually were carried out, but "the liberating features of the idea of assimilation tended to disappear in practice, and it became clear that the doctrine implied the continuing subordination of African interests to those of France."[3] The second, and accepted, draft of the constitution emphasized the indivisible character of the republic and stressed that the overseas territories, as the colonies were now known, formed integral parts of the unitary state.

Although not granted the right of self-determination by the Fourth Republic, the individual in French Africa after 1946 fared much better than he had previously. Citizenship was extended to include all subjects of French Africa, the forced labor system was eliminated, political parties and trade unions were permitted, and educational opportunities increased.

Nevertheless, African leaders, now entrenched and supported by mass parties, buoyed by the events in Ghana and Nigeria, and dealing with a weakening France, demanded more and, within a decade, succeeded. These successes were not, however, unaccompanied by internal strife. One of the consequences of the practice of association under the Third Republic had been the division of the Africans themselves into the vast, backward masses and the small, privileged, and French-cultured elite. Many of the leaders demanding independence during the 1950's were members of that group, toward which there always was a considerable amount of enmity on the part of the masses. In only one country, Guinea, did a really anti-French representative of the masses succeed in asserting himself in the face of French pressure for acceptance of the Community in 1958. Elsewhere, the French offer of autonomy within the Community was accepted, in no small measure due to the manner of education of the now politically dominant elite.

Since the establishment of the Fifth Republic and independence, several of French West Africa's territories have begun to resemble stable, viable states. If the gap between the ruling class and the masses can be reduced without revolution, the prospects of some (notably Ivory Coast) are bright. Others are frequently used as examples of utter disorganization and backwardness in newly independent Africa. In spite of their common recent history, few generalizations concerning the Community states can be made.

1. The Community States of West Africa

THE ENTENTE

Africa in recent years has seen several efforts at supranational organization, pan-Africanist unions, and political mergers. One of the most significant is the Entente, a loose economic union consisting of Ivory Coast, Upper Volta, Dahomey, and Niger. Founded in 1959, the Entente states have similar constitutions, military organizations, and administrative and governmental arrangements; they have a common currency and a common official language. The Entente surrounds comparatively wealthy Ghana and adjoins powerful Nigeria, and its population of perhaps 13 million is concentrated in the two western participants (Ivory Coast and Upper Volta), where its economic heart also lies.

The basic purpose of the Entente, which has outlived several other African attempts at unification in one form or another, is the coordination of the four members' economic and political activities. In 1959 and 1960, a common labor convention was established to regularize the salaries of workers and functionaries. The decision to request independence was made jointly, and plans were laid to hold elections at about the same time, to develop a common military authority, and to establish a Solidarity Fund, to which each member makes an annual contribution, and from which the poorest country can draw most. Since the early days, the Entente has grown, although the original four participants remain the nucleus. In 1960, at conferences in Abidjan and Brazzaville, an Abidjan Group was formed, including Senegal, Cameroun, Mauritania, and the four states of former

---

[3] *Ibid.*, p. 392.

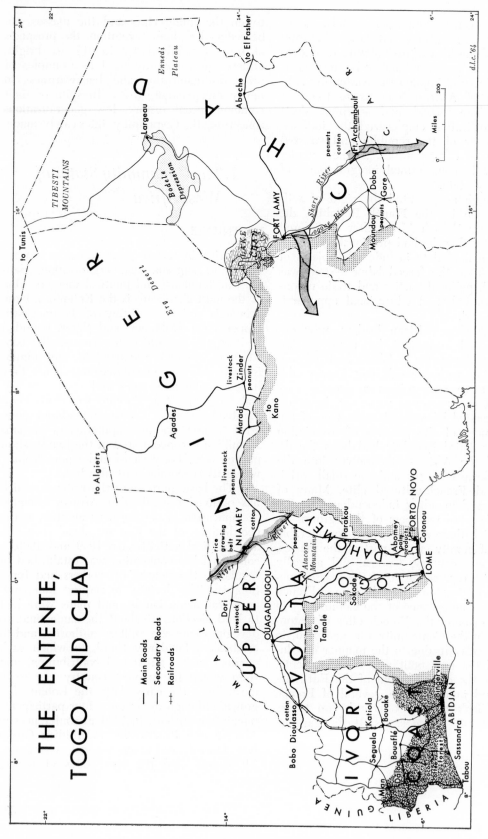

THE ENTENTE,
TOGO AND CHAD

Main Roads
Secondary Roads
Railroads

Map 87

Views of Abidjan, Capital of Ivory Coast. A city of peninsulas, fast-growing Abidjan is one of West Africa's most modern urban centers, with its 1,220-foot, four-lane Houphouet-Boigny Bridge (top, right) connecting industrial and commercial parts. The vertical development in the downtown area (top, left) is considerable, giving the city its modern appearance (below, right). A new industrial suburb is arising at Treichville (below, left) behind the new quay and port facilities. (French Embassy Press and Information Division)

Palm Grove, Ivory Coast. Palm products form a major element of both the internal and external economies of much of West Africa (French Embassy Press and Information Division)

French Equatorial Africa. This group is now associated with the Entente.

IVORY COAST

By far the wealthiest territory in former French West Africa is Ivory Coast. Its budget in the early 1960's was larger than that of any two other states in French-influenced Africa combined. Like the other Community countries, over 90 per cent of the population of about 4 million is engaged in agriculture, most still of the subsistence variety. The difference is that Ivory Coast's 128,000 square miles are capable of sustaining a variety of cash crops. The results are impressive. Coffee, introduced in 1880, now covers nearly 1½ million acres yielding about 200,000 tons an-nually, mainly robusta. Cocoa was first grown in 1912 after its introduction from the Gold Coast, and has thrived in the east. Three quarters of a million acres are under cocoa.

Once, Ivory Coast's dependence upon coffee was almost complete, as this commodity produced over 60 per cent of the annual export revenue. Cocoa, however, is challenging coffee as the most important export product. By the early 1960's, coffee's contribution had declined to 47 per cent, while that of cocoa had risen to 32. Together, these two commodities account for nearly 80 per cent of the annual export returns. The country depends, however, upon a system of price supports for coffee instituted by France, and in 1959, for instance, Ivory Coast farmers got about twice the world market price. This is the situation which led the leaders of the Ivory Coast to desire continued close association with France when the question of independence was under discussion. Nevertheless, the United States is a major consumer of both coffee (for use in instant varieties) and cocoa.

In recognition of the vulnerability of the country's economy, depending as it does upon two crops whose world price varies greatly, agricultural diversification has been encouraged, with some success in spite of labor troubles. The banana harvest is increasing each year. Cotton, pineapples, and various forest products are exported, although, compared to the major products, the revenues are yet small. Southern Ivory Coast being a forest country, excellent woods are harvested, including mahogany.

Ivory Coast benefited from its coastal location for reasons enumerated previously, but access was initially difficult. Abidjan, lying on the eastern lagoon coast (the western part of the coast is rocky), was long separated from the open ocean by a sand bar, and its port, Port Bouet, was open and unprotected. In 1950, the Vridi Canal (1.7 miles in length, 1,200 feet wide, and 50 feet deep) through this bar was completed, and deepwater quays were opened. An industrial complex is developing on the island suburb of Treichville. The city's population increased from a mere 46,000 in 1945 to 135,000 in 1955 and over

Rubber Plantation, Ivory Coast. Like Liberia, parts of Ivory Coast are suitable for rubber cultivation. Shown here is a plantation near Bingerville, just east of Abidjan. (French Press and Information Division)

200,000 in 1963, and a rapidly growing amount of trade passed through its port during the 1950's. The railroad from Abidjan northward was begun as early as 1904, reached Bobo Dioulasso in Upper Volta in 1934, and was completed to the capital of Upper Volta, Ouagadougou, in 1954.

Communications, internal as well as external, have been a serious problem to Ivory Coast. The same forests which yielded valuable exports (timber and palm products dominated the export list long ago) and grow on soils capable of sustaining coffee and cocoa formed severe obstacles to the development of an adequate road system. In general terms, it may be said that the west-central part of the country is best served by roads; extensive areas still have not been opened up by road construction. The importance of the roads of the country is underscored by the fact that over 75 per cent (by weight) of all export goods reach the coast via road transport.

More people are engaged in cash-crop farming in Ivory Coast than in any other French-influenced West African country, and, as in Ghana, the participation of the Africans in the country's economic development has led to progress in other fields. The powerful African Planters Union produces about 95 per cent of all the coffee and cocoa sold. The modernization desired by the country's leaders will take much time to accomplish, for industrialization is yet in its infancy, mining returns (from some manganese, diamonds, and gold) are negligible, and the national income, although large by West African standards, is entirely insufficient to pay for all that is desired.

Ivory Coast also needs to overcome regional differences in development and attitudes. The cash crops have always come mainly from the south, and in most aspects of development—education, social services, political consciousness, escape from subsistence agriculture—the northern savanna has lagged behind the forest south. Bouaké, a market center benefiting from its location on the railroad, on a main motor road to Abidjan, and near the forest-savanna transition zone, is the most important urban agglomeration in the interior, but its small size in spite of its advantageous position reflects the limited needs of its region. There is some hope that the cultivation of cotton will improve the position of the north.

Perhaps better referred to as the least poor of the French-influenced countries of West Africa rather than the wealthiest, Ivory Coast has taken a lead in political developments. It is the cornerstone of the Entente, to whose finances it contributes a major share. Immediately after independence, the country displayed continued pro-Western alignment and has not sought to become the object of an east-west rivalry in grant allotment. As such, Ivory Coast is almost unique in Subsaharan Africa, but the rewards have been forthcoming mainly from France, which around 1960 poured as much aid annually into this country as the United States did into all of Africa south of the Sahara.

UPPER VOLTA

The Republic of the Upper Volta, also known as the Voltaic Republic, has long been closely associated with Ivory Coast, one of its southern neighbors. Its existence as a politico-geographical entity having been interrupted between 1932 and 1947, the southern section of the country was during this period administered by Ivory Coast. The region that formed part of the Ivory Coast included the most important towns (Ouagadougou, the capital, and Bobo Dioulasso) and more than half the population, which presently numbers over 4 million. Ivory Coast is Upper Volta's natural exit to the sea, and Abidjan's port facilities as well as the railroad from Ouagadougou (75,-000) to Abidjan are jointly administered.

When Upper Volta was reconstituted in 1947, it obtained a territory of 106,000 square miles and a remarkable population. The people of Upper Volta are known for their industriousness and have long been a major source of labor for a wide area of West Africa. Many thousands migrate to Ghana for work, others go to Ivory Coast, and still others work in Dahomey, Togo, and Nigeria. What is especially noteworthy about Upper Volta's population is the fact that one tribal people dominates it numerically—a rarity in Africa. Over half the people of this country are Mossi, who inhabit primarily the east and central parts of the republic. These people show up as an organized force in West African history for a thousand years, and their strongly monarchical form of tribal authority has not prevented them from taking a leading role in the new republican organization of their state.

In addition to the Mossi, who number over 2 million, the Bobo form a large group. The Mossi headquarters has long been Ouagadougou, but the Bobo town, Bobo Dioulasso (45,000), was the country's main market center and focus of transportation lines, and long the largest urban center. With the new administrative functions of Ouagadougou, the capital has overtaken its rival in size.

These positive aspects of the country are more than offset by the all-pervading poverty of the land, the infertility of the soils, inadequate water supplies, serious erosion, and primitive methods of agriculture. Upper Volta is perhaps the poorest country in all Subsaharan Africa, and over 90 per cent of the people, uneducated, illiterate, and unchanged in spite of the political progress of their country, continue to engage in a precarious subsistence form of agriculture. The country's great asset is its population, much of which has to find work outside its boundaries, for within the republic the scope is limited. It manages to produce some thousands of cattle for export, and a few thousand tons of nuts, cotton, and fish. But France pays for the running of the government. In 1960, there were a few paved roads in the cities and none in the country. There may be some mineral deposits, but nothing significant is being exploited, and it may be said that there is no industry other than some outmoded plants processing the few agricultural products. In any event, the interior location of the country and the length of the journey to the sea form great obstacles to any kind of economic development. The value to the country of participation in the Entente is obvious.

DAHOMEY

Small (44,000 square miles) but relatively densely populated, the Republic of Dahomey is another of West Africa's poor countries, in this case depending upon palm oil and kernels. Palm products supply about 75 per cent of the country's annual export revenue, with coffee contributing a minor share.

Although possessing more or less the same climatic-vegetational series of belts found in neighboring Nigeria, Ghana, and Ivory Coast, Dahomey lags far behind these three in terms of agricultural production. Some peanuts are exported, while cotton and tobacco have been introduced, but Dahomey's economy in the 1960's is reminiscent of that of other parts of West Africa at the turn of the century.

Yet Dahomey does not rank last from the point of view of material assets. A modern deepwater port was recently opened at Cotonou, long an open roadstead. Railroads total 360 miles, linking Parakou in the interior to Cotonou (270 miles), and several shorter lines in the coastal belt linking major population centers. There are 4,000 miles of roads, a major artery leading north, forking to Niamey (Niger) and Ouagadougou. It remains true, however, that many villages are in contact with the rest of the country only during the dry periods. The lesson of Ghana and the impact of improving communications is applicable here.

As in other parts of West Africa, the majority of the Dahomey population of over 2 million are good agriculturalists in need of guidance in farming practices, suitable crops, and marketing opportunities. Meanwhile, the per capita annual income of the people is under $100 and real progress, in spite of a great deal of political awareness and activity traceable to the days of the precolonial empires, has yet to begin. Porto Novo, behind Cotonou, has a population of only 50,000, although Cotonou is likely to become the most important city in the country after the recent expansion of port facilities. Together these two centers, the only significant urban places with a prospect for early growth, contain only 5 per cent of the country's population, and the figure for all urban dwellers in the country is not much higher. France, of course, is the major trading partner, provides the bulk of all grants and loans received, and generally keeps the country, with its unfavorable balance of trade, afloat.

NIGER

The fourth member of the Entente, the Republic of the Niger, is larger than all three others combined, covering nearly a half-mil-

Women at Water Hole, Niger. The great problem of interior West Africa is water, which often must be hauled over long distances when wells run dry. These women are getting the day's supply from a well in the steppe land of Niger. (French Embassy Press and Information Division)

lion square miles. In population, however, it exceeds only Dahomey, and even when counting the many nomadic and semi-nomadic peoples who enter and leave the country each year, there are not much more than 3 million Nigerans.

The all-pervading aspect of Niger is its vastness. Among its neighbors are Algeria and Libya as well as Dahomey and Upper Volta, and more than perhaps any other country here discussed, this is a Saharan rather than a Subsaharan entity. The south is semiarid and the remainder is desert, accounting for the concentration of the sedentary agricultural population in the southern parts.

The pivotal physiographic feature of Ni-ger is of course the Niger River, upon which the capital, Niamey (50,000), is situated. From this southwestern area eastward along the southern border of the country stretches the agricultural zone, inhabited by the 1½ million Hausa and more than a half-million Djerma-Songhai. The belt stretches to Lake Chad, but Niger's share of the Chad area is the least usable of the four political regions into which it has been fragmented. Even this agricultural belt (rice is grown along the Niger, sorghum, millet, and cassava elsewhere) receives so little rainfall that it can only be described as steppe. Less than 10 per cent of the country receives over 20 inches of rain; more than half less than 5. Thus, the immediate problem in Niger is not the elimination of subsistence agriculture and its replacement by cash cropping, but the creation of an annual food production adequate to withstand years of severe drought and reduced yields.

The politico-geographical problems are no less severe than the economic. Everything seems to conspire to prevent Niger from becoming a viable state. It cannot claim even an adequate local standard of subsistence agriculture. Much of the land will not permit people to settle down and enforces nomadism not only within Nigeran boundaries but across them. Few people are truly indigenous to Niger, and far less than the official total of 3 million pay allegiance to the new government at Niamey. Economic organization and effective national control have not been achieved to the point where the country can really be described as a state; certainly its racial fragmentation prevents the application of the word "nation" to Niger's people, although in this respect Niger is not unique in Africa. But even the important, numerous, sedentary Hausa may be said to view Nigeria rather than Niger as their cultural home.

Efforts to improve the situation, mainly on the part of France, have made some headway during the past few years. A road now links southwestern Niger with the railhead at Parakou in Dahomey, and Niger's small export trade goes mainly through Cotonou. Peanuts produce the bulk of Niger's annual export revenue (which in the early 1960's was still less than $20 million), cotton has been introduced, and Africans are encouraged to sell livestock. Indeed, cattle might be Niger's chief source of wealth, but the difficulties of pastoralism in so dry a country, the lack of disease control, and, above all, the traditional unwillingness of the Peul herdsmen to sell their livestock have prevented progress in this field. Not only is there the tribal traditional problem, but the cattle are rarely in sufficiently good condition for sale.

Landlocked, vast, dry, poor, and divided in a number of ways, Niger presents one of the bleakest aspects in the politico-geographical scene of West Africa. Its blessings from membership in the Entente are many, not least of which is the major share to which it is entitled, on account of its poverty, from the Solidarity Fund. Although a political entity on the political map, Niger is a state only in name.

MALI

Formerly known as Soudan (Français), the Republic of Mali in some ways resembles Niger, although it is less poor. Its area (450,-000 square miles) is nearly that of Niger, although its population (4 million) is somewhat greater. Like Niger, Mali extends in a general southwest to northeast direction, is landlocked, depends heavily upon the Niger River, and is run from a capital peripherally located in the southwest.

Mali, however, was not a member of the original Entente, and looked westward in a federation with Senegal. This federation (Mali Federation of Senegal and what was then known as the Soudan Republic) has broken up; Soudan Republic has taken the name Mali, and relations between Mali and Senegal have not been good, with important economic consequences. Dakar is the obvious outlet for Mali, especially since a railroad connects the capital, Bamako, with this port. But with the deterioration of relations with Senegal, the railroad ceased to function in the intended manner, and road transport southward through Ivory Coast has handled most of the exports of the early 1960's. This, of course, was a costly development for all concerned except Ivory Coast, which profited from the new trade handled.

The bulk of Mali's population is concentrated, predictably, in the wetter south and southwest, where rainfall totals nearly 40 inches and irrigation possibilities exist. At Sansanding, the Niger River spreads into an interior delta and annually floods a large area. In 1948, France completed the construction of a large dam at the head of this delta, raising the water level some 16 feet and permitting the use of the old channels of the braided river as irrigation canals. The scheme, reminiscent of that at Gezira, is intended eventually to irrigate nearly 2½ million acres, and a similar, small-scale project succeeded below a barrage built near Bamako. The major project did not make much progress until

Views of Bamako, Capital of Mali. Located on the Niger River in western Mali, Bamako is Mali's largest and most important city. The dryness of the surrounding areas and the oasis-like character of the town are well shown (above), while the market (below) reflects its peculiar architectural flavor (French Embassy Press and Information Division)

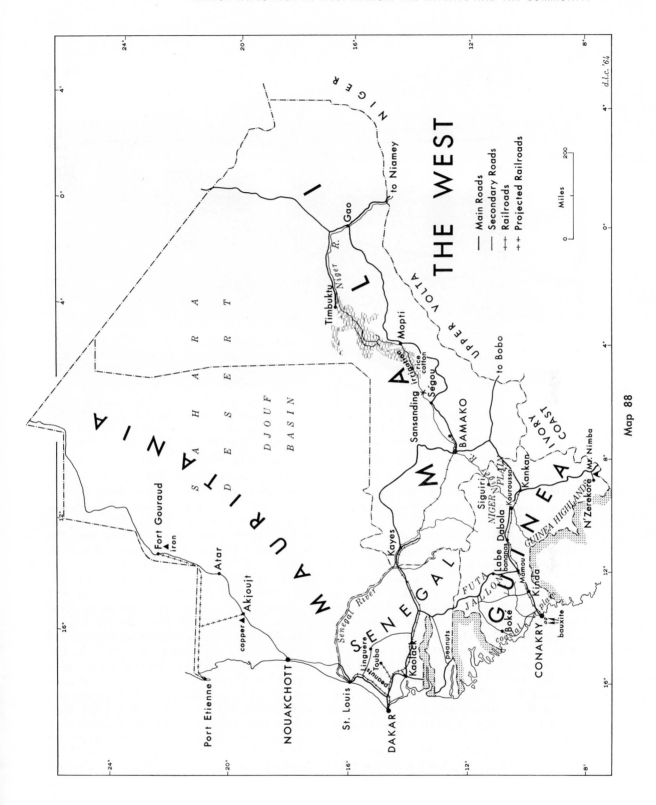

THE WEST

Main Roads
Secondary Roads
Railroads
Projected Railroads

Miles
0   200

Map 88

The Sansanding Barrage, Mali. In central Mali lies one of Africa's most important irrigation projects, which, it is hoped, will eventually be greatly expanded. The dam shown here lies east of Ségou and is the most important structure in the scheme to distribute the waters of the Niger over its extensive floodplain. (French Embassy Press and Information Division)

after 1948 (although it had been planned as early as 1932), and even in 1960, less than 150,000 acres were actually under irrigation. But the families who had been settled on the land, though numbering less than 50,000 people in 1960, were successful farmers of rice and cotton and were making money far in excess of the average per capita income. Mali's Office du Niger is naturally intent upon the continuation of the project, which cannot be done without foreign assistance. But it is a break in the poverty of interior West Africa, and although relatively few Mali citizens are yet affected, the implementation of all phases of the Sansanding Scheme, involving an area extending from just below Segou almost to Timbuktu, is at least a basis for some optimism in the economic sphere. As many as a million people may at some future time be supported there.

Meanwhile, however, Mali continues to share the problems of other landlocked West African states. There is little industry, and mining is unimportant. Subsistence agriculture still is the most common form of economic activity, and the country depends for its revenue upon such commodities as peanuts, shea nuts, some livestock, rice from the Sansanding Scheme, a few thousand tons of cotton, and hides and skins. Quantities are small, and the country's annual budget in the early 1960's was less than one-quarter of that of Ivory Coast. Urbanization and the modernization of the country have barely begun; Bamako has less than 100,000 inhabitants and is the only really important center in the country. Kayes, on the Senegal River, is a significant river port where livestock is marketed, and famed Timbuktu has a population of less than 10,000. Northward, beyond Timbuktu, Mali extends far into the desolation of the interior Sahara, beyond the Tropic of Cancer. There, the country faces problems similar to those confronting Niger in its efforts

Mopti, Niger River, Mali. Mopti is the main fishing center of the Republic of Mali, and fish is exported to the Ivory Coast, Ghana, Upper Volta, and Guinea, in addition to the heavy consumption of the domestic market. (United Nations)

to consolidate its territory under effective national control.

MAURITANIA

The Islamic Republic of Mauritania is less a part of Subsaharan Africa than perhaps any of the countries here discussed. Vast, compact, but inhabited by less than 1 million people, mostly nomadic, this territory of scanty vegetation, barren surfaces, poor communications, and negligible commerce is among the most backward in the world. It was administered from Saint Louis in Senegal until as recently as 1957. Its present capital, Nouakchott (6,000), was constructed from the ground up when the need for an internal capital was recognized, although there was a small village on the site prior to its selection. The port of Port Etienne was hurriedly im-

proved to lessen the dependence on the outlet used throughout the decades of federation, Dakar.

The extreme southern part of Mauritania, along the Senegal River valley, is the only area capable of sustaining sedentary agriculture. Elsewhere, the Trarza and other peoples trek endlessly across the dry, dusty country with its sparse vegetation, seeking pasture for their cattle, goats, and sheep. Livestock (sold in Senegal and Mali) form the most important export product of the country, in addition to which some gum arabic is exported.

Mauritania's hope is pinned upon several recent discoveries of ore deposits. In the northwest, about 400 miles from Port Etienne, a rich iron deposit was located during the 1950's. Its exploitation necessitated the construction of a railroad some 420 miles long from the harbor, skirting the boundary of

395

Port Etienne, Mauritania. Among Mauritania's few exports is sun-dried fish, sent each year to other parts of West Africa. (United Nations)

Spanish Sahara (Rio de Oro) to Fort Gouraud. Several Western European countries are investing in both the railroad and the expansion of the facilities at Port Etienne. The major share, of course, is French. At Akjoujt, about 180 miles northeast of Nouakchott, lie significant copper deposits. The quality of the copper ores varies considerably, and the various compounds require separate treatment processes. In addition to 125 miles of branch railroad (from the Fort Gouraud–Port Etienne line), therefore, reduction plants are likely to be necessary, and selective mining is essential. The prospect is that exploitation there will for some time remain a matter for the future. Exploration for oil has recently begun in Mauritania as it has elsewhere in Saharan Africa, and the possibility exists that another source of income may thus be found.

Port Etienne, among the oldest permanent settlements in the country, has long (since just after the turn of the present century) been a fishing port. Off shore are rich fishing grounds, and fish has figured among the country's small export volume for some decades. Although the new facilities to handle the iron ore are being built some six miles

south of the fishing port, the arrival of modern times in Port Etienne will no doubt lead to the improvement of the fishing port also. A plentiful supply of fish will be a great asset to the poverty-stricken north, and a freezing plant will increase exports.

All this, however, is yet to come. For uncounted decades, Mauritania has been isolated, landlocked in spite of her coast, and virtually completely deprived of all modern amenities. Even the subsistence agriculture is a precarious one. Its entire population is less than that of some African cities, and much of it has not even seen the changed way of life that has been brought, however slowly, to tropical Africa. In terms of size, its 420,000 square miles may exceed all European states. Unquestionably, Mauritania possesses ample territory; it possesses few of the other rudiments of a state.

SENEGAL

While Mauritania is one of the most backward of all former French territories in Africa, the Republic of Senegal is among the most advanced. This is partly due to the fact

Views of Dakar, Senegal. Long the capital of French West Africa, Dakar grew to become French Africa's largest city and major port. When the federation broke up, it became a major asset of the new Republic of Senegal. With a well-appointed port and one of Africa's most modern commercial districts, Dakar is the prototype of the French city in Africa. Shown here are a part of the city center (above) and port (below).

that the earliest French settlements in Subsaharan Africa were established in Senegal, which retained a privileged status within the French colonial empire during its expansion. It also is a result of its position as the former headquarters of the entire French West African realm, one of the legacies of which is the city of Dakar (400,000), the seat of government.

Senegal is somewhat better endowed with agricultural possibilities than Mauritania, but its best soils are generally only fair, and rainfall becomes adequate only in the south. Peanuts, not surprisingly, form the country's major source of export revenue, but the economy is diversified to some extent. Food crops are imported, especially rice, and aluminum phosphate, from the immediate hinterland of Dakar, is exported. Senegal is the most highly industrialized country in former French West Africa, and in addition to the usual plants processing agricultural products, there is some light industry which depends upon imported raw materials.

Senegal is also among the most highly urbanized countries of the former federation, mainly because of the large urban concentration at Dakar, where over 10 per cent of the country's 3,500,000 people live. Dakar has grown rapidly after the transfer of government from Saint Louis in 1902, when it ranked behind that town. By 1940, there were well over 100,000 people, and the city was the major outlet for almost all of French West Africa north of the forest belt. The natural harbor has been improved by artificial protection and is among the best in Subsaharan Africa. Its governmental and business centers, including stately ornamental structures and impressive skyscrapers, form a dramatic contrast to the poverty of the Medina slums. Communication lines focus upon the metropolis. In addition to the railroad to Bamako, which has stimulated peanut-growing, there is a line to Saint Louis in the north and Linguere in the interior. The northern line serves the important agricultural region in the Senegal Valley, where an agricultural improvement project (based upon rice) is under way, and also penetrates a livestock producing area. Since the serious diplomatic conflict with Soudan and the breakup of the

Mali Federation, the Bamako line has carried a reduced volume of trade. The port of Dakar, which in 1959 handled 3,700,000 tons of trade, has experienced something of a leveling off of the trend prevalent during previous years, when the volume of cargo handled increased rapidly.

One of Senegal's peculiarities is its territorial relationship with what may be described as an enclave, Gambia. If Gambia were a part of Senegal, the country would be compact in shape. Colonial rivalry, however, has resulted in a situation whereby Senegal's 76,000 square miles consist of a northeastern bulk and a southwestern proruption, for some time situated between colonial Gambia and Portuguese Guinea. Although there are physiographic and ethnic grounds for the unification of Gambia and Senegal, over half a century of contrasting cultural influence has driven the leaders of the two countries apart. There are road connections from the southern proruption across Gambia into the north, but the situation contains elements of potential political trouble.

Although only medium-sized, Senegal has a very varied population, which is mostly Moslem (especially in the north), while retaining its traditional religions elsewhere, notably in the south. The numerically dominant Wolof also are among the most highly urbanized, as many hold jobs in government and business. Since the Second World War, education has made great strides, including the opening of the first university in French West Africa at Dakar in 1957. The Senegalese, urban and rural alike, have demonstrated considerable political maturity and an ability to grasp the significance of the issues facing them. Although the balance of trade is yet unfavorable and the difference has to be made up by France, the prospects for success of the nation-state experiment in Senegal are perhaps better than in most other former French West African colonies.

CHAD

Although the Republic of Chad was not a part of French West Africa, it is for various reasons discussed as a Community state of

Senegal River, Senegal. The Senegal River forms the boundary between Senegal and Mauritania, and its waters are used for irrigation as well as transportation and fishing. A fisherman here is about to cast his net. (United Nations)

West Africa today. In terms of physiographic, ethnic, environmental, historical, and economic realities, Chad, at the crossroads of Northeastern, Western, and equatorial Africa, is very much a part of the interior West African scene. Its focus is in the Lake Chad area —indisputably a West African feature—and its internal conditions are reminiscent of those of Niger and Mali rather than of Gabon and Congo (Brazzaville).[4]

Chad is perhaps the most landlocked of all African political entities. Although its compact area is huge, covering nearly a half-million square miles, its boundaries are always hundreds of miles from the nearest coast. Furthermore, physiographic barriers impede communications with the nearest coast (the Gulf of Guinea), the southern connection through Cameroun involving a crossing of the North Equatorial divide. Chad will

[4] Although geographically a part of West Africa, Chad has joined in the Union of Central African Republics with the Republic of the Congo, Central African Republic, and Gabon.

no doubt benefit from Nigeria's extension of the Lagos-Kano railroad northwestward, bringing the railhead closer to Chad and probably consolidating Chad's West African ties.

North of the latitude of Lake Chad, the republic is bounded by geometrical boundaries reflecting the emptiness of the territory through which they are drawn. The bulk of the Tibesti Massif lies within Chad's borders, and in the east the boundary corresponds more or less with the edge of the more diversified terrain in the Sudan. Thus, most of Chad is a vast, relatively unbroken pediplane, sloping gently toward the higher mountains. The physiographic region including the Shari River and its inland basin forms Chad's core area, and the Shari (over 700 miles in length), depending upon the volume of its floodwaters, manages alternately to inundate and partially fill the lake. The alarming evidence is, however, that Lake Chad's fluctuations recede steadily, and the lake may dry up, as has the former lake beyond the Zambezi inland (Okovango) delta. In the early 1960's,

In the Steppes of Chad. Much of Chad's population is nomadic, moving across the country's boundaries into adjacent territories and back again. (French Embassy Press and Information Division)

the inundated area of Lake Chad varied between 4,000 and 10,000 square miles annually.

Like its giant eastern neighbor, Chad has a divided population consisting of a Caucasian, Moslem north and a Negro, non-Moslem south. Unlike the Sudan, however, the largest single group is a southern people, the Saras. In general terms, the northern peoples are nomadic and seminomadic pastoralists (such as the Peuls), and traders (the Hausa), while the southerners engage in sedentary agriculture and fishing. There are less than 3 million people in the entire country, and problems of politico-territorial unification are similar to those encountered in Niger. A glance at any map of Chad will show how far the peoples of the Tibesti (the Tubu) are from any center of authority. Communications on the ground are so difficult that the French developed a system of air connections to overcome this problem in part. Chad's size

has hampered development; education has lagged, the country is less than 5 per cent urbanized (the capital, Fort Lamy, has under 100,000 people and is more than twice as large as the next two towns, Mundu and Fort Archambault, combined), and modern development has touched few parts of the republic.

The economy of the country is almost exclusively agricultural, and there is little prospect that changes will come about. Prohibitive transportation problems, both internal and external, restrict Chad's opportunities in other spheres. There is, however, an exportable agricultural product upon which the country depends almost completely for its trade revenues. The south and the lake area, possessing the required moisture conditions, have been found suitable for cotton cultivation on a commercial basis, and well over a half-million acres have been planted. Since the end of the Second World War, exports of cotton have increased to exceed 100,000 tons annually. Small returns are also being produced by exports of livestock and livestock products, and small quantities of peanuts.

The Republic of Chad is a long way from self-sufficiency and continues to rely heavily upon outside assistance. The towns, such as the old slave-trading center of Abeche in the east, have only local importance as exchange markets. The resource base is severely limited; the water situation is frequently precarious. Of the few assets interior Africa north of the equator has to offer, Chad has the misfortune of having almost none.

2. Republic of Guinea

Having for over a half-century been a part of the French West African Federation, Guinea in 1958 was the only prospective

Change in West Africa's Towns: Conakry, Guinea. A tall apartment building rises above mud-walled shacks in Guinea's capital. (United Nations)

Community state to refuse further participation in the French framework. This was the result of a variety of political and economic, as well as historical, factors and caused the immediate cessation of French aid (then amounting to some $17 million annually), the removal of many essential facilities, and the immediate departure of over half the white population, numbering more than 7,000.

Guinea's territory of under 100,000 square miles (the largest coastal West African country after Nigeria and Ivory Coast) bounds no less than six political entities with varying characteristics. One, Portuguese Guinea, is a remnant of the West Africa of another century. In the south are British-influenced Sierra Leone and long-independent Liberia; in the east and north, the French-influenced countries of Ivory Coast, Mali, and Senegal. Despite its comparatively large area, Guinea has a short and rather difficult coast line with muddy and mangrove-infested estuaries. Conakry, the largest city (90,000), was founded upon the one ridge jutting out into the ocean, permitting both deepwater port development and contact by modern means with the interior.

Guinea is a land of variety, physiographically, ethnically, and economically, and it is a country of considerable potential. Its physiography is dominated by the highland mass of the Futa Jallon, rising several thousand feet and consisting of a dissected plateau with prominent peaks and deep valleys. The Futa Jallon forms the central backbone of the country, beyond which the land begins its gentle decline into the Niger Basin. In the north, elevations of over 5,000 feet are sustained, and southward, the mountains (here referred to as the Guinea Highlands and mainly crystalline) are shared by Sierra Leone and Liberia, and so are the iron ores they contain as, for instance, in Mount Nimba on the Liberian border.

The highlands support cattle rearing and plantation agriculture of coffee and bananas; the last has long been the country's major export product. They draw a large amount of precipitation from the air rising along their slopes, concentrated especially during the months of July and August but lasting from March to December; soil erosion is a major problem. Conakry receives some 170 inches annually, but in the lee of the mountains the totals drop rapidly, and savanna conditions prevail. The coastal plain, less than 50 miles in width, is hot and humid, being low in elevation and wedged between the swampy coast and the sudden slopes of the Futa Jallon. In spite of its character, the plain is rather densely populated and supports the cultivation of a variety of subsistence crops, including rice, corn, and kola nuts, while the oil palm provides additional means of subsistence. In the vicinity of Conakry, the coastal plain narrows on account of the jutting ridge upon which the town is located, and there some banana cultivation is carried on.

Bananas have accounted for over a quarter of Guinea's exports by value, but the industry received a blow when France refused to purchase the harvest after the negative vote of 1958; Guinea, in financial trouble, was forced to turn elsewhere for support. But the country has many opportunities for diversification: the cooler highlands carry several varieties of fruit, including pineapples and oranges, as well as coffee. Rubber and timber are produced in the extensive forest areas.

Guinea's mineral resources are likewise varied, and gold and diamonds have long been mined, gold in the Niger Plains in the far northeast (Siguiri is the center) and diamonds in the southeast. More important, however, are the huge bauxite deposits and iron ores; several bauxite areas are located very near Conakry and on the small islands near the mainland, and Guinea is Africa's largest producer. The iron ores lie within five miles of Conakry, and mining operations are cheap. With the short haulage and easy handling, the ores form one of Guinea's major assets.

Thus Guinea, in rejecting France's Community concept and opting for complete independence, possessed at least some of the ingredients necessary to go an independent course, more, at any rate, than most other French-influenced West African states. Of course, the decision brought serious problems with it. The per capita income of Guinea's 3½ million people (made up of diverse tribal representations, including Mandingos and Sousou in addition to the numerous Fulani of the interior) still is very low, and the balance

of trade in recent years has not been favorable, although the gap has been closing. New markets have had to be found, and bananas, coffee, and palm products now go in quantity to Eastern European countries.

The utilization of some of Guinea's plentiful hydroelectric potential and the improvement of communications constitute two of the country's main hopes for future growth. The important trunk railroad from Conakry to the interior trading center of Kankan (410 miles), which benefited the country by opening the interior, fell into disrepair but is being repaired by the Soviet Union; its main cargo was bananas from the highlands, and reconstruction is expected to stimulate the agricultural industries of the interior. Furthermore, coffee cultivation in the south has increased with the opening of the road to Monrovia, the nearest port, and rice from

Banana Packing, Guinea. A major part of Guinea's annual export revenue is derived from the banana harvest. Here, packers near Kindia are putting stalks in polyethylene bags prior to shipment to Conakry and overseas markets (United Nations)

View in the Republic of Togo. Villages in the interior of Togo lie among the omnipresent palm trees; this area is one of subsistence cultivation. Note terraces to reduce erosion. (United Nations)

the Niger Plains is exported to Mali. Meanwhile, Guinea has managed to survive the stresses and strains culminating in 1958 and the years immediately thereafter.

3. Republic of Togo

Togoland has seen as much political activity as any country in Subsaharan Africa. Its artificiality is evident from an examination of any map of the physical, economic, or ethnic conditions in the region of which the Togolands[5] form a part. The people of the Republic of Togo are of the same kind as those of Ghana, Dahomey, and Nigeria, and when the original boundaries defined by the

European powers were demarcated, they ran through unified tribal-political entities. After having become Germany's only self-supporting colony, Togoland was involved in the First World War which resulted, ultimately, in its fragmentation, first along one boundary, then along another. Eventually, French Togoland (22,000 square miles) was established as a Class C Mandate, and, except for a brief period of incorporation into Dahomey during the period between the two world wars, remained a separate political entity.

It is important to recognize the individual contributions made by both Germany and France in the development of the present-day Republic of Togo. During its brief period of rule, Germany established a good railroad and road system, focusing upon Lomé and its poor harbor. The Germans introduced crops and developed the economy, founded an educational, judicial, and administrative

---

[5] See Chapter 18. One of the Togolands has been absorbed by Ghana.

A Village in the Republic of Togo. Houses are made of mud and thatch; careful terracing permits the growing of some corn in the immediate vicinity. (United Nations)

system, and made considerable progress in the unification of the country. The French, on their part, never attempted formally to integrate their section of Togoland into the federation, although Britain was administering its territory as part of the Gold Coast. In 1946, French Togoland became an associated territory rather than an overseas territory, and was made a United Nations Trust Territory. There were efforts, however, to tie French Togoland more closely to Paris than the Trusteeship Agreement appeared to permit, and during the 1950's the Togoland question became a major issue before the United Nations.

The 1954 constitution drawn up by the French government had consequences far beyond the limits of French Togoland. Although the constitution was an effort to accommodate Togo nationalists and did not satisfy their demands, it was a major step in the direction of African self-government at a time when the African leaders in the territories of the federation were searching for bases upon which to argue for a revision of French-African relationships. The Togo constitution was the example they sought, and they used it with force, bringing about the 1956 *loi-cadre* and the 1958 vote on self-determination.

Togoland's position in the limelight was brief, however, and in 1960 it received sovereignty along with the other French-influenced countries of West Africa. Since then, it has not played a leading role in West African affairs, but the consequences of irredentism have at times been felt. The assassination in 1963 of President Sylvanus Olympio briefly reminded the world that the Togo problems had not all been solved when independence was attained.

Although in terms of area the smallest of France's former territories in West and equatorial Africa, Togo's population is over 1½ million, and parts of the country are therefore rather densely settled. As in Cameroun, France did not continue the rapid pace of development initiated by Germany, and for several decades the country floated upon what the Germans had founded. It has a favorable balance of trade based upon a variety of agricultural and forest products, including cocoa, coffee, cotton, and peanuts as well as palm products. Most of the production comes from the southern part of the republic, where the communications are best and the soils better than in the north. A phosphate deposit near Lomé (50,000) may increase export revenues and perhaps lead to the improvement of the port facilities at the capital.

The Republic of Togo may not survive the tensions of West Africa's politico-geographical evolution. It has many liabilities, including its small area, pronounced elongation, proximity to relatively powerful and hostile Ghana, irredentist problems both within and without the borders, and ill-founded boundaries. Its favorable balance of trade is an asset, but should be seen in the light of total external trade, which is small. Its continued special association with the Community is rewarded by some French financial assistance. The Republic of Togo shares much with its neighbors, but possesses little upon which to base its own individualism, which it will need to foster a popular national spirit. It is a far cry from individual nationalist aspirations to the general awareness of nationhood. In Togo, early success in this sphere may be an essential ingredient of politico-territorial survival.

4. The Malagasy Republic

The inclusion of the island of Madagascar in a study of Subsaharan Africa frequently leads to arguments concerning the justifica-

tion for the practice. Anthropologists, pointing to the ethnic characteristics of the vast majority of the population of Madagascar, often eliminate the island from consideration because of its Asian rather than African connections. But Madagascar, in physiographic terms, probably once was a part of the African land mass, and physical geographers would be unable to discuss the continent's southern bulk adequately without reference to the island, as shown in Chapter 1. Moreover, Madagascar underwent a period of colonial occupation by France which began and ended about the same time as in West and Central Africa. And Madagascar has taken a leading role in political affairs, its capital having been the site for several meetings of African heads of state. The Malagasy Republic has made clear its intentions to retain its ties with Subsaharan Africa; it has joined the community. Finally, it may become a major exporter of food products, and its obvious markets, from the economic geographical point of view, lie on the African mainland.

Geographically, therefore, it is not difficult to justify the inclusion of Madagascar in a Subsaharan framework. Nevertheless, linguistic, somatic, and cultural connections of the Malagasy people are indisputably with Indonesia and Southeast Asia. There are traces of Hindu influence introduced many centuries ago; subsequently, the Arabs made contact, establishing trading posts and initiating commercial connections with the African mainland. They also brought a black African element into the population through their manipulation of slaves. An important wave of immigration was that of the Hova, who came from Malaya after the first Europeans had sighted the coasts, and who constitute perhaps 25 per cent of the total population of 5½ million.

Prior to and during the first period of European contact, Madagascar may be said to have been in a feudal state, during which various kingdoms arose and failed through internal division. Portuguese, Dutch, and English coastal settlements were established, and the first French post was built in 1642 at Fort-Dauphin. But white settlement remained peripheral, and in the 1700's the Merina (Hova) developed a powerful king-

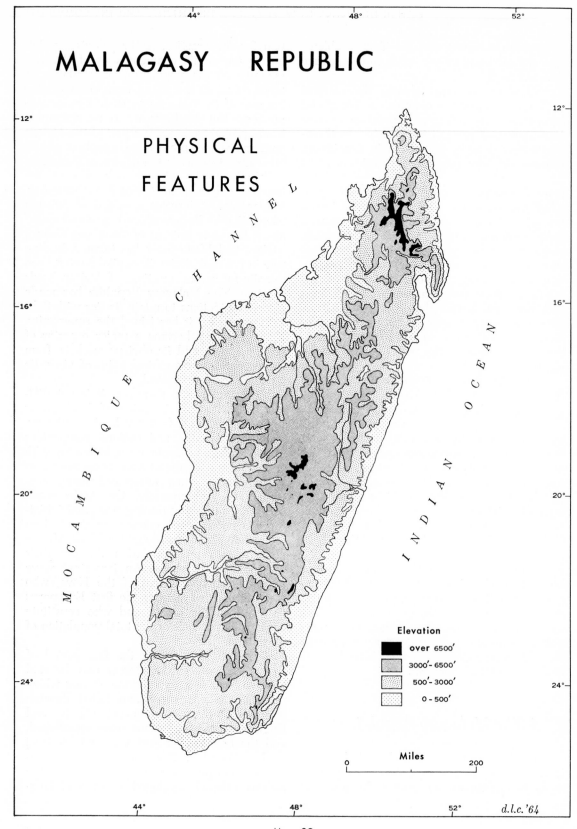

MALAGASY REPUBLIC

PHYSICAL FEATURES

C H A N N E L

M O C A M B I Q U E

I N D I A N   O C E A N

Elevation

■ over 6500'

▓ 3000'- 6500'

□ 500'- 3000'

⬚ 0 - 500'

Miles

0   200

d.l.c. '64

Map 89

dom in the heart of Madagascar, centered upon the present capital, Tananarive. Its success attracted European penetration during the 1800's, mainly that of the English and the French. King Radama I yielded to English pressure for the abolition of the slave trade in the area under his control and encouraged the development of legitimate commerce. In this effort he was assisted by the English, and his reign (1810–28) was a favorable one for the island in general.

After the death of Radama I, however, relations between the Merina monarchs and the Europeans deteriorated. Virtually all whites were expelled during the rule of his successor, a queen. Her son, Radama II, attempted to repair some of the damage done, but was assassinated by opponents among his people to the reintroduction of European influence. Eventually, rivalry between the British and French on the one hand, and between the Europeans and the Hovas of the Merina Kingdom on the other, led to political and economic chaos. In some areas, the usual process of treaty signing between local chiefs and Europeans was taking place, while the leaders of the Merina Kingdom claimed to have jurisdiction over such areas as the chiefs were ceding away. Hostilities erupted, whose eventual consequence was the departure of the British in favor of the French and the defeat of the Hovas in 1885 after a war which had begun in 1882.

In 1885, the French assumed a rather ill-defined protectorate over the kingdom of the Hovas. Foreign affairs of the Merina Kingdom thus became the province of the French, but the Merina monarch retained some internal power. Friction continued, and in the mid-1890's the French set out to conquer the island for good. The ruling queen was exiled, and in 1896 the succession of Merina monarchs came to an end.

The conditions of French control in Madagascar resembled those prevalent in the African mainland under France's jurisdiction. Although some material achievements were made, including the modernization of communications, improvement of the port of Tamatave and the urban center of Tananarive, and the introduction of social services on a limited scale, the French formula did not

accommodate continuing nationalist aspirations. France in Madagascar was dealing with a number of peoples some of whom, by virtue of their absorption of Arab invaders and because of their non-African heritage, had experience in politics and a desire for a return to pre-French days. Unlike the decaying West African empires of previous centuries, France in Madagascar had actually helped destroy an indigenous kingdom which had made considerable strides in the direction of modernization, and which had survived until near the turn of the present century. Thus, in 1947, a wave of uprisings based upon a resurgent nationalism occurred, indicating that while the terms of the Fourth Republic might suit West and equatorial Africa, they did not satisfy Malagasy nationalist aspirations.

The unsavory events of the late 1940's—tens of thousands of lives were lost in the rebellion—were followed by a now familiar pattern. Madagascar in 1958 voted, along with the French West and equatorial overseas territories, on the terms of the Fifth Republic and accepted membership in the Community as the Malagasy Republic. In 1960, sovereignty was attained.

ASSETS AND LIABILITIES

Madagascar is among the world's five largest islands. The physiography of its 228,000 square miles, dominated by a plateau backbone extending nearly 1,000 miles from north to south in the east, presents considerable variety. In the extreme east, the crystalline plateau, which reaches elevations near 10,000 feet, plunges steeply into the Indian Ocean. Having been faulted, this eastern escarpment possesses a few terraces and fewer usable harbors. Dangerous offshore coral reefs add to the hazards of this coast, which nevertheless accommodates the country's leading port, Tamatave. Coastal communications take place between Tamatave and Farafangana along the Pangalanes Canal, which lies at the foot of the escarpment but just inland from the sea. In the west, a series of sedimentary accumulations lead gently from the edge of the plateau to the low, smooth, mangrove-studded coast. Only in the northwest are there some inlets resulting from hard vol-

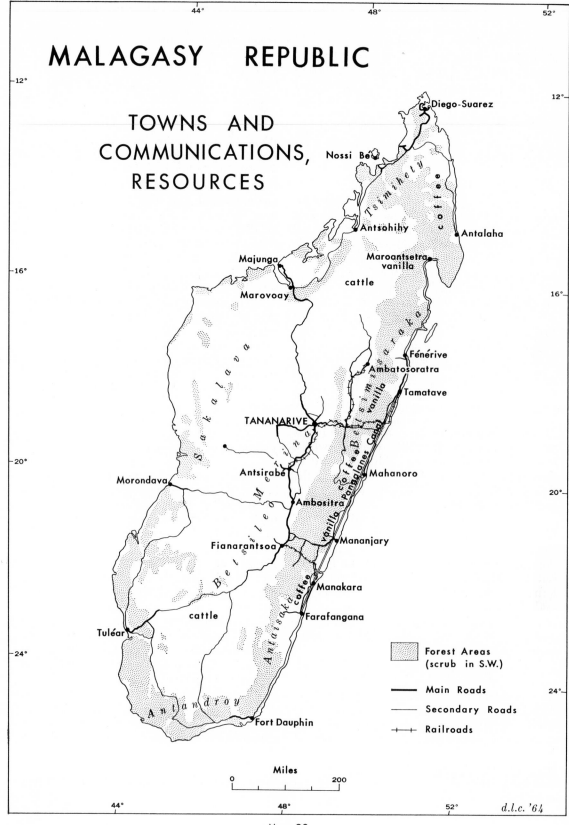

MALAGASY REPUBLIC

TOWNS AND COMMUNICATIONS, RESOURCES

Diego-Suarez

Nossi Bé

Tsimihety

coffee

Antsohihy

Antalaha

Maroantsetra
vanilla

Majunga

cattle

Marovoay

Sakalava

Tsimanasaraka

Fénérive

Ambatosoratra

Tamatave

vanilla

TANANARIVE

Merina

Antsirabé

coffee

Mahanoro

Pangalanes Canal

Ambositra

Morondava

vanilla

Betsileo

Mananjary

Fianarantsoa

Antaisaka

coffee

Manakara

cattle

Farafangana

Tuléar

Antandroy

Fort Dauphin

	Forest Areas (scrub in S.W.)
	Main Roads
	Secondary Roads
	Railroads

Miles

0   200

d.l.c. '64

Map 90

canic rocks. In general terms, therefore, Madagascar is poor in natural harbors adequate to handle overseas trade. Nevertheless, a number of ports have been established—more than a dozen handle external trade—whose facilities have had to be artificially improved at considerable expense. Development plans include the decision to limit further appropriations to the major port, Tamatave, which is connected by rail to Tananarive, the capital, and two other leading centers, Majunga, still an open roadstead but the country's second port because of its vast hinterland, and Diego-Suarez, which has one of the largest and best-protected bays in the world and is a port of call for ships on international routes.

A second element of physiographic diversification is that of climate. Lying across the twentieth parallel south and actually crossing the Tropic of Capricorn, while in the path of the moist southeast trades, Madagascar experiences high rainfall (over 100 inches) along the eastern slopes, moderate precipitation over the relatively cool plateau, and a drying, rainshadow effect in the west. Tananarive's warmest month (February) averages only 67° Fahrenheit, and its coolest month (July) records 55°. This is comparable to the highlands of Kenya and Southern Rhodesia, and the effect of the plateau's elevation is quickly appreciated when a comparison is made to nearby Tamatave, where the figures are 81° and 68°, respectively.

Madagascar, however, is hampered by the latosolic soils which have developed over most of its area and which are very infertile, requiring expensive treatment to be enabled to carry cash or staple crops. Where volcanic rocks have penetrated to the surface, better pedologic conditions have resulted. In a few areas, alluvial soils are under cultivation. The variety of agricultural products which can be produced is considerable, and includes rice, the country's staple and most important food crop, coffee, which produces some 40 per cent of the annual export revenue, and sugar, cloves, tobacco, vanilla, and cassava.

Mineral resources are varied, but small in quantity. The Malagasy Republic exports graphite and mica, and there are nickel and chromium in the subsoil in addition to a host of other minor deposits. But Madagascar is poor in this sphere, and the mining industry's contribution to the national economy is negligible.

One of the Malagasy Republic's liabilities is the inadequacy of its transport network. Improved communications are essential to help effect development. Many parts of the country simply have not yet been opened up, and agricultural production, occupying over 90 per cent of all Malagasy people, is mainly of the subsistence variety, being commercial only in those areas which are connected to the markets and outlets. More than half the country's coffee was long grown in a single region, that around Fianarantsoa. Rice covers by far the greatest acreage in the country, but contributes only a fraction of the annual export returns. Industrial development has not yet commenced, except for the processing of agricultural products on a minor scale.

The great asset of the Malagasy Republic is its people, of whom there are an insufficient number; this is a country which may be described as underpopulated. Although divided into a number of major groups, including, in addition to the Merina, the Betsimisaraka (somewhat less than 1 million), who live in the Tamatave area and are skillful weavers, and the Betsileo (over a half-million), who reside around Fianarantsoa and are competent farmers and craftsmen. Although groupings are thus identifiable, all Malagasy peoples are able to communicate through the same language of Indonesian origin, and they share certain religious practices. There are differences among them, and old divisions have not been forgotten. But in the effort to forge a Malagasy nation, the republic's peoples are able to start from a common base which is long strides ahead of that in most political entities on the mainland.

409

APPENDIX

APPENDIX

A NUMBER OF TERRITORIES in Subsaharan Africa in 1964 continue to exist as political anomalies in a rapidly changing scene. Their future is uncertain, but it appears inevitable that their present status will be altered. Each is very small in area, and relatively small in terms of population. Below is an outline of the salient features of these entities.

1. Gambia

The Past First a British slave trading station, subsequently the object of French–British rivalry, eventually a British base against the slave trade. Neglected during French expansion in West Africa, today no more than an enclave within the Republic of Senegal.

The Area An elongated entity covering 4,000 square miles, extending just over 200 miles along Gambia River. Width 12–20 miles. Boundaries geometrical in the west, based upon arcs drawn from the Gambia River elsewhere.

Status, 1964 Colony and Protectorate of Britain; the colony covers about 150 square miles and lies at the river's mouth, where the capital, Bathurst (35,000) is located upon St. Mary's Island. Population (Wolof, Fulani, Mandingo) 350,000.

Conditions Almost total dependence upon peanut crop; balance of trade is unfavorable. Much water transport, since the river is navigable for small ocean-going vessels to Georgetown and for small craft beyond the Senegal boundary. Great tidal contrasts in the river valley occur. A backward country, and the scene of another abortive attempt to accelerate development in Africa: the Poultry Scheme. Perhaps the most striking example of the artificiality of colonial fragmentation in Africa.

2. Portuguese Guinea

The Past Visited by Portuguese explorers during the first half of the fifteenth century; before the end of the seventeenth, Bissau was a flourishing slave-

413

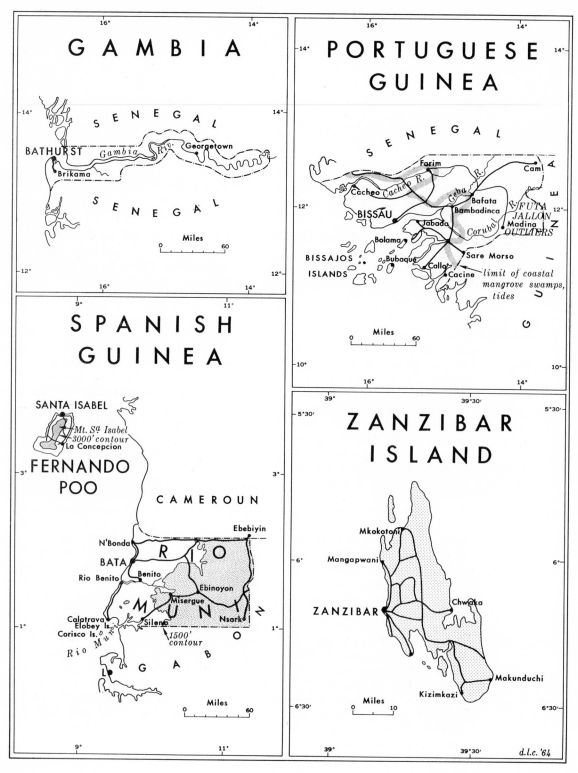

GAMBIA

SENEGAL

BATHURST
Gambia Riv. • Georgetown
• Brikama

SENEGAL

Miles
0   60

PORTUGUESE GUINEA

SENEGAL

Farim
Cam
Cacheo *Cacheo R.*
Geba R.
Bafata
BISSAU
Bambadinca
Jabada
Corubal
FUTA JALLON OUTLIERS
Madina
Bolama
Bubaque
Callo
Sare Morso
BISSAJOS ISLANDS
Cacine
limit of coastal mangrove swamps, tides

GUINEA

Miles
0   60

SPANISH GUINEA

SANTA ISABEL
Mt. Sᵃ Isabel
3000' contour
La Concepcion

FERNANDO POO

CAMEROUN

Ebebiyin
N'Bonda
RIO
BATA
Rio Benito
Benito
MUNI
Ebinoyon
Misergue
Nsork
Calatrava
Elobey Is.
Sileno
Corisco Is.
1500' contour
Rio Muni
GABON

Miles
0   60

ZANZIBAR ISLAND

Mkokotoni
Mangapwani
Chwaka
ZANZIBAR
Makunduchi
Kizimkazi

Miles
0   10

d.l.c. '64

Map 91

trading station. Portuguese-French boundary settlements did not come until 1886, after a long period of friction.

The Area   A compact unit of 14,000 square miles with a heavily indented, mangrove-covered coast. Dense forests behind the mangrove swamps merge into an interior savanna.

Status, 1964   An Overseas Province of Portugal centered upon Bissau, the capital (10,000). Population (Fulani, Mandingo) 700,000.

Conditions   Among Africa's least developed countries, exporting palm products, rice, peanuts, hides, and skins. Waterways are navigable for considerable distances inland, and most transportation is by this means.

3. Spanish Guinea (Rio Muni and the Islands)

The Past   Long excluded from Africa by the Treaty of Tordesillas and its own preoccupation with the Americas, Spain obtained Fernando Poo and Annobon in 1778, when the Portuguese ceded the islands for use in the slave trade. British administration was effective during the activities against slavery, and in 1844 Spain made another effort to settle there. In 1879 Fernando Poo became a Cuban penal settlement. Rio Muni (includ-

ing several estuary islets) was located between a German and a French sphere of influence, owed its survival partly to this factor, and was finally defined only in 1900 by the Treaty of Paris, which nevertheless guaranteed French rights of pre-emption.

The Area   A fragmented unit consisting of the islands of Fernando Poo (779 square miles) and Annobon (7 square miles), several other small islets, and the mainland, compact territory of Rio Muni (10,040 square miles). Fertile volcanic soils on Fernando Poo with considerable range in elevation; Rio Muni rises to a plateau-like central and eastern area with mediocre soils and dense forest growth along the coastal belt.

Status, 1964   Metropolitan Provinces of Spain centered upon Santa Isabel (Fernando Poo) and Bata (Rio Muni). Population 250,000, of whom 60,000 live on the islands.

Conditions   Fernando Poo's population, considerably mixed, includes 50 per cent Bubi (Bantu) and numerous immigrant workers from the mainland tending European cocoa and coffee plantations. Fishing is the livelihood of densely settled Annobon. Palm products, some coffee and cocoa, as well as sisal come from Rio Muni, where development, now relatively rapid, only began after the end of the Second World War. There are many timber concessions; communications are improving.

415

Zanzibar Town on Zanzibar Island. Once a thriving slave market and subsequently the world's major clove producer, Zanzibar remains today an important station for coastal traffic in East Africa. Its importance has declined with the rise of the mainland ports, and the clove industry has been attacked by disease. Trade with the mainland by dhows (see offshore) continues.

Street Scene, Zanzibar Town. Zanzibar is a mixture of peoples and cultures. The town, long the most important in East Africa, shows the evidence of its age and mixed origins. (United Nations)

416

4. Zanzibar and Pemba

The Past

An Arab stronghold whose domain extended onto the African mainland and with political connections with Arabia, Zanzibar first thrived as an entrepot for a large section of coastal East Africa. Contact with the Portuguese during the fifteenth century eventually led to friction and prolonged hostilities. Having long been a major slave and ivory port, Zanzibar's very existence was threatened by British efforts to stamp out the slave trade during the eighteenth century, but the Sultan (Seyyed Said) ordered plantation owners to plant clove trees while encouraging legitimate trade. Revenues from the slave trade, carried on illegally, continued to flow in, and the clove industry thrived. In 1861, the political ties between Zanzibar and Arabia were severed; in 1869, the port attained unprecedented significance with the opening of the Suez Canal. Finally, Britain succeeded in her efforts to eliminate the slave trade, and the scramble for East Africa's land began. Toward the end of the nineteenth century, the sultanate crumbled, and Britain established a protectorate over Zanzibar and the remainder of its possessions, including Pemba and a stretch of Kenya coastline.

The Area

The fragmented country (without the mainland area) consists of Zanzibar Island (640 square miles) and Pemba Island (380 square miles). Fertile alluvial soils overlie the coral base of the islands, formerly densely covered by forest, most of which has been cleared. Hot and humid, they sustain a variety of tropical crops.

Status, 1964

Independent state within British Commonwealth. A mixed Arab, Indian, and African population of well over 300,000 (50,000 Arabs, 20,000 Asiatics) is governed from Zanzibar Town (60,000).

Conditions

The world's largest clove producer today sees its industry threatened by several diseases attacking the clove trees, and diversification is required. Coconut oil, copra, and ropes and matting are exported. Trade remains substantial, although the world importance of Zanzibar has disappeared, and ports on the African mainland now compete for coastal traffic. Nevertheless, Zanzibar takes a sizeable share of this activity.

417

Index

(Italic page numbers refer to maps and photographs.)

Cam, *414*
Cambamba Dam, *173*
Cameia Game Reserve, *173*
Camels, 400
Cameron, Governor, 237
Cameroon, Mount, *5*, 225
Cameroon-Bamenda Highlands, 325
Cameroun, *209*, 223–227, 399
  early German administration, 225
  export routes, 211
  history, 223
  location, consequences, 227
  outlets of, 323
  Republic of, 383
  as Trust Territory, 206
Cameroun Highlands, 323, 337
Canicado, *165*
Cape Coast, 7, 352, *353*
Cape Colony, 59, 114
Cape Cross, *139*
Cape Delgado, *165*
Cape of Good Hope, 58
Cape Middleveld, 82
Cape Peninsula, 83
Cape Province, 88
Cape Ranges, *5, 6, 7, 82, 85*
Cape Three Points, 39
Cape Town, 59, 83, *88, 94, 95, 100, 104*
  climatic data, 34
  Colored population, 89
  and effect of Berg Wind, 40
  population of, 108
Capela, *169*
Caprivi (Kaprivi) Strip, 134, 137, *145, 169*
  dimensions of, 142
  origin of, 68, 142
Carter Commission, 253
Carter, D. B., 24, 42
Cashew nuts, *244*
Cassava, *266*
Castor, *244*
Catholicism, 291
Cattle, *200, 220, 222, 266, 364, 384, 408*
  in Bechuanaland, 118
  in Ghana, 360, 362
  in Kenya, 261, 262
  in Niger, 391
  in Rwanda, 281
  in South Africa, 89
  in South West Africa, 141
  in Uganda, 270
Caucasians, 306, 400
Cavalla (Cavally) River, 375, 379
Cazombo, *169*
Cela, 175
Cela Colonization Project, *173*
Central African Republic, *197*, 206, *209*, 221–223
Central Line, 241

Central Province
  Gold Coast, *348*, 350
  Kenya, 250
  Liberia, *372*
  Tanganyika, *232, 242, 243*
Central Region (Ghana), *348*, 357
Centrifugal forces, Nigeria, 330, 341 ff.
Centripetal forces, Nigeria, 344
Cestos (Cess) River, *375*
Chad, 204, 306
  boundaries, *209*
Chad, Lake, 6, *209*, 225, 323, *384*, 390, 399, 400
Chad, Republic of, 324, 380, *384*, 398–401
  assets, 400, 401
  and neighbors, 399
  outlets of, 399
  pacified, 382
  physiography, 399
  population, 400
  as West African state, 399
Chad Basin, *5, 6, 187*, 225, 325, 325, 330, 339
Chagga, 235
Chaka, *50*
Chambeshi River, 155
Chiange, *169*
Chibuto, *165*
Chicamba Dam, *167*
Chidzero, B. T. G., 235
Chilwa, Lake, *145, 167*
Chimoio District, 170
Chinde, *165*
Chingola, *145*, 153
Chirundu, 144, *145, 156*, 158, 161
Choma, *145*
Christian Ethiopia, causes of isolation, 291
Christianity, 272, 306
  in the Horn, 290
  in Nigeria, 328, 329
Christians
  struggle with Moslems, Horn, 291
  in Sudan, isolation of, 312
Chrome, 148, 364, *364*
Chromium, 88
Church Missionary Society, 365
Chwaka, *414*
Circulation, problems in Horn, 292, 294
Circumscription, in Portuguese Africa, 180
Ciskei, 103
Citrus fruits, *167*
Clay, *375*
Cloves, 409, 416
  industry, threatened, 417
  introduced in Zanzibar, 417
Coal, *88, 167, 200*, 240, 336
  for Katanga, 202

Coal, *Continued*
  in Rhodesia, 150
  in Swaziland, 125
Coast Province (Kenya), *250*
Coastal plain
  Nigeria, 325
  Sierra Leone, *364*
Cobalt, *200*
Cocoa, *200*, 202, 220, *344, 359, 363, 364, 376, 377, 384*, 405
  in Ghana, 355, 357
  in Nigeria, 330, 331, 332
Coconut oil, 417
Coconuts, *244*
Clapperton, H., 63
Coffee, *173, 175, 200*, 202, 220, 241, *244, 266*, 283, *364, 376, 377, 384*, 402, 405, *408*, 409
  Cameroun, 226
  C.A.R., 222
  Ethiopia, 298
  Ivory Coast, 386
  Kenya, 255
  along Kilimanjaro, 235
Cold Snap, South Africa, 40
Cole, S., 13
Coleman, J. S., 350
Colonial aims, in the Horn, 292
Colonial Charter (Portugal), 71
Colonial Development Corporation, 243
Colonial Development and Welfare Act, 241, 336
Colonial Office, 237
Colonialism, expansion of, 1890–1964, *65*
Colony Peninsula (Sierra Leone), 368
Colony Province (Nigeria), *329*
Colored population, 89–91
  birth and death rates, 90
  church preference of, 90
  economic condition of, 90
  elite, class consciousness, 91
  languages spoken, 90
  origins, 89
Coloreds, 82, 83
  in South West Africa, 138
  in Swaziland, 123
  urbanized, 87
Columbite, *240*
Comité Spécial du Katanga, 190
Common Market, of East Africa, 277
Commonwealth, 93, 363
Communications
  Ivory Coast, 388
  Nigeria to outside world, 323
  Rwanda and Burundi, 280
Conakry, *393*, 400
  climate, 402
  population, 401
  railroad to, 402

PRINTED IN U.S.A.

435